CHEMISTRY RESEARCH AND APPLICATIONS

# RECENT ADVANCES IN GINSENG AND GLYCOSIDES RESEARCH

# CHEMISTRY RESEARCH AND APPLICATIONS

Additional books in this series can be found on Nova's website
under the Series tab.


Additional e-books in this series can be found on Nova's website
under the e-book tab.

CHEMISTRY RESEARCH AND APPLICATIONS

# RECENT ADVANCES IN GINSENG AND GLYCOSIDES RESEARCH

## CLAUDE J. HOPKINS
### EDITOR

nova
publishers
*New York*

**Library of Congress Cataloging-in-Publication Data**

Library of Congress Cataloging-in-Publication Data

Recent advances in ginseng and glycosides research / editor, Claude J. Hopkins.
    pages cm
 Includes bibliographical references and index.
  ISBN: 978-1-62417-765-1 (hardcover)
 1. Ginseng. 2. Ginseng--Therapeutic use. 3. Glucosides. 4. Glucosides--Therapeutic use. I. Hopkins, Claude J., editor of compilation.
  RM666.G49R43 2013
  615.3'2384--dc23
                            2012049996

*Published by Nova Science Publishers, Inc. † New York*

# CONTENTS

# PREFACE

In this book, the authors present current research in the study of glycosides and gingseng. Topics include the synthesis and physico-chemical properties of benzimadazolone derivatives with N-bound glycosidic units; motif-based exploration of glycoside hydrolases family 1; ginsenoside and gintonin; Mediterranean medicinal plants; isoflavone c-glycosides isolated from the root of Kudzu (pueraria lobata) and their estrogenic and antimutagenic activities; changes in the composition of saccharides in rice grains through cooking and digestion using synthetic human saliva; and the effects of ultrasound assisted extraction of water soluble constituents on Brazilian ginseng roots.

Chapter 1 – Ginseng, the root of *Panax ginseng* C.A. Meyer, is one of the oldest herbal medicines and induces a variety of physiological and pharmacological effects in nervous systems. Ginsenosides, which are also called ginseng saponins, were first identified as one of active ingredients from ginseng. Recent studies have shown that ginsenosides including ginsenoside $Rg_3$ regulate various types of membrane ion channels, such as voltage-dependent and ligand-gated ion channels, in neuronal and heterologously expressed cells. Ginsenoside $Rg_3$ inhibits voltage-gated $Ca^{2+}$ and $Na^+$ channel activities but exhibits the differential effects on $K^+$ channels. Ginsenoside $Rg_3$ also inhibits receptor-mediated ligand-gated ion channel activities such as 5-hydroxytryptamine type 3 (5-$HT_3$), some subtypes of nicotinic acetylcholine, and N-methyl-D-aspartate (NMDA) receptors. However, ginsenosides enhances $GABA_A$ and glycine receptor-gated ion channel currents. A line of evidence shows that ginsenoside $Rg_3$-induced ion channel regulations are achieved by sharing the common interaction site(s) with ion channel blocker or toxin-binding sites. Taken together, ginsenoside $Rg_3$ decreases the excitability of excitable cells by inhibiting voltage-gated $Ca^{2+}$ and $Na^+$ channels and by inhibiting 5-$HT_3$, nicotinic acetylcholine, and NMDA receptor activities or by stimulating $GABA_A$ and glycine receptors that are present at pre- and post-synapses.

In contrast to ginsenoside $Rg_3$, crude ginseng total saponin (cGTS) fraction induces an elevation of $[Ca^{2+}]_i$ transient in mammalian cells and activates endogenous $Ca^{2+}$-activating $Cl^-$ channels (CaCC) in *Xenopus* oocytes via the same signaling pathways used by $G\alpha_{q/11}$ protein-coupled receptors. Repeated treatment of cGTS induces rapid desensitization of CaCC activation in *Xenopus* oocytes. cGTS is about 50% ginsenosides in composition, but the remainder is not defined clearly. Recent reports have revealed that the cGTS fraction contains novel glycolipoproteins, designated the gintonin. Gintonin, but not ginsenosides, interacts with unidentified membrane proteins to generate $[Ca^{2+}]_i$ transient in mammalian cells and to activate endogenous CaCC channels in *Xenopus* oocytes using the same signaling pathway with that of cGTS. Gintonin is novel lysophosphatidic acids (LPAs)-ginseng protein complexes. Gintonin targets G protein-coupled lysophosphatidic acid (LPA) receptors. LPAs are well-known as a lipid-derived growth factor or neurolipid with a variety of physiological and pharmacological actions in neuronal and non-neuronal cells including cell proliferation, migration, survival, and morphological changes. Gintonin can selectively activate LPA receptors with an affinity greater than that of free LPA. The activation of LPA receptors by gintonin induces a transient elevation of $[Ca^{2+}]_i$ in neuronal and non-neuronal cells via pertussis toxin-sensitive and -insensitive G proteins, phospholipase C, and inositol-3-phosphate ($IP_3$) pathway. $Ca^{2+}$ is a second messenger. Therefore, gintonin-mediated transient elevation of $[Ca^{2+}]_i$ via LPA receptor activations is coupled to a variety of $Ca^{2+}$-dependent cellular responses such as neurotransmitter release, muscle contraction, and gene transcription.

Ginsenoside and gintonin show the differential effects in nervous systems, although both are originated from ginseng root. Ginsenoside $Rg_3$ tends to attenuate cell excitations by blocking cation influxes such as $Ca^{2+}$ and $Na^+$ or by enhancing anion $Cl^-$ influx, whereas gintonin induces a transient $[Ca^{2+}]_i$ elevation via G protein-coupled LPA receptors to evoke $Ca^{2+}$-dependent cellular responses. This chapter will deal with the biochemical characteristics of ginsenosides and gintonin, describe the molecular mechanisms of ginsenosides or gintonin actions in the regulations of ion channels and receptors, and further extend cellular effects of ginsenosides or gintonin. This chapter will also describe the pharmacological applications of ginsenosides or gintonin as a drug that targets ion channels and receptors.

Chapter 2 – Medicinal plants from the Mediterranean region have been used in medicine since ancient times and are well known for their successful therapeutic activity. Many glycosides isolated from these plants showed various medicinal properties. The purpose of this review is to provide the verified data on the anti-viral, anti-microbial, anti-cancer, anti-inflammatory, anti-aging, anti-oxidant and anti-diabetic activities of the glycosides extracted from the medicinal plants of the Mediterranean flora and to discuss the various mechanisms of their actions.

Chapter 3 – New water-soluble benzimidazolone derivatives bearing a glucosyl unit were synthesized using an efficient glycosylation method. Also a series of new non-ionic amphiphiles based on bis-galactobenzimidazolones have been synthesized by grafting alkyl bis-benzimidazolone units as hydrophobic tails on glucopyranose and on hydroxypropyloxygalactopyranose moieties as hydrophilic heads. Their surface and self-aggregation properties in water were investigated. The new amphiphiles show characteristic UV-Vis absorption and fluorescence emission bands associated with the benzimidazolone moiety. The fluorescence emission is quenched with a certain degree of selectivity by cations, due to their strong affinity towards the benzimidazolone group, which shows ion complexation properties. Reaction of 1,5-benzodiazepine-2,4-dione with 3-O-substituted-5,6-anhydro-1,2–isopropyli-dene-α-D-glucofuranose gave the unexpected N,N'-di-glucofuranosyl benzimidazol-2-one by a novel rearrangement and ring closure reaction. A mechanism is proposed.

Chapter 4 – The kudzu root (*Pueraria lobata*) is used as an ingredient in kudzu-starch which is an important material for cooking as well as processed foods in Japan. On the other hand, this root is a kind of oriental crude drug and has been used for various medicinal purposes. In this chapter, chemical structures, and estrogenic and antimutagenic activities of isoflavone C-glycosides isolated from the root of kudzu are investigated. Kudzu root, which was obtained from the Gose city area, Nara, Japan, was cut, crushed, and extracted with water, and the extract was purified with various chromatographic techniques to afford four compounds. The chemical structures of these isolated compounds were elucidated on the basis of the NMR and MS analyses to be 6''-O-α-D-glucopyranosylpuerarin, puerarin, 3'-methoxypuerarin, and 6''-O-α-D-apiofranosyl- puerarin, respectively. 6''-O-α-D-Glucopyranosylpuerarin was obtained from the natural origin for the first time, and 6''-O-α-D-apiofranosylpuerarin was a novel compound. Estrogenic activity of isolated compounds was evaluated using yeast two-hybrid assay. Four isoflavone C-glycosides, which are 8-C-β-D-glucosyl derivatives of daidzein, showed no activities, on the other hand, daidzin, which is 7-O-β-D-glucoside of daidzein, exhibited the activity. These differences of the activity might be depended on the binding position (C-7 or C-8) or combination style (O- or C-) of glucose moiety to daidzein. Antimutagenic activity of daidzein, daidzin, puerarin, and 3'-methoxypuerarin was further assayed on the basis of Ames method using *Salmonella typhimurium* TA98 and TA100. Daidzein showed the activity, on the other hand, three glucosides of daidzein showed no activity to suggest that regardless of the position or the style, binding of glucose moiety inhibit the antimutagenic potency of daidzein.

Chapter 5 – Glycoside hydrolases cleave a wide variety of glycosidic linkages, including several industrially important enzymes. These enzymes are currently classified into 130 families based on amino acid sequence similarities. Members of glycoside hydrolase family 1 (GH1) are widely distributed in all three domains of life and hydrolyze various glycosides with physiological roles. In addition to hydrolytic activity, GH1 enzymes exhibit glycosylation activity to form glycosidic linkages. These properties suggest their utility not only as saccharolytic catalysts, but also as inexpensive glycosylation catalysts for the synthesis of valuable glycoconjugates. Many GH1 enzymes have been characterized to reveal that these contain β-glucosidases, β-fucosidases, β-mannosidases, 6-phospho-β-galactosidases, and 6-phospho-β-glucosidases. However, GH1 enzymes that are functionally characterized are extremely low compared to the entries described in the Carbohydrate-Active enZymes database, which accumulates over 4,000 entries for GH1 sequences. This fact suggests that the entries may harbor novel GH1 enzymes useful for glycoside research and applications. This chapter, aiming at the discovery of useful GH1 enzymes, reviews their general features and the authors' approaches to generate or identify novel GH1 enzymes. The approaches are based on a motif sequence conserved in GH1 members, termed as the DG motif. Distribution and variation of DG motifs are also discussed to facilitate novel GH1 discovery.

Chapter 6 – Various factors, such as texture, smell, taste and external, influence the delicious quality of rice. Attention to taste in these factors, the amounts of mono-, di- and trisaccharides, such as glucose, fructose, sucrose, maltose and maltotriose, which largely contribute to the taste of rice, in raw, cooked and digested rice were measured. Three cultivars of Koshihikari, Akitakomachi and Hoshinoyume were selected. As rice samples, not only freshly harvested rice but also two types of rice preserved at the milled state of the fresh rice at 40°C for one and two months were used. The digested rice was prepared through *in vitro* enzymatic reaction for cooked rice using artificially synthetic human saliva containing a digestive enzyme. Moreover, amylose and reducing saccharides contents in rice starch were also measured to examine the relationship between the changes in the amount of the tastable saccharides and the state of starch through cooking and subsequent digestion.

For raw rice of three cultivars, glucose contents were the largest in the tastable saccharides. The decrease of sucrose and the increases of fructose and glucose in cooked rice grains during the preservation were concurrently observed. These phenomena would be due to the hydrolysis of sucrose, which consists of fructose and glucose. The large amounts of maltose and maltotriose were detected in the digested rice samples, suggesting that these oligosaccharides would be liberated through the hydrolysis of α-1,4 glucoside bonds in amylose and amylopectin molecules by the catalysis of α-amylase in the synthetic saliva as these were hardly detected in the raw and cooked rice samples. It was found that the heating preservation affected the sweetness of rice and the heating-dependency of the sweetness was different among rice cultivars by the estimation of the relative sweetness of rice samples from the amount of tastable saccharides. The structure of the rice grains of the Koshihikari cultivar has difficulty with the heating effect during the preservative period, in contrast with the other two cultivars. The amylose contents for all cooked rice cultivars increased during preservation. It was observed that the amylose content in digested rice of each cultivar was lower than those in raw and cooked rice. This is mainly due to the hydrolysis catalyzed by α-amylase in synthetic saliva in the digestion process. The reducing saccharides in all rice samples increased 20 to 50 fold by the debranching treatment.

Chapter 7 – Ultrasound-assisted extraction (UAE) is an effective technique to recovery analytes from different matrices in shorter time than other extraction techniques. The recognition of the efficiency of dynamic UAE coupled with the additional advantages offered by the use of water as an environmentally friendly solvent has prompted researchers to investigate the potential of UAE for industrial-scale extraction of natural products. Species of the genus Pfaffia (Amaranthaceae) are commercialized in Brazil as substitutes for Panax spp. (ginseng, Araliaceae). Due to the similar morphology of its roots to those of ginseng, they are popularly known as "Brazilian ginseng". Recently, highly chemical constituents used in the pharmaceutical, cosmetic and food industries have been identified in Brazilian ginseng (Pffafia glomerata) roots. Thus, the effects of dynamic ultrasound assisted extraction of water soluble constituents on Brazilian Ginseng (Pffafia glomerata) roots were evaluated in order to understand how ultrasound interacts with cell walls and enhance mass transfer of the cell contents. The roots were analyzed before and after being subjected to the extraction process by scanning electron microscopy (SEM), X-ray diffraction (XRD), Fourier transform infrared spectroscopy (FTIR) and Differential Thermal (DT) analyses.

In: Recent Advances in Ginseng and Glycosides Research          ISBN: 978-1-62417-765-1
Editor: Claude J. Hopkins                                        © 2013 Nova Science Publishers, Inc.

*Chapter 1*

# GINSENOSIDE AND GINTONIN: ONE ROOT BUT TWO DIFFERENT FACES IN THEIR ACTIONS

## *Seung-Yeol Nah**

Ginsentology Research Laboratory and Department of Physiology,
College of Veterinary Medicine and Bio/Molecular Informatics Center,
Konkuk University, Seoul, Korea

## ABSTRACT

Ginseng, the root of *Panax ginseng* C.A. Meyer, is one of the oldest herbal medicines and induces a variety of physiological and pharmacological effects in nervous systems. Ginsenosides, which are also called ginseng saponins, were first identified as one of active ingredients from ginseng. Recent studies have shown that ginsenosides including ginsenoside $Rg_3$ regulate various types of membrane ion channels, such as voltage-dependent and ligand-gated ion channels, in neuronal and heterologously expressed cells. Ginsenoside $Rg_3$ inhibits voltage-gated $Ca^{2+}$ and $Na^+$ channel activities but exhibits the differential effects on $K^+$ channels. Ginsenoside $Rg_3$ also inhibits receptor-mediated ligand-gated ion channel activities such as 5-hydroxytryptamine type 3 (5-$HT_3$), some subtypes of nicotinic acetylcholine, and N-methyl-D-aspartate (NMDA) receptors. However, ginsenosides enhances $GABA_A$ and glycine receptor-gated ion channel currents. A line of evidence shows that ginsenoside $Rg_3$-induced ion channel regulations are achieved by sharing the common interaction site(s) with ion channel blocker or toxin-binding sites. Taken together, ginsenoside $Rg_3$ decreases the excitability of excitable cells by inhibiting voltage-gated $Ca^{2+}$ and $Na^+$ channels and by inhibiting 5-$HT_3$, nicotinic acetylcholine, and NMDA receptor activities or by stimulating $GABA_A$ and glycine receptors that are present at pre- and post-synapses.

* Address correspondence to the author at the Ginsentology Research Laboratory and Department of Physiology, College of Veterinary Medicine and Bio/Molecular Informatics Center, Konkuk University, Seoul 143-701, Korea; Tel: + 82 2 450 4154; Fax: +82 2 450 2809; E-mail: synah@konkuk.ac.kr.

In contrast to ginsenoside Rg$_3$, crude ginseng total saponin (cGTS) fraction induces an elevation of [Ca$^{2+}$]$_i$ transient in mammalian cells and activates endogenous Ca$^{2+}$-activating Cl$^-$ channels (CaCC) in *Xenopus* oocytes via the same signaling pathways used by Gα$_{q/11}$ protein-coupled receptors. Repeated treatment of cGTS induces rapid desensitization of CaCC activation in *Xenopus* oocytes. cGTS is about 50% ginsenosides in composition, but the remainder is not defined clearly. Recent reports have revealed that the cGTS fraction contains novel glycolipoproteins, designated the gintonin. Gintonin, but not ginsenosides, interacts with unidentified membrane proteins to generate [Ca$^{2+}$]$_i$ transient in mammalian cells and to activate endogenous CaCC channels in *Xenopus* oocytes using the same signaling pathway with that of cGTS. Gintonin is novel lysophosphatidic acids (LPAs)-ginseng protein complexes. Gintonin targets G protein-coupled lysophosphatidic acid (LPA) receptors. LPAs are well-known as a lipid-derived growth factor or neurolipid with a variety of physiological and pharmacological actions in neuronal and non-neuronal cells including cell proliferation, migration, survival, and morphological changes. Gintonin can selectively activate LPA receptors with an affinity greater than that of free LPA. The activation of LPA receptors by gintonin induces a transient elevation of [Ca$^{2+}$]$_i$ in neuronal and non-neuronal cells via pertussis toxin-sensitive and -insensitive G proteins, phospholipase C, and inositol-3-phosphate (IP$_3$) pathway. Ca$^{2+}$ is a second messenger. Therefore, gintonin-mediated transient elevation of [Ca$^{2+}$]$_i$ via LPA receptor activations is coupled to a variety of Ca$^{2+}$-dependent cellular responses such as neurotransmitter release, muscle contraction, and gene transcription.

Ginsenoside and gintonin show the differential effects in nervous systems, although both are originated from ginseng root. Ginsenoside Rg$_3$ tends to attenuate cell excitations by blocking cation influxes such as Ca$^{2+}$ and Na$^+$ or by enhancing anion Cl$^-$ influx, whereas gintonin induces a transient [Ca$^{2+}$]$_i$ elevation via G protein-coupled LPA receptors to evoke Ca$^{2+}$-dependent cellular responses. This chapter will deal with the biochemical characteristics of ginsenosides and gintonin, describe the molecular mechanisms of ginsenosides or gintonin actions in the regulations of ion channels and receptors, and further extend cellular effects of ginsenosides or gintonin. This chapter will also describe the pharmacological applications of ginsenosides or gintonin as a drug that targets ion channels and receptors.

**Keywords:** Ginseng, ginsenoside, ion channels, gintonin, G protein-coupled LPA receptors, Ca$^{2+}$.

# PART I

## I. Introduction

Ginseng, the root of *Panax ginseng* C.A. Meyer, contains a variety of ingredients and ginsenoside is one of the derivatives of triterpenoid dammarane consisting of thirty carbon atoms. Each ginsenoside has a common hydrophobic four ring steroid-like structure with carbohydrate moieties attached. Thus, ginsenosides have amphiphilic property. About 30 different types of ginsenosides have been isolated and identified from the root of *Panax ginseng* (Fig. 1). They are mainly classified into protopanaxadiol (PD), protopanaxatriol (PT) and oleanolic ginsenosides according to the position of different carbohydrate moieties at the carbon-3, carbon-6 position, and aliphatic side chain (Nah et al., 2007).

Each type of ginsenosides could divide into three portions. First, carbohydrate portions, as mentioned above, are attached to carbon-3, carbon-6 or carbon-20. Sugars of these side chains consist of monomer, dimer, or trimer. The compositions of sugar are also diverse with arabinose, glucose, rhamnose, and xylose. These sugar components provide an amphiphilic property of ginsenoside. Second, the backbone of ginsenosides, aglycone, is hydrophobic with four ring steroid-like structure with several methyl group. Third is the aliphatic side or alkene chain $CH_2CH_2CH=C(CH_3)_2$ at the carbon-20 of backbone structure (Figure 2) but the aliphatic side of ginsenoside could be also modified during metabolism of ginsenosides (Figure 1). *In vitro* study shows that ginsenosides regulate membrane ion channel activities outside of cells (Lee et al., 2004). Thus, it seems that acute treatment of ginsenosides does not penetrate into the cells, rather ginsenosides interact with membrane proteins (i.e. ion channels and receptors) for the regulations of cellular activities. The three main portions of ginsenosides might contribute to exert their cellular effects outside of cells. This section will first focus on the chemical structure-activity relationship of ginsenosides in ion channel regulations before see how ginsenosides interact with ion channels and receptors.

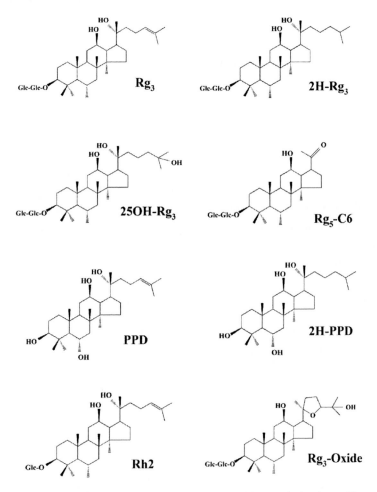

Figure 1. Chemical Structures of ginsenoside Rg₃ and ginsenoside Rg₃ derivatives. Glc, glucopyranoside. Ginsenoside Rg₃ and ginsenoside Rg₃ derivatives differ in the three side chains and carbohydrates attached to a common steroid-like ring. Subscripts indicate the carbons in the glucose rings that link the two carbohydrates. Adapted from Lee *et al.* (2008c).

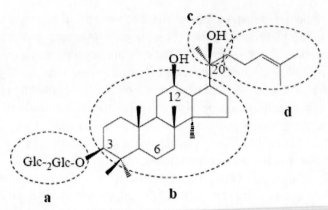

Figure 2. 20(*S*)-Ginsenoside Rg$_3$ consists of three main portions. Carbohydrate portion at the carbon-3 (a); The main backbone (b); epimer (c); aliphatic side chain (d). The possible functions of these portions in voltage-gated ion channel or ligand-gated ion channel regulations are in detail described in text.


## II. Ginsenoside Rg$_3$ As a Model Compound for Structure-Activity Relationship Study

20(*S*)-ginsenoside Rg$_3$, (20-*S*-protopanaxadiol-3-[O-β-D-glucopyranosyl (1→2)-β-glucopyranoside]), is one of protopanaxadiol ginsenosides. The chemical structure of ginsenoside Rg$_3$ is shown in Figure 1. Ginsenoside Rg$_3$ has two glucoses at the carbon-3 position and has no sugar at the carbon-20. Its chemical structure is quiet contrast to protopanaxatriol ginsenoside Rf (20-*S*-protopanaxadiol-6-[O-β-D-glucopyranosyl (1→2)-β-glucopyranoside]), which has two glucoses at the carbon-6 but not at the carbon-20. Ginsenoside Rg$_3$ exists as a pair of stereoisomers, with a change in the position of the hydroxyl group at the carbon-20 differentiating between the epimers, 20(*R*)-ginsenoside Rg$_3$ and 20(*S*)-ginsenoside Rg$_3$ (Figure 3).

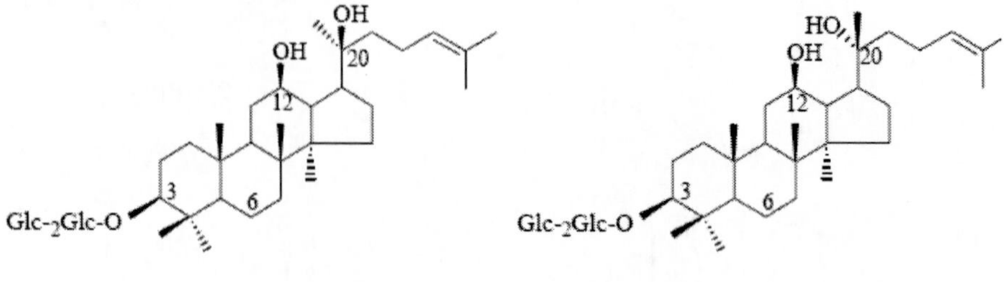

20(*S*)-Ginsenoside Rg$_3$                    20(*R*)-Ginsenoside Rg$_3$

Figure 3. Ginsenoside Rg$_3$ exists as epimers at the carbon-20. They differ at the position of hydroxyl group. Abbreviations for carbohydrates are as follows: Glc, glucopyranoside. Superscripts indicate the carbon in the glucose ring that links the two carbohydrates.

Ginsenoside Rg$_3$ is suitable for a model compound among various ginsenosides with following reasons. First, ginsenoside Rg$_3$ is the most potent regulator of various types of ion channels such as voltage-dependent Ca$^{2+}$, K$^+$ and Na$^+$ channels and ligand-gated ion channels such as 5-HT$_3$, NMDA and brain, muscle- and neuronal-types of nicotinic acetylcholine receptors (Nah et al., 2007). Second, ginsenoside Rg$_3$ exists as stereoisomers and it is relatively easy to obtain the individual 20(R)-ginsenoside Rg$_3$ and 20(S)-ginsenoside Rg$_3$ epimer without contamination of the other form.

## 1. The Contribution of Carbohydrate Portion of 20(S)-Ginsenoside Rg$_3$ in the Regulation of Ion Channels

Ginsenoside is one of kinds of saponins, which are characterized by glycosides with sugars at specific position of backbone structure, called aglycone. Thus, 20(S)-ginsenoside Rg$_3$ is O-glycosylated with saponin at the carbon 3 position with two glucoses. To know the role of carbohydrates in Na$^+$ (Nav1.2) channel regulation, Kim et al. (2005a) prepared a derivative of 20(S)-ginsenoside Rg$_3$ by conjugating second glucose of 20(S)-ginsenoside Rg$_3$ with a small compound called 3-(4-hydroxyphenyl) propionic acid hydrazide (HPPH) (Fig. 4A) and further examined the effect of 20(S)-ginsenoside Rg$_3$ derivative on the Na$^+$ channel regulation. They demonstrated that a ginsenoside Rg$_3$ derivative had no effect on Na$^+$ channel activity (Figure 4B). Furthermore, a simple opening of second glucose by oxidation with periodate also did not exhibit any effects on Na$^+$ channel activity. Interestingly, even though treatment of cells with the protopanaxadiol (PPD) alone (which is aglycone with backbone structure of 20(S)-ginsenoside Rg$_3$), sophorose alone (which is only dimmer of two glucoses attached to the carbon-3), or combination of PPD and sophorose did not inhibit Na$^+$ currents (Kim et al., 2005). The carbohydrate portion 20(S)-ginsenoside Rg$_3$ needs to be intact state without any modifications. What is the role of hydroxyl group of carbohydrate portion of ginsenoside Rg$_3$ in Na$^+$ channel regulation? Lee et al. (2008) demonstrated that the hydroxyl groups of carbohydrate portion of 20(S)-ginsenoside Rg$_3$ help 20(S)-ginsenoside Rg$_3$ to bind ion channel proteins by forming hydrogen bonds.

The modifications of hydrophilic carbohydrate portion of ginsenoside Rg$_3$ by introduction of other compound might induce conformational changes of carbohydrate portion, and finally interrupt the stable hydrogen bonds between 20(S)-ginsenoside Rg$_3$ and ion channel proteins. The sugar portion of ginsenoside Rg$_3$ might contribute to interactions of 20(S)-ginsenoside Rg$_3$ with channel proteins outside of cells without complete penetration into cells.

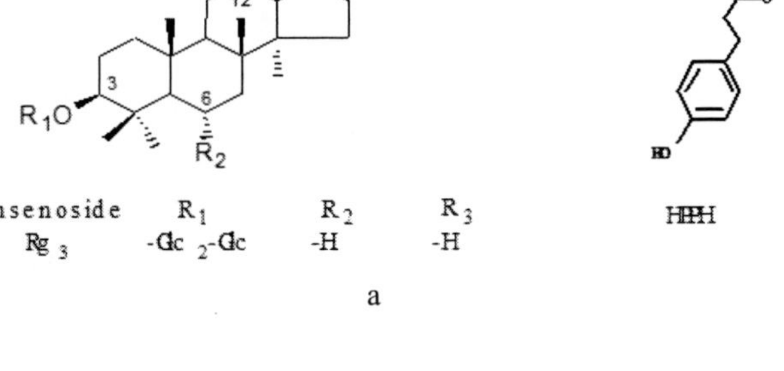

| Ginsenoside | R$_1$ | R$_2$ | R$_3$ |
|---|---|---|---|
| Rg$_3$ | -Glc$_2$-Glc | -H | -H |

a

Figure 4. (Continued)

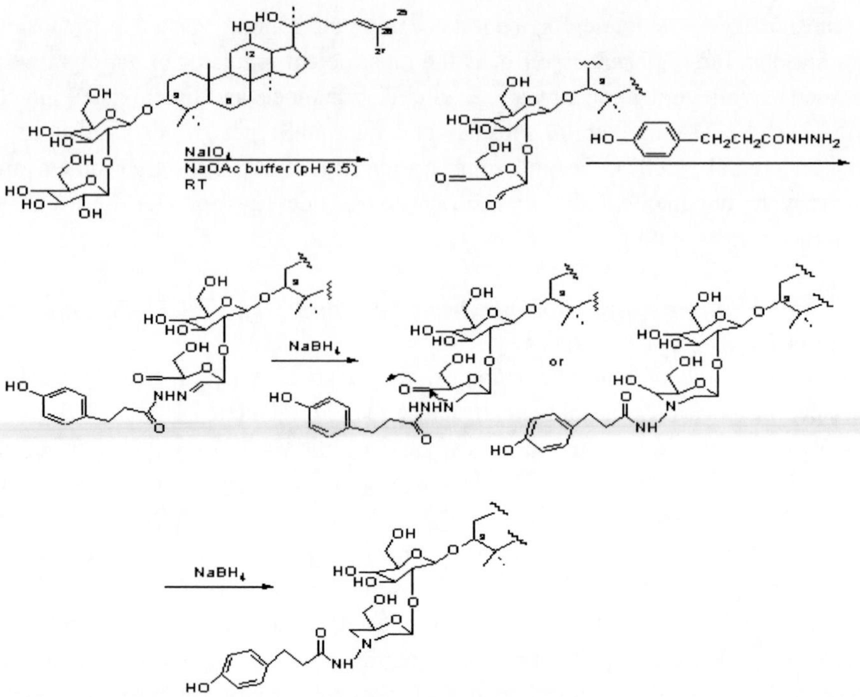

b

Figure 4. Structures of ginsenoside Rg$_3$ and 3-(4-Hydroxyphenyl) propionic acid hydrazide (HPPH) and proposed mechanism for conjugation of ginsenoside Rg$_3$ to HPPH by periodate oxidation method. A. *Left panel,* Ginsenoside Rg$_3$ has two glucoses at the carbon-3 position. Abbreviations for carbohydrates are as follows: Glc, glucopyranoside. *Right panel,* Structures of HPPH. B. The detail procedure for ginsenoside Rg$_3$-HPPH conjugate was described in Kim *et al.* (2005). Adapted from Kim *et al.* (2005).

## 2. 20 (R)- And 20(S)-Ginsenoside Rg$_3$ Epimers in Ion Channel Regulations: A Role of Hydroxyl Group at the Carbon-20

Some of ginsenosides exist as stereoisomers at the carbon-20. Ginsenoside epimers are distinguished by the position of hydroxyl group at the carbon-20 of ginsenoside (Fig. 3). 20(R)-ginsenoside Rg$_3$ maintains as more straight form, whereas 20(S)-ginsenoside Rg$_3$ maintains as a little bent form to the direction of backbone of ginsenoside Rg$_3$ (Kang et al., 2005). In study for structure and biological activity relationships, 20(S)- but not 20(R)-ginsenoside Rg$_3$ inhibited voltage dependent Ca$^{2+}$, K$^+$, and Na$^+$ channels, indicating that these channels interact with ginsenoside Rg$_3$ with stereospecific manner (Jeong et al., 2004). In modeling studying using 20(R)-ginsenoside Rg$_3$ and 20(S)-ginsenoside Rg$_3$, 20(S)-ginsenoside Rg$_3$ has more tight hydrophobic packing near the chiral center than 20(R)-ginsenoside Rg$_3$. Tertiary structures and activities of 20(S)-ginsenoside Rg$_3$ has more tight hydrophobic packing near the chiral center than 20(R)-ginsenoside Rg$_3$ and indicate that 20(S)-ginsenoside Rg$_3$ may have stronger interactions with the interaction region in Na$^+$ channels than 20(R)-ginsenoside Rg$_3$ (Kang et al., 2005). The position of hydroxyl group at carbon-20 in 20(S)- rather than 20(R)-form might play a key role in providing a favorable environment for 20(S)-ginsenoside Rg$_3$ to access the interaction sites of pore when voltage-dependent ion channels are in the resting or open state following the voltage steps for channel activation. In addition, ginsenoside Rg$_3$ inhibits agonist stimulated-blood vessel contractions. In *ex vivo* experiments using swine coronary artery, it was further demonstrated that treatment with 20(*S*)- but not 20(*R*)-ginsenoside Rg$_3$ caused a potent concentration-dependent, endothelium-independent relaxation of coronary artery contraction induced by high K$^+$. However, treatment with both 20(*S*)- and 20(*R*)-ginsenoside Rg$_3$ induced a significant, concentration-dependent relaxation of 5-HT-induced coronary artery contractions in intact samples, while only 20(*S*)-ginsenoside Rg$_3$ inhibited coronary artery contraction in endothelium-denuded arteries (Kim et al., 2006). Thus, in addition to ion channel regulations in single cell, ginsenoside Rg$_3$ epimers might also exhibit differential regulations in smooth muscle contractions. These results also show further possibility that ginsenoside Rg$_3$ epimers might differ from each other in their *in vivo* actions depending on the position of hydroxyl group of the carbon-20.

Interestingly, both epimers inhibited ligand-gated ion channel activities such as 5-HT$_{3A}$ and nicotinic acetylcholine receptors, although the inhibitory effects on these ligand-gated ion channel activities by 20(*R*)-ginsenoside Rg$_3$ was less than that of 20(*S*)-ginsenoside Rg$_3$ (Jeong et al., 2004). Ginsenoside Rg$_3$ epimers act less stereospecific in ligand-gated ion channel regulations than voltage-gated ion channels. These results indicate that voltage-dependent ion channels and ligand-gated ion channels interact with ginsenoside Rg$_3$ epimers with differential manners. Taken together, a slight difference in the position of hydroxyl group at the carbon-20 of backbone structure between the ginsenoside Rg$_3$ epimers produces a large difference in ion channel regulation.

### 3. Contribution of Aliphatic Side Chain at the Carbon-20 of 20(S)-Ginsenoside Rg$_3$ in Ion Channel Regulations

As shown in Figure 2, ginsenosides isolated from ginseng have aliphatic side chain CH$_2$CH$_2$CH=C(CH$_3$)$_2$ at the carbon-20 of backbone structure. This aliphatic side chain is similar to that of cholesterol except the double bonds at the carbon-24 and -25. The aliphatic side chain of 20(*S*)-ginsenoside Rg$_3$ was oxygenated when it was orally administered to experimental animals. In feces the oxygenated 20(*S*)-ginsenoside Rg$_3$ metabolites and backbone metabolites without the moiety of the CH$_2$CH$_2$CH=C(CH$_3$)$_2$ were found (Qian et al., 2005). Although this aliphatic side chain of 20(*S*)-ginsenoside Rg$_3$ undergoes metabolic processes *in vivo*, it is unknown about the functional role of the intact aliphatic side chain in ion channel regulations. Lee *et al.* (2008) prepared 20(*S*)-ginsenoside Rg$_3$ derivatives by modifying the aliphatic side chain of ginsenoside Rg$_3$, remaining with backbone structure and carbohydrate portion intact and demonstrated that the reduction of double bond in aliphatic side chain of 20(*S*)-ginsenoside Rg$_3$ exhibited agonistic actions in Na$^+$ channel current inhibitions by shifting concentration-response curve to leftward by three-fold. However, they showed that deletion, hydroxylation, or oxygenation of aliphatic side chain caused an attenuation or loss of Na$^+$ channel current inhibitions (Lee et al., 2008). These results provide evidences that the aliphatic side chain of 20(*S*)-ginsenoside Rg$_3$ is also involved in Na$^+$ channel regulations and further show a possibility that the aliphatic side chain of ginsenoside Rg$_3$ could be also one of contributors in ion channel regulations.

### 4. A Possible Role of Ginsenoside Rg$_3$ Backbone Structure in Ion Channel Regulations

The steroid-like backbone structure of 20(*S*)-ginsenoside Rg$_3$ is the common skeleton portion of all ginsenosides. The pathway of ginsenoside backbone synthesis in *Panax* ginseng is almost same with that of mammalian sterol synthesis (Haralampidis et al., 2002). The initial steps for backbone structure synthesis of ginsenosides begin with squalene as sterols and are divided into two pathways. One is for sterols, the other one is for triterpenoid dammarane. Thus, the backbone structure of ginsenosides is not much different from plant or mammalian sterols except several methyl and hydroxyl groups at several positions (Haralampidis et al., 2002). Although the backbone structure of ginsenoside is a main portion of ginsenoside, it is not simple to explain how the backbone structure, non-polar hydrophobic portion of 20(S)-ginsenoside $Rg_3$, contributes 20(S)-ginsenoside $Rg_3$-induced ion channels or ligand-gated ion channel regulations. One hypothesis is that the hydrophobic steroid-like component of ginsenoside could be inserted as a wedge into channel pore regions or pore entrance, when channel pore is open and permeable for ions after depolarization or receptor activations. It is unlikely that ginsenoside $Rg_3$ penetrates into cell membrane, since the carbohydrate of carbon 3 position of ginsenoside $Rg_3$ makes the hydrophobic bonds with channel pore amino acids (Lee et al., 2008). In addition, although the hydrophobic non-polar backbone of 20(S)-ginsenoside $Rg_3$ inserts as a wedge into ion channel or ligand-gated ion channel pore region when these channels are open or resting state, the degree of insertion of 20(S)-ginsenoside $Rg_3$ into pore region might be dependent on the pore sizes of ion channels or ligand-gated ion channels. It is known that the pore sizes of voltage-dependent ion channels or ligand-gated ion channels are not homogenous, depending on types of ion channels (Hille, 2001). For example, muscle-type nicotinic acetylcholine receptor has larger pore size than other $Na^+$ or $K^+$ channels in order of sequence of muscle-type nicotinic acetylcholine receptor > $Na^+$ channel > $K^+$ channel. Therefore, it is likely that the three dimensional size of backbone structure of 20(S)-ginsenoside $Rg_3$ might determine how much 20(S)-ginsenoside $Rg_3$ interacts with and at which position of ginsenoside $Rg_3$ interacts with channel pore amino acid residues with helps of hydrogen bond formations by sugars with channel proteins. If the pore size of ion channels or ligand-gated ion channels is not enough large for 20(S)-ginsenoside $Rg_3$ to go into pore, 20(S)-ginsenoside $Rg_3$ might interact with pore entrance, slightly inside of pore, or more deep inside of pore. Thus, the degree of penetration of backbone structure of 20(S)-ginsenoside $Rg_3$ into channel pore of ion channels or ligand-gated ion channels might be dependent on three dimensional conformations of ion channel or ligand-gated ion channel proteins. Supporting this notion is that site-directed mutations of channel pore or channel entrance of ion channel or ligand-gated ion channels abolished or greatly attenuated 20(S)-ginsenoside $Rg_3$-induced inhibitions (Lee et al., 2007; Lee et al., 2008).

## Conclusion

Ginsenosides, unique saponins only found in *Panax* ginseng, exert their various pharmacological and physiological effects in biological systems. Ginsenosides regulate a variety of ion channels at single cellular level. However, until now it was not explained on the main functional group of ginsenosides. To explain action mechanisms of ginsenosides, ginsenoside $Rg_3$ was chosen as one representative ginsenoside. Structure-activity relationships of ginsenoside $Rg_3$ was examined in ion channel regulations after modification of carbohydrate portion and ginsenoside $Rg_3$ derivatives at aliphatic side chain. In addition, the role of ginsenoside $Rg_3$ stereoisomers was also examined at the carbon-20. Based on reports, it is unlikely that the functional group of ginsenoside $Rg_3$ is not limited to a specific portion of ginsenoside $Rg_3$, since the position of hydroxyl group (i.e. stereoisomers) and aliphatic side chain at the carbon-20 of backbone structure, both contribute to membrane ion channels and receptor regulations. The carbohydrate portion of ginsenoside Rg3 is also essential for membrane voltage-gated ion channel regulations. Altogether, the further elucidations on the exact role of each portion that consists of ginsenosides will be required in membrane ion channels and receptor regulations.

## III. The Regulations of Ginsenoside-Induced Membrane Ion Channels

The activation of voltage-gated $Na^+$ channels initiates depolarization and voltage-gated $K^+$ channels are involved in repolarization after depolarization. The activation of voltage-gated $Ca^{2+}$ channels are mainly involved in neurotransmitter releases from presynaptic terminals (Hille, 2001). Voltage-gated $Ca^{2+}$, $K^+$, and $Na^+$ channels are play important roles in action potential induction, duration, and frequency in excitable cells such as muscle fiber, myocytes, and neurons. The agents that target these channel activities could be developed for drugs against excitotoxicities in nervous systems or anti-hypertension. It has been reported that ginsenoside Rg3 regulates voltage-gated ion channels such as $Ca^{2+}$, $K^+$, and $Na^+$ channels (Nah et al., 2007). The characteristics of ginsenoside Rg3-induced ion channel regulations are to exhibit a differential regulations; Ginsenoside Rg3 inhibits voltage-gated $Ca^{2+}$ and $Na^+$ channels (Lee et al., 2005; Lee et al., 2006). Interestingly, ginsenoside Rg3 inhibits voltage-gated $K^+$ channels (Lee et al., 2008) but activates KCNQ $K^+$, $BK_{Ca}$, and decelerates hERG $K^+$ channel deactivation (Choi et al., 2010; Choi et al., 2011a; Choi et al., 2011b). Thus, although ginsenoside Rg3 lacks a specificity or selectivity of ion channels, it seems that ginsenoside Rg3 attenuates excitability of neurons and dilates blood vessel and relaxes heart. The following section will show ginsenoside Rg3 interaction site(s) with ion channel proteins after site-directed mutagenesis.

### 1. Ginsenoside Has Specific Interaction Site(S) in Voltage-Gated Ion Channel Regulations

Although the affinities on ginsenoside Rg3 for the regulation of various ion channels and ligand-gated ion channels are relatively lower than those of channel blockers or toxins, the accumulating evidences that ginsenosides regulate ion channels and ligand-gated ion channels outside of cells, regulate ion channel activity with stereospecific manner, and require carbohydrate components for ion channel regulations show the possibility that ginsenoside might have specific binding or interaction site(s) with ion channel and ligand-gated ion channel proteins. The conventional way to identify ginsenoside interaction site(s) with ion channels or ligand-gated ion channels is to use site-directed mutagenesis and *Xenopus* oocytes gene expression systems (Dascal, 1987). It is generally accepted that if the excitatory or inhibitory effects of a certain channel blocker or toxin were greatly attenuated or abolished after substitution of a specific amino acid into other amino acid by point mutation, the channel blocker or toxin achieves its effects through the interaction with the amino acid residue (Lee et al., 2008). This section will provide the evidences that ginsenoside Rg3 has interaction site(s) with ion channels and show how 20(*S*)-ginsenoside Rg3 interacts with amino acids of channel proteins in the regulation of voltage-gated and ligand-gated ion channels.

## 2. Identification of Ginsenoside Interaction Sites in Voltage-Gated $Ca^{2+}$ Channel Regulations

$Ca^{2+}$ is one of second messengers. $Ca^{2+}$ is an important regulator for many neuronal functions including exocytosis and excitability (Miller, 2001). Voltage-dependent $Ca^{2+}$ channels play an important role in control of cytosolic free $Ca^{2+}$. The neurons possess a variety of voltage-dependent $Ca^{2+}$ channels such as L-, N-, P/Q-, R-, or T-types depending on cell types. However, excessive elevation of cytosolic free $Ca^{2+}$ level induces cell damages and finally cell death (Berridge et al., 1998; Miller, 2001). $Ca^{2+}$ channels are transmembrane proteins that consist of a pore-forming $\alpha$ subunit and several auxiliary subunits. The $\alpha$ subunit is composed of four homologous domains (I-IV), each composes of six $\alpha$-helical transmembrane segments (S1-S6) like $Na^+$ channels, and is responsible for voltage-dependent increases in $Ca^{2+}$-selective permeability (Lee et al., 2006). $\beta$ subunits could also affect the various states in response to time- and voltage-dependent signaling (Lee et al., 2006). Site-directed mutagenesis studies have allowed characterization of the detailed actions and binding sites of various $Ca^{2+}$ channel antagonists or toxins (Kraus et al., 1998; He, 1997; Yamaguchi et al., 2003)

Previous reports show that ginseng extract and ginsenosides inhibit $Ca^{2+}$ channels in sensory neurons. Among various ginsenosides such as ginsenosides $Rb_1$, Rc, Re, Rf, and $Rg_1$, ginsenoside Rf was more potent for the inhibition of $Ca^{2+}$ channels (Nah et al., 1995). On the other hand, Kim *et al.* (1998) demonstrated that ginsenosides inhibit $Ca^{2+}$ channels in rat chromaffin cells, which are one of the representative neurosecretory cells in catecholamine releases under various stress situations. The order of inhibitory potency on $Ca^{2+}$ channel in rat chromaffin cells was ginsenoside Rc > Re > Rf > $Rg_1$ > $Rb_1$. Ginsenosides also showed a selectivity in $Ca^{2+}$ channel regulation by inhibiting N-, P-, Q/R- but not L-type $Ca^{2+}$ channel in bovine chromaffin cells (Choi et al., 2001a). Rhim *et al.* (2002) showed that ginsenoside $Rg_3$ more potently inhibits L-, N-, and P-types of $Ca^{2+}$ channels than other ginsenosides tested in rat sensory neurons. In addition to $Ca^{2+}$ channel inhibition by ginsenosides, Kim *et al.* (1998) also showed that ginsenosides attenuated the stimulated membrane capacitance increase ($\Delta C_m$) in rat chromaffin cells. The order of inhibitory potency on $\Delta C_m$ was ginsenoside Rf > Rc > Re > $Rg_1$ > $Rb_1$. Thus, the attenuation of $Ca^{2+}$ channel and membrane capacitance by ginsenosides suggests that ginsenosides might be closely involved in the regulation of neurotransmitter releases from presynaptic nerve terminal(s). Ginsenoside $Rg_3$ inhibits $Ca^{2+}$ channel currents in a stereospecific manner and affects the steady-state activation but not inactivation (Jeong et al., 2004). These reports suggest that ginsenoside has specific interaction site(s) on $Ca^{2+}$ channels.

Among various voltage-gated $Ca^{2+}$ channels, Choi *et al.* (2009) chose and tried to identify ginsenoside interaction site(s) in *Xenopus* oocytes expressing wild-type and mutant L-type $Ca^{2+}$ channels using the two-microelectrode voltage-clamp technique. Choi *et al.* (2009) assessed how various point mutations of the L-type $Ca^{2+}$ channel affect the ginsenoside $Rg_3$ action. They have first examined whether ginsenoside $Rg_3$ shares the overlapping sites with dihydropyridine (DHP) and diltiazem binding sites in the regulation of L-type $Ca^{2+}$ channels (Kraus et al., 1998; He, 1997; Yamaguchi et al., 2003) but found that these sites did not affect ginsenoside $Rg_3$-mediated inhibition of L-type $Ca^{2+}$ channel activity (Choi *et al.*, 2009). Next, after finding that ginsenoside $Rg_3$ regulates Nav1.2 and Nav1.4 channel currents by interacting with amino acid residues such as N418, L421 and L437 of transmembrane domain IS6.18), Choi *et al.* (2009) examined some structural homologies of

$Ca^{2+}$ channel with $Na^+$ channels. They mutated the analogous amino acids from Val426 to Gly432 in transmembrane domain IS6 of the L-type $Ca^{2+}$ channel and examined ginsenoside $Rg_3$ action. Among various domains of L-type $Ca^{2+}$ channels, mutations of L427R, N428R and L431K in transmembrane domain-I-segment 6 (IS6) of the channel significantly attenuated the ginsenoside $Rg_3$ action and caused rightward shifts in dose-response curves, although the inhibitory effects of ginsenoside $Rg_3$ on $Ca^{2+}$ currents was not completely abolished. In addition, ginsenoside $Rg_3$ treatment produced a negative shift in the inactivation voltage but did not alter the steady-state activation voltage, and none of the mutant channels affected the ginsenoside $Rg_3$-induced negative shift of inactivation voltage. Ginsenoside $Rg_3$ had no effects on inactivation time constant in wild-type and mutant channels. Thus, mutations of L427R, N428R and L431K in transmembrane domain-I-segment 6 (IS6) of the channel partially attenuated ginsenoside $Rg_3$ action. In other ion channels or receptors such as Kv1.4, $Na^+$ channels and 5-$HT_{3A}$ receptor, point mutation of specific amino acid residues almost abolished ginsenoside $Rg_3$ sensitivity (Lee et al., 2007a; Lee et al., 2008a; Lee et al., 2008b) The difference in the severity of the ginsenoside $Rg_3$ effect on the L-type $Ca^{2+}$ channel *versus* other channels and receptors provide us to two possibilities; first the point mutations in the L-type $Ca^{2+}$ channel may not be effective enough to confer complete resistance to ginsenoside $Rg_3$. The other possibility is that the amino acid residues identified are only one part of the interaction site(s) for ginsenoside $Rg_3$ regulations of L-type $Ca^{2+}$ channel. Ginsenoside $Rg_3$-induced inhibition of L-type $Ca^{2+}$ channel currents is attenuated by mutations of Leu427, Asn428 and Leu431 in transmembrane IS6 residues. Leu427, Asn428 and Leu431 residues of the L-type $Ca^{2+}$ channel play important roles in the ginsenoside $Rg_3$ effect on L-type $Ca^{2+}$ channel properties.

## 3. Identification of Ginsenoside Interaction Sites in Various $K^+$ Channel Subtype Regulations

There are many kinds of $K^+$ channels in living cells. The representative $K^+$ channels are voltage-dependent $K^+$ (Kv) channel, $Ca^{2+}$-activated $K^+$ channel ($BK_{Ca}$), ATP-sensitive $K^+$ channel ($K_{ATP}$), KCNQ $K^+$ channel, hERG $K^+$ channel, and G protein coupled inwardly rectifying $K^+$ (GIRK) channel in neuronal or non-neuronal systems (Hille, 2001). Most of $K^+$ channels are involved in regulation of repolarization and in control of frequency of action potential in excitable cells or in relaxation of smooth muscle by allowing the efflux of $K^+$ ion from cytosol (Hille, 2001). This section will show how ginsenoside $Rg_3$ regulates with Kv, $BK_{Ca}$, KCNQ $K^+$, or hERG $K^+$ channel and also provides that there is a consistent pattern in the ginsenoside $Rg_3$-induced $K^+$ channel regulations.

Voltage-gated $K^+$ (Kv) channels play critical roles in a wide variety of physiological processes, including the regulation of neurotransmitter release, neuronal excitability, heart rate, muscle contraction, hormone secretion, epithelial electrolyte transport, cell volume and cell proliferation in both neuronal and non-neuronal cells (Hille, 2001). Kv channels consist of tetramers of pore-forming $Kv\alpha$ and auxiliary $Kv\beta$ subunits (Armstrong and Bezanilla, 1977). The $Kv\alpha$ subunit is composed of six $\alpha$-helical transmembrane segments (S1-S6). The S4 segment acts as the voltage-sensing module of the $K^+$ channel (Armstrong and Bezanilla, 1977), while the pore forming S5 and S6 segments constitute a selectivity filter and govern voltage-dependent increases in $K^+$ permeability. There are numerous Kv channel subtypes: some Kv channel $\alpha$ subunits exhibit transient A-type $K^+$ currents and N-type inactivation, while others exhibit long-lasting, delayed-rectifying C-type $K^+$ currents and C-type inactivation, depending on the channel conductance and gating characteristics (Hoshi et al., 1990). Site-directed mutagenesis studies using Kv$\alpha$ subunits have clarified the detailed actions and binding sites of various drugs or toxins that regulate Kv channel activity (Armstrong and Bezanilla, 1977).

It is well-known that ginsenosides relax blood vessels and other smooth muscles but the mechanism was not clearly demonstrated (Kim et al., 1999). Recent report shows that ginseng total saponins and ginsenoside Rg$_3$ activate Ca$^{2+}$-activated K$^+$ and ATP-sensitive K$^+$ channel in rabbit coronary artery smooth muscle cells (Chung and Kim, 1999; Chung and Lee, 1999). Li et al. (2001) demonstrated that the activation of Ca$^{2+}$-activated K$^+$ channels by ginsenosides in vascular smooth muscle cells were mediated by mobilization of intracellular free Ca$^{2+}$ following ginsenoside treatment. These results show the possibility that ginseng might stimulate membrane components for intracellular Ca$^{2+}$ mobilization cascades and the mobilized Ca$^{2+}$ activates Ca$^{2+}$-activated K$^+$ channels, which in turn mediate repolarization of smooth muscle cells in blood vessel from depolarization induced by various endogenous or exogenous stimuli.

Regarding to ginsenoside Rg$_3$ action on voltage-gated K$^+$ channels, Jeong et al. (2004) showed that ginsenoside Rg$_3$ inhibits voltage-dependent K$^+$ channel (Kv1.4) expressed in Xenopus laevis oocytes, although the subsets of Kv channel currents were not blocked by ginsenoside Rg$_3$ (data not shown), indicating that ginsenoside Rg$_3$ exhibited a differential regulation of Kv channel subtypes. Jeong et al. (2004) have also demonstrated that ginsenoside Rg$_3$ regulates human Kv1.4 channel activity in a stereospecific manner: 20(S)-ginsenoside Rg$_3$ but not 20(R)-ginsenoside Rg$_3$ inhibits Kv1.4 channel currents. Based on these results, ginsenoside Rg$_3$ might regulate Kv1.4 channel activity through specific interaction site(s) in the Kv1.4 channel protein.

Interestingly, Lee et al. (2008) found that the inhibitory effects of ginsenoside Rg$_3$ on Kv1.4 channel currents was abolished by K$^+$ activation, which is induced by increasing the extracellular K$^+$ concentration. The regulatory effect of ginsenoside Rg$_3$ on Kv1.4 channel activity are strongly dependent on the extracellular K$^+$ concentration by shifting ginsenoside Rg$_3$ concentration-response curve rightward, indicating that ginsenoside Rg$_3$ competes with extracellular [K$^+$] for the same interaction site (s). The K$^+$ activation site, which is known to locate at the outer pore entry, consists of several amino acids including lysine 531 (K531) (Pardo et al., 2002; Claydon et al., 2004).

Some subsets of Kv channel currents, including Kv1.4, are also affected by extracellular and intracellular tetraethylammonium (TEA), which is a well-known K$^+$ channel blockers. The wild-type Kv1.4 channel, however, is nearly insensitive to TEA. Thus, although extracellular TEA treatment did not inhibit the wild-type Kv1.4 channel, it appeared that extracellular TEA also competed with ginsenoside Rg$_3$ for the inhibition of Kv1.4 channel currents by shifting the ginsenoside Rg$_3$ concentration-response curve rightward (Lee et al., 2008). Interestingly, one of the extracellular TEA binding sites also contains the K531 residue. Mutations in this K531 residue (e.g., K531Y) increased the sensitivity of the Kv1.4 channel to extracellular TEA and also abolished K$^+$ activation. These results indicate that ginsenoside Rg$_3$-mediated regulation of Kv1.4 channel activity might be achieved through common interaction site(s) for K$^+$ activation and TEA binding sites. Alternatively, the ginsenoside Rg$_3$ interaction site(s) might overlap with the K$^+$ activation site or TEA binding site. Lee et al. (2008a) proved it using various mutants in the Kv1.4 channel, including the K531 residue. Mutants were made in the channel pore regions: channel pore sites (S510K, D513Q, V525L, and V535Q) and outer pore sites (K531A, P532A, I533A, T534A, V535A) (Watanabe et al., 2004). Kv1.4 channel mutants were also made in the N-glycosylation site (N353Q) (Judge et al., 1999), the voltage sensor site (R447C and R450C) (Claydon et al., 2004), the voltage shift sites (L478F and G548P) (Bett et al., 2004), the pH sensitive site (H507Q) and the C-type inactivation site (V560A) (Claydon et al., 2004). The K531A mutant, located in one of the outer pores, significantly attenuated ginsenoside $Rg_3$ inhibition of Kv1.4 channel currents, while the other mutants had no significant effects. These results suggest the possibility that ginsenoside $Rg_3$ regulates Kv1.4 channel activity by interacting with Lys531, which is also known to be one of the $K^+$ activation sites and one of the extracellular TEA binding sites. Other mutant channels at the K531 residue such as K531Y, I533M, and K531Y-I533M showed that the K531Y but not I533M substitution and the K531YI533M double substitution nearly abolished ginsenoside $Rg_3$ inhibition of Kv1.4 channel currents (Lee et al., 2008a). These results indicate clearly that ginsenoside $Rg_3$-mediated regulation of Kv1.4 channel activity is closely related to the Lys531 residue.

Since site-directed mutagenesis experiments provide an evidence that ginsenoside $Rg_3$ has interaction sites with Kv1.4 channel protein, Lee et al. (2008a) also used homology and virtual docking model methods, which give three dimensional configurations, to know how ginsenoside $Rg_3$ could bind to the Kv1.4 channel protein through various interactions such as hydrogen bonds or hydrophobic interactions. They found that the carbohydrate portion of ginsenoside $Rg_3$ plays an important role in its interaction with the Kv1.4 channel. The second, but not the first, carbohydrate attached at carbon-3 of the ginsenoside $Rg_3$ backbone forms six hydrogen bonds with amino acids in the pore entryway of the Kv1.4 channel. Among the amino acids forming hydrogen bonds with ginsenoside $Rg_3$, K531 forms three bonds and threonine and histidine form the other hydrogen bonds. However, the K531Y mutant in the Kv1.4 channel shows only two hydrogen bonds with ginsenoside $Rg_3$. Homology and virtual docking model methods demonstrated that mutation of K531 to K531Y induces a conformational change and results in only two hydrogen bonds with ginsenoside $Rg_3$. Finally, ginsenoside $Rg_3$-mediated Kv1.4 channel regulation is achieved through interaction with a specific amino acid residue of Kv1.4 channel protein.

In addition, Lee et al. (2008a) also demonstrated that homology and virtual docking model methods could be used to identify the role of the ginsenoside $Rg_3$ backbone in the regulation of Kv1.4 channel. In this modeling study, ginsenoside $Rg_3$ backbone is located in the pore portion of the Kv1.4 channel, and this position could block the pore and interrupt $K^+$ efflux when the channel is stimulated by depolarization. The second carbohydrate portion of ginsenoside $Rg_3$ forms stable hydrogen bonds with amino acids in the outer pore entryway. Thus, the backbone of ginsenoside $Rg_3$ could acts as a physical plug or wedge in ginsenoside $Rg_3$-mediated Kv1.4 channel regulation. Taken together, the use of a site-directed mutagenesis method and homology and virtual docking model methods allows us to get information on the confirmation and identification of ginsenoside $Rg_3$ interaction site on the Kv1.4 channel.

Large-conductance $Ca^{2+}$-activated $K^+$ ($BK_{Ca}$) channels are a family of potassium-selective ion channels activated in response to elevation of intracellular free $Ca^{2+}$ level following membrane depolarization (Hille, 2001). $BK_{Ca}$ channels are composed of two subunits: the $\alpha$ (also called Slo) subunit, which forms the channel pore (Ghatta et al., 2006; Salkoff et al., 2006), and the $\beta$ subunit (Wanner et al., 1999), which modifies the voltage and calcium sensitivity of the pore-forming subunit (Qian et al., 2002). The $\alpha$ subunit has large cytoplasmic C terminus, is responsible for the calcium-dependent activation of the channel (Schreiber and Salkoff, 1997; Schreiber et al., 1999; Wei et al., 1994). $BK_{Ca}$ channels are activated by increased intracellular $Ca^{2+}$ and/or $Ca^{2+}$-dependent kinases including CaM kinases, PKA, and PKC (Toro et al., 1998; Weiger et al., 2002). $BK_{Ca}$ channels play key roles in a variety of neuronal and non-neuronal cell functions. For example, in neurons, since elevation of $[Ca^{2+}]_i$ in presynaptic sites is also coupled to activation of $BK_{Ca}$ channels, which are usually co-localized with voltage-dependent $Ca^{2+}$ channels in presynaptic sites for repolarization or return to resting membrane potential (Berkefeld et al., 2006), $BK_{Ca}$ channels regulate frequency of firing, action potential afterhyperpolarization and neurotransmitter release. $BK_{Ca}$ channels are also one of the main ion channels that contribute action potential repolarization and afterhyperpolarization during excitation-contraction coupling in vascular smooth muscle cells (Ohi et al., 2001).

$BK_{Ca}$ channel activators or openers could be utilized as neuroprotective agents against excessive $Ca^{2+}$ influx through depolarization or excitatory neurotransmitters (Lawson, 2000). For example, NS-1619, BMS-204352 and TIBC act independently from the β subunit (Coghlan et al., 2001; Dick et al., 2002; Ha et al., 2006; Imaizumi et al., 2002; Valverde et al., 1999; Vergara et al., 1998), whereas other openers such as dehydrosoyasaponin-I and 17-β-estradiol require β subunit for their action (Giangiacomo et al., 1998; Valverde et al., 1999). Li *et al.* (2001) demonstrated that the activation of $Ca^{2+}$-activated $K^+$ channels by ginsenosides in vascular smooth muscle cells were mediated by mobilization of intracellular free $Ca^{2+}$ following ginsenoside treatment. These results show the possibility that ginsenosides might stimulate membrane components for intracellular $Ca^{2+}$ mobilization cascades and the mobilized $Ca^{2+}$ activates $Ca^{2+}$-activated $K^+$ channels, which in turn mediate repolarization of smooth muscle cells from depolarization induced by various endogenous or exogenous stimuli.

Choi *et al.* (2011a) observed that ginsenoside $Rg_3$ enhanced $BK_{Ca}$ channel currents. Ginsenoside $Rg_3$-enhancement of $BK_{Ca}$ channel currents was independent of intracellular $Ca^{2+}$ and was not desensitized, since BAPTA, a $Ca^{2+}$ chelator, did not block ginsenoside $Rg_3$-induced enhancement of $BK_{Ca}$ channel currents. $BK_{Ca}$ channel was sensitive to TEA and rather the presence of TEA significantly shifted the concentration response curve of ginsenoside $Rg_3$ towards the right and vice versa in wild-type channel, indicating that ginsenoside $Rg_3$ compete extracellular TEA binding site(s). In addition, Choi *et al.* (2011a) also found that ginsenoside $Rg_3$-enhancement of $BK_{Ca}$ channel current was independent of β subunit, suggesting that ginsenoside $Rg_3$ effects on $BK_{Ca}$ channel are achieved through direct interaction with α subunit.

Next, Choi et al. (2011a) investigated the mechanisms by which ginsenoside $Rg_3$ achieved the enhancement of $BK_{Ca}$ channel currents through interaction with α subunit. Based on the previous report by Lee et al. (2008a), Choi et al. (2011a) also constructed mutant channels at the channel pore entryway of α subunit and found that ginsenoside $Rg_3$ effects on $BK_{Ca}$ channel current enhancements were also greatly attenuated in Y360I mutant channels, which residue is located at similar position with Kv1.4 channel and is also known as extracellular TEA binding site of $BK_{Ca}$ channel.

On the other hand, a variety of ion channels regulate the electrical activities of animal heart (Hille, 2001). For example, when voltage-dependent $Na^+$ (Nav1.5) and $Ca^{2+}$ (L-type) channels are activated, heart muscle leads to excitation and contraction. Activation of voltage-dependent $K^+$ channels leads to cardiac repolarization and relaxation of the heart. In addition, cardiomyocytes contain two kinds of delayed rectifier $K^+$ channels that are involved in shortening the action potential duration (Robbins, 2001). The delayed rectifier $K^+$ current consists of two components: the rapidly activating ($I_{Kr}$) and the slowly activating component ($I_{Ks}$). Now, the biochemical and electrophysiological studies revealed that hERG ($I_{Kr}$) and KCNQ 1 + KCNE1 ($I_{Ks}$) $K^+$ channels are mainly responsible for the repolarization of heart cardiac action potential (Tristani-Firouzi and Sanguinetti, 2003). Clinically, the genetic or pathological dysfunctions of hERG or KCNQ $K^+$ channels are one of main cardiac diseases such as arrhythmias. Arrhythmias are known as one of causes of sudden cardiac death in the world (Robbins, 2001). Since hERG $K^+$ and KCNQ $K^+$ channel activities play a crucial role in the induction of late rapid cardiac repolarization (Sanguinetti et al., 1996), hERG as well as KCNQ $K^+$ channels are one of the primary pharmacological targets for development of therapeutic drugs against cardiovascular diseases including arrhythmias.

Ginsenosides have also been shown to exhibit anti-hypertension and cardio-protective effects (Attele et al., 1999). Bai et al. (2003) and Furukawa *et al.* (2006) have shown that ginseng extract shortened action potential duration and that ginsenoside Re regulated $I_{Kr}$ and $I_{Ks}$ channel currents of guinea pig cardiomyocytes. However, relatively little is known how ginseng extract and ginsenosides shortened action potential duration through activation of hERG ($I_{Kr}$) and KCNQ ($I_{Ks}$) $K^+$ channels at molecular level. Regarding to hERG ($I_{Kr}$) $K^+$ channel regulations by ginsenoside Rg$_3$, First, Choi et al. (2010, 2011b) demonstrated in *Xenopus* oocytes gene expression systems that ginsenoside Rg$_3$ enhanced $I_{hERG}$ and $I_{tail}$ in concentration- and voltage-dependent manners. Ginsenoside Rg$_3$ not only caused a persistent $I_{deactivating-tail}$ without decay but also decelerated deactivating time constants in both concentration- and voltage-dependent manners. Bepridil, a hERG channel $K^+$ blocker, blocked ginsenoside Rg$_3$ actions. Ginsenoside Rg$_3$ significantly shifted steady-state activation but not inactivation of hERG $K^+$ channel. Finally, mutations of S631 to S631C hERG $\alpha$ subunit abolished ginsenoside Rg$_3$-mediated regulations on hERG $K^+$ channels. Thus, ginsenoside Rg$_3$ enhanced $I_{hERG}$ and $I_{tail}$ and induced a persistent $I_{deactivating-tail}$ with delayed deactivation in hERG $K^+$ channel through interaction with S631 residue (Choi et al., 2011b).

Regarding to KCNQ ($I_{Ks}$) $K^+$ channel, which consists of KCNQ1 plus KCNE1 subunits, Choi et al. (2010) revealed that ginsenoside Rg$_3$ enhanced $I_{Ks}$ currents. Using site-directed mutagenesis to further characterize ginsenoside Rg$_3$ regulation of KCNQ1 plus KCNE1 channel activity, the K318 and V319 residues of the KCNQ1 or KCNQ1 plus KCNE1 channel is involved in ginsenoside Rg$_3$-mediated KCNQ1 or KCNQ1 plus KCNE1 channel regulations. The homology docking modeling shows that K318 residue plays an important role in ginsenoside Rg$_3$ interaction with the closed or open state of the channels. Ginsenoside Rg$_3$-mediated cardio-protective effects by shortening action potential duration through activation of $I_{Kr}$ and $I_{Ks}$ activity are achieved through interaction with S631 residue of hERG $K^+$ channel and K318 and V319 residues of KCNQ1 plus KCNE1 channel, respectively.

Ginsenoside Rg$_3$ regulations of BK$_{Ca}$ channel, hERG $K^+$ channel, and KCNQ1 plus KCNE1 channel could be applied to its *in vivo* pharmacological effects in cardiovascular systems. The enhancing effects of ginsenoside Rg$_3$ on hERG $K^+$ ($I_{Kr}$) channel, KCNQ1 plus KCNE1 ($I_{Ks}$) channel, and BK$_{Ca}$ channel currents might contribute to a facilitation of repolarization of cardiac action potential and shorten action potential duration and could induce blood vessel relaxation. One important finding in ginsenoside Rg$_3$-mediated various $K^+$ channel subtype regulations is that ginsenoside Rg$_3$ interaction site(s) in $K^+$ channel proteins show some consistent patterns. As shown in Figure 5, $K^+$ channels have a common feature in that they all have pore-lining P-loop with a consensus amino acid sequence – TXGYGD–, which is called the $K^+$ channel "signature sequence" (Heginbotham et al., 1992; 1994). These residues, repeated in each of the four α subunits, form the $K^+$ selectivity filter. Ginsenoside $Rg_3$-mediated human Kv1.4, KCNQ ($I_{Ks}$), hERG, and $BK_{Ca}$ $K^+$ channel regulations are achieved through interaction with K531, K318 and V319, S631, and Y360 residue, respectively, of which all residues are present first or second amino acid after – TXGYGD– and are located at the channel pore entryway (Choi et al., 2010, 2011a, 2011b; Lee et al., 2008a) (Figure 5). These results indicate that ginsenoside $Rg_3$ interacts with amino acid residues in common interaction regions near the "signature sequence" in subsets of $K^+$ channels examined. Another important finding in Kv1.4 and $BK_{Ca}$ $K^+$ channel regulation by ginsenoside $Rg_3$ is to share other $K^+$ channel regulator binding site such as extracellular TEA binding site (Lee et al., 2008a).

## 4. Identification of Ginsenoside Interaction Sites in Voltage-Gated Na⁺ Channel Regulations

Activation of voltage-dependent $Na^+$ channels is directly involved in induction of action potentials of axonal and somatic portion of neurons. They are also involved in actively propagating axonal or dendritic information from one part to another part of neuron. There are three subtypes of $Na^+$ channels in excitable cells or organs: neuronal (Nav1.2)-, heart (Nav1.5)- and muscle (Nav1.4)-type $Na^+$ channels. These channels are further divided into at least nine different subtypes (Goldin, 1995). $Na^+$ channels are transmembrane proteins consisting of a pore-forming α subunit and auxiliary β1, β2 and β3 subunits (Goldin, 1995). The α subunit is made up of four homologous domains (I–IV), each composed of six α-helical transmembrane segments (S1–S6), and is responsible for voltage-dependent increases in $Na^+$-selective permeability. The transient inward $Na^+$ current initiates axonal and somatic action potentials in nerve and muscle fibers and may also be involved in intraneuronal axonal or interneuronal information transfer (Goldin, 1995). The $Na^+$ channel α subunit is the primary domain forming the channel pore and voltage sensor, and site-directed mutagenesis has been applied to identify drug/toxin binding sites in this region (Catterall et al., 2007). For example, tetrodotoxin (TTX), a neurotoxin from pufferfish (*fugu*), is a very strong neuronal $Na^+$ channel blocker, and incorrect cooking of this fish still causes the deaths of many people. Using site-directed mutagenesis, investigators identified the TTX binding site, containing several amino acid residues such as phe385 and phe387 (Catterall et al., 2007). As a second example, the local anesthetic lidocaine exhibits its anesthetic effects by inhibiting $Na^+$ channel currents. Also using site-directed mutagenesis, the interaction sites for lidocaine were identified at Phe1764 and/or Tyr1771 of the $Na^+$ channel (Linford et al., 1998). In addition to these two agents, there are many kinds of drugs and toxins that affect $Na^+$ currents.

Recent reports show the regulation of $Na^+$ channel by ginsenosides; Liu et al. (2001) and Jeong et al. (2004) showed that ginsenosides inhibit neuronal $Na^+$ channels expressed in tsA201 cell and *Xenopus laevis* oocytes, respectively. Liu et al. (2001) used much higher concentrations of ginseng extract and ginsenoside $Rb_1$ than those used in other channel regulation to inhibit $Na^+$ channel currents. Jeong *et al.* (2004) showed that ginsenoside $Rg_3$ was much more potent in $Na^+$ channel current inhibitions than other ginsenosides tested. In structure-activity relationship of the ginsenoside $Rg_3$ stereoisomers, using 20(*R*)-ginsenoside $Rg_3$ and 20(*S*)-ginsenoside $Rg_3$, Jeong *et al.* (2004) demonstrated that 20(*S*)-ginsenoside $Rg_3$ but not 20(*R*)-ginsenoside $Rg_3$ inhibited the neuronal $Na^+$ channel currents in a dose- and voltage-dependent manner and showed that the hydroxyl group at carbon-20 of 20(*S*)-ginsenoside Rg$_3$ might be geometrically better aligned with the hydroxyl acceptor group in the ion channels than that of 20(*R*)-ginsenoside Rg$_3$.

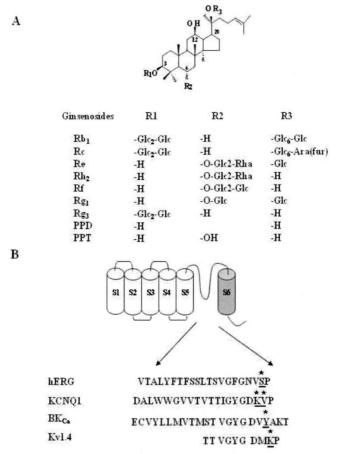

| Ginsenosides | R1 | R2 | R3 |
|---|---|---|---|
| Rb$_1$ | -Glc$_2$-Glc | -H | -Glc$_6$-Glc |
| Rc | -Glc$_2$-Glc | -H | -Glc$_6$-Ara(fur) |
| Re | -H | -O-Glc2-Rha | -Glc |
| Rh$_2$ | -H | -O-Glc2-Rha | -H |
| Rf | -H | -O-Glc2-Glc | -H |
| Rg$_1$ | -H | -O-Glc | -Glc |
| Rg$_3$ | -Glc$_2$-Glc | -H | -H |
| PPD | -H | | -H |
| PPT | -H | -OH | -H |

hERG      VTALYFTFSSLTSVGFGNVSP

KCNQ1      DALWWGVVTVTTIGYGDKVP

BK$_{Ca}$      ECVYLLMVTMST VGYG DVYAKT

Kv1.4      TT VGYG DMKP

Figure 5. Chemical structures of various individual ginsenosides and the primary amino acid sequence of BK$_{Ca}$, hERG, KCNQ1, and Kv1.4 K$^+$ channel α subunit mutated. (A) Structures of various ginsenosides and ginsenoside metabolites, protopanaxadiol (PPD) and protopanaxatriol (PPT) used in this study. Abbreviations for carbohydrates are as follows: Glc, glucopyranoside; Ara (pyr), arabinopyranoside; Rha, rhamnopyranoside. (B) Topology and sequence alignment of BK$_{Ca}$, hERG, KCNQ1, and Kv1.4 K$^+$ channels and the mutated amino acid residues are underlined in the pore helix. The specific amino acid residues in K$^+$ channels that were proposed to interact with 20(*S*)-ginsenoside Rg$_3$ (Rg$_3$) are marked (*). Adapted from Choi et al. (2011b).

In addition, Lee et al. (2008c) also showed the role of aliphatic side chain, [-CH$_2$CH$_2$CH=C(CH$_3$)$_2$], which is coupled to the carbon-20 of backbone structure of 20(*S*)-ginsenoside Rg$_3$ in Na$^+$ channel regulations. The reduction of double bond in aliphatic side chain of 20(*S*)-ginsenoside Rg$_3$ exhibited agonistic actions in Na$^+$ channel current inhibitions by shifting concentration-response curve to leftward by three-fold. However, deletion, hydroxylation, or oxygenation of aliphatic side chain caused an attenuation or loss of Na$^+$ channel current inhibitions. The aliphatic side chain of 20(*S*)-ginsenoside Rg$_3$ as well as the hydroxyl group of carbon-20 of ginsenoside Rg$_3$ stereoisomers plays an important role in Na$^+$ channel regulations. Lee et al. (2008c) further showed a possibility that the aliphatic side chain of ginsenoside Rg$_3$ could be the target of chemical modifications for abolishment or potentiation of ginsenoside Rg$_3$ actions in Na$^+$ channel regulations.

In further characterizing studies about ginsenoside Rg$_3$-mediated voltage-gated neuronal Na$^+$ channel regulations, two main characteristics of ginsenoside Rg$_3$-mediated regulation of wild-type Na$^+$ channels have been identified. One is that ginsenoside Rg$_3$ treatment causes a depolarizing shift in the activation voltage step in wild-type Na$^+$ channels, indicating that ginsenoside Rg$_3$ binding to the Na$^+$ channel does not allow the Na$^+$ channel to easily open at a given voltage step, requiring greater depolarizing stimulation compared to without ginsenoside Rg$_3$ (Lee et al., 2005). The other characteristic is that ginsenoside Rg$_3$ induces use-dependent inhibition, meaning that the channel pore blocking actions of ginsenoside Rg$_3$ are enhanced by rapid, repeated stimulation over a very short time period, indicating that ginsenoside Rg$_3$ might be a kind of open channel blocker. The idea that ginsenoside Rg$_3$ is an open channel blocker of Na$^+$ channel is supported by experiments using inactivation-deficient Na$^+$ channel mutants, in which the inactivation gate has been deleted and transient inward currents are converted into long-lasting inward currents (Lee et al., 2008b). Thus, ginsenoside Rg$_3$ more potently inhibited the plateau than peak $I_{Na}$ and facilitated channel closing in inactivation deficient channel mutants. Interestingly, mutations of one amino acid (lys859 to glu859) in the voltage-sensor domain in the S4 helix abolished the ginsenoside Rg$_3$-mediated depolarizing shift without affecting ginsenoside Rg$_3$-mediated peak current ($I_{Na}$) inhibition. These results indicates that ginsenoside Rg$_3$ might act through interactions with the Na$^+$ channel, and conformational changes of the Na$^+$ channel through mutations in specific amino acid residues affect ginsenoside Rg$_3$ action.

Although ginsenoside Rg$_3$ regulates neuronal Na$^+$ channels as open channel blocker by showing use-dependent inhibition and a depolarizing shift in the activation voltage step in wild-type Na$^+$ channels, these results did not identify, however, the exact interaction sites in the Na$^+$ channel proteins. Since ginsenoside Rg$_3$ regulates K$^+$ channel subtypes through common interaction sites shared with other drugs, Lee et al., (2008b) examined whether ginsenoside Rg$_3$ also inhibits Na$^+$ currents at common interaction sites shared with representative Na$^+$ channel blockers such as tetrodotoxin (TTX) and lidocaine. However, ginsenoside Rg$_3$ still exerts its inhibitory effects on mutant channels in which the lidocaine and TTX binding sites were disrupted, indicating that ginsenoside Rg$_3$ inhibition of Na$^+$ currents is not achieved via the lidocaine or TTX interaction sites.

Batrachotoxin (BTX) is another neurotoxin that acts on Na$^+$ channels. BTX toxin is first found in the skin of South American frog *Phyllobates terribilis* and persistently activates brain Na$_V$1.2 and skeletal muscle Na$_V$1.4 channels rather than inhibiting Na$^+$ currents as lidocaine and TTX do (Wang et al., 1998). In addition, BTX is a kind of steroidal alkaloid toxin, and the backbone structure of BTX is similar to that of ginsenoside Rg$_3$. Interestingly, ginsenoside Rh$_2$ inhibits [$^3$H]BTX-B binding in rat brain membrane fractions (Duan et al., 2006), showing that the ginsenoside Rg$_3$-induced rat brain Na$_{V1.2}$ channel effects may involve the BTX binding sites and that the interference by ginsenoside with [$^3$H]BTX-B binding in rat brain membrane fractions is relevant to ginsenoside Rg$_3$-induced Na$^+$ channel regulations. BTX interaction sites are located at the I433, N434 and L437 residues of the Na$_{V1.4}$ channel and equivalent residues such as I417, N418 and L421 of brain Na$_V$1.2 channel in domain-I segment 6 (IS6). Channel mutations in BTX binding sites, such as N418K and L421K in the rat brain Na$_V$1.2 and L437K in the mouse skeletal muscle Na$_V$1.4 channel, attenuate or abolish ginsenoside Rg$_3$ inhibition of Na$^+$ currents. In addition, channel mutants in BTX binding sites also greatly attenuate the ginsenoside Rg$_3$-mediated depolarizing shift of the activation voltage, which is observed in wild-type channels. Moreover, ginsenoside Rg$_3$-mediated use-dependent inhibition was also almost abolished in these mutant channels.

Lee et al. (2008b) demonstrated that the characteristics of ginsenoside Rg$_3$ action on Na$^+$ channels, such as the ginsenoside Rg$_3$-mediated depolarizing shift in the activation voltage and ginsenoside Rg$_3$-mediated use-dependent inhibition, are achieved through BTX binding sites and that BTX binding sites play an important role in modifying ginsenoside Rg$_3$-mediated Na$^+$ channel properties. Finally, BTX, but not lidocaine and TTX, binding sites in brain- and muscle-type Na$^+$ channels play important roles in ginsenoside Rg$_3$-mediated Na$^+$ channel regulation at cellular and molecular levels. Finally, since Na$^+$ and Ca$^{2+}$ channels are one of the targets of neuroprotective substances (Alzheimer, 2002), ginsenoside Rg$_3$ could be one of candidates for neuroprotective applications and drug development.

## Conclusion

The carbodydrate portion at the carbon-3, the position of hydroxyl group at the carbon-20, and the aliphatic side chain at carbon-20 are involved in the regulations of voltage-gated ion channels by ginsenoside Rg$_3$. In addition, site-directed mutagenesis experiments and homology docking modeling allow us to identify ginsenoside Rg$_3$ interaction site(s) and three dimensional configurations between ginsenoside Rg$_3$ and channel proteins. The characteristics in ginsenoside Rg$_3$ interaction with channel proteins are as follows: First, ginsenoside Rg$_3$ interacts with amino acids at channel pore or channel entrance of voltage-gated ion channels. Second, ginsenoside Rg$_3$ shares with ion channel antagonist (i.e., TEA) or toxin (i.e., BTX) interaction sites in K$^+$ and Na$^+$ channel subtype regulations, respectively. And, the hydroxyl groups of carbohydrate portions of ginsenoside Rg$_3$ forms stable hydrogen bonds with channel proteins, since mutations of specific amino acids induce a change of position of amino acids and interfere stable hydrogen bonds with hydroxyl group of carbohydrates. This section might contribute to increased understanding how ginsenoside Rg$_3$ interacts with voltage-gated-ion channel proteins to regulate ion channel activities and might be a molecular basis of ginsenoside Rg$_3$-derived natural drug development.

## IV. The Regulations of Ginsenoside-Induced Membrane Ligand-Gated Ion Channels

There are several types of ligand-gated ion channels. Most of ligand-gated channels are members of the large "Cys-loop" super-family of evolutionarily related and structurally similar ligand-gated ion channels including GABA$_A$ and glycine, 5-HT$_3$, and muscle- and neuronal-type nicotinic acetylcholine receptors. They are present at postsynaptic terminals. The main role of these ligand-gated ion channels is to produce a fast excitatory postsynaptic potential (5-HT$_3$, muscle- and neuronal-type nicotinic acetylcholine, and NMDA receptors) or inhibitory postsynaptic potential (GABA$_A$ and glycine receptors) and regulate synaptic transmission. Ionotropic glutamate receptors belong to other family of ligand-gated channels and activation of them exhibits also fast excitatory postsynaptic potential. Ginsenoside Rg$_3$ also exhibits a differential behavior in ligand-gated ion channel regulations. For example, ginsenoside $Rg_3$ stimulates $GABA_A$ and glycine receptor channel activity, whereas ginsenoside $Rg_3$ inhibits 5-$HT_3$, muscle- and neuronal-type nicotinic acetylcholine, and NMDA receptor channel activities. Thus, it is likely that ginsenoside $Rg_3$ might play an important role for a fine balance through the inhibition of excitatory ligand-gated or stimulation of inhibitory ligand-gated ion channel activities in the central nervous systems. The below section will show how ginsenosides regulate and interact with ligand-gated ion channel proteins through site-directed mutagenesis.

### 1. Regulations of GABA$_A$ and Glycine Receptor Channel Activity by Ginsenosides

$GABA_A$ and glycine receptors are one family of inhibitory ligand-gated ion channels. GABA receptor is predominantly expressed in the brain (Bloom and Iversen, 1971; McCabe and Wamsley, 1986), whereas glycine receptor is predominantly expressed in spinal cord and brain stem (Rajendra et al., 1997). Both receptors form a $Cl^-$-permeable and $Cl^-$-selective transmembrane channel and are responsible for fast inhibitory synaptic transmission (Macdonald and Olsen, 1994; Whiting et al., 1995; Betz, 1990). The physiological roles of $GABA_A$ receptors predominantly include emotion such as fear and anxiety and sleep, and these receptors have several clinically important drug binding sites (Rudolph and Knoflach, 2011). The activation of glycine receptors in spinal cord and brain stem also mediates fast post-synaptic inhibition for reflex responses, voluntary motor control and the processing of sensory signals (Rajendra et al., 1997).

Ginseng has been shown to have an anxiolytic effect in animal model studies (Bhattacharya et al., 1991; Park et al., 2005). Recent studies show that ginsenosides regulate $GABA_A$ receptor. First, in biochemical studies, ginsenosides might regulate the ligand binding with $GABA_A$ receptor. Kimura et al. (1994) showed that ginsenosides differentially regulate the binding of [$^3$H]-flunitrazepam or [$^3$H]-muscimol to the $GABA_A$ receptor in a rat brain membrane fraction (Kimura et al., 1994). On the other hand, Kim *et al.* (2001) showed that prolonged infusion with ginsenoside Rc but not with ginsenoside $Rg_1$ into rat brain elevates [$^3$H]-muscimol binding to the $GABA_A$ receptor in a brain region-specific manner (Kim et al., 2001). Thus, these results have shown that ginsenosides may regulate the $GABA_A$ receptor by affecting the binding affinities of its ligands. In addition, Choi *et al.* (2003) showed that ginsenosides also regulate $GABA_A$ receptor channel activity by enhancing GABA-mediated channel activity (Choi et al., 2003). Thus, in studies using *Xenopus* oocytes expressing human recombinant $GABA_A$ receptor, ginsenoside $Rb_1$, $Rb_2$, Rc, Rd, Re, Rf, $Rg_1$, and $Rg_2$ affected $GABA_A$ receptor channel activity and among them ginsenoside Rc most potently enhanced the GABA-induced inward peak current. Both bicuculline, a $GABA_A$ receptor antagonist, and picrotoxin, a $GABA_A$ channel blocker, blocked the stimulatory effect of ginsenoside Rc on $I_{GABA}$. Niflumic acid (NFA) and 4,4'-diisothiocyanostilbene-2,2'-disulfonic acid, both $Cl^-$ channel blockers, attenuated the effect of ginsenoside Rc on GABA-induced inward peak current.

Compared to $GABA_A$ receptor, ginsenosides-mediated regulation of glycine receptor channel activity was not much performed. Noh *et al.* (2003) investigated the effect of ginsenosides on human glycine $\alpha1$ receptor channel activity expressed in *Xenopus* oocytes using a two-electrode voltage clamp technique. Noh *et al.* (2003) demonstrated that treatment of ginsenoside Rf enhances glycine-induced inward peak current with dose dependent and reversible manner but ginsenoside Rf itself did not elicit membrane currents as ginsenoside $Rg_3$ does in $GABA_A$ receptor. Ginsenoside Rf action on glycine receptor channel activity was blocked by strychnine, glycine receptor antagonist and 4,4'-disothiocyanostilbene-2,2'-disulfonic acid (DIDS), a Cl⁻ channel blocker. Among various ginsenosides, the order of potency for the enhancement of glycine-induced inward Cl⁻ current was ginsenoside $Rb_1$ > $Rb_2$ > $Rg_2$ ≥ Rc > Rf > $Rg_1$ > Re. Further study will be required to elucidate how ginsenosides interact with glycine receptor proteins to enhance glycine-induced inward Cl⁻ current.

## 2. Identification of Ginsenoside Interaction Sites in 5-HT₃ Receptor

5-HT₃ receptor is also one of ligand-gated ion channel superfamily (Maricq et al., 1991). The 5-HT₃ receptor is a cationic ion channel that allows $Ca^{2+}$ and $Na^+$ to flow into cells, causing depolarization when the receptor is activated by serotonin or other agonists. The activation of this channel also is permeable to $K^+$ ions for repolarization that is similar in many ways to nicotinic acetylcholine receptors. 5-HT₃ receptors are sparsely distributed on primary sensory nerve endings in the periphery and widely expressed in the mammalian central nervous system (Maricq et al., 1991). Various agents exert their pharmacological effects by targeting 5-HT₃ receptors, which are mainly involved in vomiting and irritable bowel syndrome (Trigg and Higa, 2010). This receptor is also clinically significant because antagonists of 5-HT₃ receptor have important applications as analgesics, anxiolytics, and antipsychotics (Engleman et al., 2008). The structure of the 5-HT₃ receptor is well-characterized, consisting of a large extracellular N-terminal and intracellular C-terminal, and each subunit has four hydrophobic transmembrane domains (TM1- TM4). The assembly of four homomeric pentamers is required for full functional activity of the 5-HT₃ receptor. Studies have shown that serotonin and agonist binding sites are located in the N-terminal domain at the subunit-subunit interfaces, while the TM2 domains of the five subunits combine to form the channel pore. Reeves et al. (2001) and Panicker et al. (2002) revealed using the substituted cysteine accessibility method that amino acids from D274 to D298 in TM2 form the putative pore-lining face, and that residues D274, G276, E277, S280, T284, L285, L287, S290, V291, F292, L293, I295, and V296 appear to form a gating region that is susceptible to sulfhydryl reagents (Reeves et al., 2001). This putative gating region in the 5-HT₃A receptor is similar to that of the nicotinic acetylcholine receptor.

In traditional medicine, ginseng is also utilized for the alleviation of emesis, which includes nausea and vomiting. Nausea and vomiting are significant adverse effects of anti-cancer agent like cisplatin, and cause significant patient morbidity. Ginseng exhibits in vivo anti-nausea and anti-vomiting properties. For example, Kim et al. (2005) demonstrated that Korean red ginseng total extract has attenuated cisplatin-induced nausea and vomiting using ferrets. 5-HT₃ receptors are involved in vomiting and irritable bowel syndrome (Kim et al., 2005b; Kim et al., 2005c). Ginsenoside $Rg_2$ and ginsenoside metabolites also inhibit 5-HT₃ receptor-gated ion currents ($I_{5-HT}$) in Xenopus oocytes expressing 5-HT₃ receptors (Lee et al., 2004a). The inhibitory effect by ginsenoside $Rg_2$ on 5-HT-induced inward current was also non-competitive and voltage-independent, which is similar manner with that of ginsenoside-induced modulation of nicotinic acetylcholine receptor. In addition, the inhibitory effect of ginsenoside $Rg_3$ on serotonin-induced currents ($I_{5-HT}$) is observed when it is applied extracellularly but not intracellularly (Lee et al., 2004b). Moreover, mutations in pre-TM1, which causes facilitation of 5-HT₃A receptor channel activity, not only abolish the inhibitory effects of 20(R)-ginsenoside $Rg_3$ on 5-HT-induced inward current, but also greatly attenuate the action of 20(S)-ginsenoside $Rg_3$ on 5-HT-induced inward current (Lee et al., 2007b). These results indicate that ginsenoside $Rg_3$ achieves its inhibitory effects through interactions with unidentified amino acids, which are not in the serotonin or agonist binding sites, in a stereospecific manner.

Recently, Lee *et al*. (2007a) used site-directed mutagenesis technique to characterize the detailed actions and binding sites of ginsenoside Rg$_3$ that regulate the 5-HT$_3$ receptor. Mutations in the TM2 region affect $I_{5-HT}$ inhibition in response to anesthetics, cadmium and the open channel blocker TMB-8, so it was thought that ginsenoside Rg$_3$ might interact with the 5-HT$_3$ receptor pore regions of TM2. Based on this hypothesis, Lee *et al*. (2007a) constructed a series of mutant 5-HT$_3$ receptors in the TM2 region and screened one by one. Lee *et al*. (2007a) found that V291A, F292A and I295A mutations in the TM2 region greatly attenuated or abolished ginsenoside Rg$_3$-induced inhibition of peak $I_{5-HT}$. These results further suggest that ginsenoside Rg$_3$ is acting through 5-HT$_3$ receptor, and alterations in TM2 of the 5-HT$_3$ receptor could affect the action of ginsenoside Rg$_3$. Lee *et al*. (2007a) also showed that the V291A mutation but not the F292A or I295A mutations induced constitutively active ion currents, with a decreased current decay rate. Ginsenoside Rg$_3$ treatment of this mutant receptor accelerated the rate of current decay in a dose-dependent manner in the presence of 5-HT, suggesting that the presence of ginsenoside Rg$_3$ caused channel closure rather than opening. Thus, ginsenoside Rg$_3$ and TMB-8, an open channel blocker, inhibited the constitutively active ion currents in a dose-dependent manner. Diltiazem, another open channel blocker, did not prevent ginsenoside Rg$_3$-induced inhibition of the constitutively active ion currents in occlusion experiments (Lee et al., 2007a). This report provides the following further insights: first, ginsenoside Rg$_3$ inhibits 5-HT$_{3A}$ receptor channel activity through interactions with residues V291, F292 and I295 in the channel gating region of TM2, and second, ginsenoside Rg$_3$ regulates 5-HT$_{3A}$ receptor channel activity in the open state at different site(s) from those used by TMB-8 and diltiazem. Thus, ginsenoside Rg$_3$ inhibits the 5-HT$_3$ receptor in the open state through interactions with V291, F292 and I295. The identification of ginsenoside Rg$_3$ interacting sites in the 5-HT$_3$ receptor indicates that ginsenoside Rg$_3$ interacts with 5-HT$_3$ receptor to achieve its biological functions.

### 3. Identification of Ginsenoside Interaction Sites in Nicotinic Acetylcholine Receptor

Nicotinic acetylcholine receptors are one of most extensively investigated receptors among various ligand-gated ion channels. The activation of this receptor by acetylcholine allows influx of cations, most of Na$^+$ ions, into cells through this channel pore. Muscle-type nicotinic acetylcholine receptor consists of α1β1δγ (embryonic form) or α1β1δε (adult form) subunits and are involved in muscle contraction (Lindstrom, 1996; Sargent, 1993). Neuronal type of nicotinic acetylcholine receptors consist of α (α2–α9) and β (β2–β4) subunits. α7 and α9 subunits alone can form functional homomeric receptors or α and β subunits can form functional heteromeric receptors and their distribution are found in the central and peripheral nervous systems, depending on type of organs or regions of nervous systems (Gotti et al., 2009).

Recent reports showed that ginsenosides regulate bovine chromaffin cells that are stimulated by acetylcholine and inhibit catecholamine release from chromaffin cells, which mainly contain α3β4 nicotinic acetylcholine receptors involved in catecholamine release (Tachikawa et al., 1995; Tachikawa et al., 2001). Furthermore, ginsenosides also inhibited acetylcholine-induced inward currents in oocytes expressed with nicotinic receptor α$_1$β$_1$δε or α3β4 subunits, showing the possibility that ginsenosides regulate nicotinic acetylcholine receptor channel activities (Choi et al., 2002). But ginsenosides themselves had no effect on basal currents in oocytes expressing nicotinic acetylcholine receptor $\alpha\beta\delta\varepsilon$ or $\alpha3\beta4$ subunit. The inhibition of acetylcholine-induced inward current by ginsenosides in oocytes expressed with nicotinic acetylcholine receptor $\alpha\beta\delta\varepsilon$ or $\alpha3\beta4$ subunit was reversible, voltage-independent, and non-competitive manner, indicating that ginsenosides do not compete with acetylcholine for those receptor regulations (Choi et al., 2002). Interestingly, it appears that protopanaxatriol ginsenosides such as Re, Rf, $Rg_1$, or $Rg_2$ was more potent than protopanaxadiol ginsenosides such as $Rb_1$, $Rb_2$, Rc, Rd for the inhibition on acetylcholine-induced inward current (Choi et al., 2002). Sala *et al.* (2002) also demonstrated that ginsenoside $Rg_2$ reduced the peak current and increased the desensitization on acetylcholine-induced inward current in oocytes expressing human neuronal nicotinic acetylcholine receptors such as $\alpha3\beta4$, $\alpha3\beta2$, $\alpha4\beta4$, and $\alpha4\beta2$.

Interestingly, ginsenosides had no effect on homomeric $\alpha7$ nicotinic acetylcholine receptors-mediated ion currents (Lee et al., 2009). The homomeric $\alpha7$ nicotinic acetylcholine receptors are the major binding site for $\alpha$-bungarotoxin in the mammalian central nervous system and are $Ca^{2+}$ permeable and are predominantly expressed in cortical and limbic areas (Gotti et al., 2000). $\alpha7$ nicotinic acetylcholine receptor and $5-HT_{3A}$ receptors are both homomeric ligand-gated ion channels. Furthermore, these two receptors share many homologous amino acid sequences in TM2. In previous report, Lee *et al.* (2007) showed that ginsenosides, including ginsenoside $Rg_3$, inhibit 5-HT-mediated ion currents in *Xenopus* oocytes expressing $5-HT_{3A}$ receptors. Moreover, mutation F292A in TM2 of the homomeric $5-HT_{3A}$ receptor abolished ginsenoside $Rg_3$-induced inhibition of peak current, showing that ginsenoside-induced ligand-gated cation channel regulation is achieved via interactions with amino acids residing in the channel pore (Lee et al., 2007). However, since ginsenosides regulate heteromeric nicotinic acetylcholine receptor channel activities, it is difficult to find out ginsenoside interaction site(s) using heteromeric nicotinic acetylcholine receptors.

In addition, many lines of evidence have shown that single point mutation in the highly conserved Leu247 to Thr247 in transmembrane domain 2 (TM2), which forms the channel pore region, creates gain-of-function alterations (i.e., slower desensitization, increased acetylcholine affinity, and a linear current-voltage relationship) and alters pharmacological properties (i.e., conversion of various $\alpha7$ nicotinic acetylcholine receptor antagonists into agonists) (Bertrand et al., 1992). Thus, the L247 residue of $\alpha7$ nicotinic acetylcholine receptor could be a useful target for the study of $\alpha7$ nicotinic acetylcholine receptor-related pharmacology (i.e., drug developments) and channel gating of acetylcholine receptor (Lyford et al., 2003). In addition, the Leu residue corresponding to position 247 of the chick $\alpha7$ nicotinic acetylcholine receptor channel is highly conserved in all nicotinic, $GABA_A$, $5-HT_3$ and glycine receptors, and has been believed to be positioned at the gate (Lester et al., 2004). Recently acquired high resolution structures of the nicotinic acetylcholine receptor channel also show that the conserved Leu, is located at the narrowest part of the channel, and the side chain of the amino acid head point toward to the lumen of the pore (Miyazawa et al., 2003). The importance of position 247 for gating and conductance has also been demonstrated in a functional study (Bertrand et al., 1992).

Lee *et al.* (2009) examined whether mutation of Leu247 to various other amino acid residues induce changes in the receptor sensitivity to ginsenoside $Rg_3$ and they further characterized ginsenoside $Rg_3$-mediated mutant $\alpha7$ nicotinic acetylcholine receptor regulation and identified potential ginsenoside Rg$_3$ interaction sites with the mutant receptor using three-dimensional modeling techniques. In their report, Lee *et al.* (2009) showed that mutation of the highly conserved Leu247 to Thr247 in the transmembrane domain 2 (TM2) channel pore region of α7 nicotinic acetylcholine receptor induces alterations in channel gating properties and converts α7 nicotinic acetylcholine receptor antagonists into agonists. Interestingly, mutation of L247 to L247A, L247D, L247E, L247I, L247S, and L247T, but not L247K, rendered mutant receptors sensitive to ginsenoside Rg$_3$. They further characterized ginsenoside Rg$_3$ regulation of L247T receptors. Ginsenoside Rg$_3$ inhibition on mutant α7 nicotinic acetylcholine receptor channel currents was reversible and concentration-dependent. Ginsenoside Rg$_3$ inhibition was strongly voltage-dependent and noncompetitive manner. These results indicate that the interaction between ginsenoside Rg$_3$ and mutant receptors might differ from its interaction with the wild-type receptor. The homology docking model between ginsenoside Rg$_3$ and mutant receptor revealed that ginsenoside Rg$_3$ forms hydrogen bonds with amino acids, such as Ser240 of subunit I and Thr244 of subunit II and V at the channel pore, whereas ginsenoside Rg$_3$ localizes at the interface of the two wild-type receptor subunits. Thus, mutation of Leu247 to Thr247 induces conformational changes in the wild-type receptor and provides a binding pocket for ginsenoside Rg$_3$ at the channel pore. This is the first finding on the identification of ginsenoside Rg$_3$ interaction site using mutant but not wild-type nicotinic acetylcholine receptors (Fig. 6).

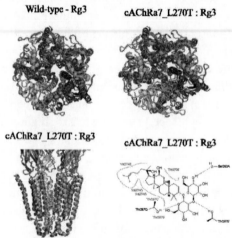

Figure 6. Virtual dockings of ginsenoside Rg$_3$ to chick wild-type and L247T α7 nicotinic acetylcholine receptor (AChR) channel homology models. (A) Top view of the highest-ranked docking model of ginsenoside Rg$_3$ to the wild-type channel. The channel is shown as a cartoon diagram and ginsenoside Rg$_3$ is indicated as a ball and chain model. Each subunit is shown in different colors. (B) Top view and side view of the highest-ranked docking model of ginsenoside Rg$_3$ to the L247T receptor. One of the subunits is omitted in the side view for clarity. All of the top 10 docking results displayed pore blocking of the mutant channel by ginsenoside Rg$_3$. (C) Poseview analysis of proteinligand interactions. Hydrogen bonding is denoted by a dotted line. The spline sections indicate hydrophobic contacts, highlighting the hydrophobic regions of ginsenoside Rg$_3$ and the identity of the contacting amino acid. The roman numerals in parenthesis indicate each subunit of the pentamer. Adapted from Lee *et al.* (2009).

## 4. Identification of Ginsenoside Interaction Sites in NMDA Receptor

Glutamate is a major excitatory neurotransmitter in the central nervous system (Morisyoshi et al., 1991). Glutamate not only interacts with GTP-binding protein coupled receptors (i.e., metabotropic glutamate receptor subtypes) but also binds to various ionotropic ligand-gated glutamate receptors, which include α-amino-3-hydroxy-5-methyl-4-isoxazolepropionic acid (AMPA), kainic acid, and $N$-methyl-D-aspartic acid (NMDA) receptors (Moriyoshi et al., 1991; Hollmann and Heinemann, 1994). Glutamate can interact with both NMDA- and non-NMDA receptors, which are also another class of ligand-gated ion channel. The activation of these receptors by glutamate makes permeable to cations such as $Ca^{2+}$, $Na^+$, or $K^+$ ions, although the selectivity of these cations is dependent on receptor subtypes (Moriyoshi et al., 1991; Hollmann and Heinemann, 1994). Among them NMDA receptors play a pivotal role in the regulation of synaptic functions in the central nervous system (Carroll and Zukin., 2002). In the hippocampus, the activation of NMDA receptors induces long-term potentiation (LTP), which is a key contribution for learning and memory (Lisman et al., 2012). Thus, NMDA receptors have important roles in physiological functions in learning and memory. Currently, NMDA receptors are one of the target proteins for clinical applications against neurotoxicity as well as drug development related to learning and memory (Timofeeva and Levin, 2011).

In regarding ginseng-related effects, ginsenosides $Rb_1$ and $Rg_3$ attenuated glutamate- and NMDA-induced neurotoxicity by inhibiting the overproduction of nitric oxide, formation of malondialdehyde, and influx of $Ca^{2+}$ in rat cortical cultures (Kim et al., 1998). In addition, Kim *et al.* (2002) showed that in rat hippocampal cultures, ginsenosides and ginsenoside $Rg_3$ attenuated high $K^+$-, glutamate-, and NMDA-induced $Ca^{2+}$ influx (Kim et al., 2002). Seong *et al.* (1995) showed that ginsenosides attenuated glutamate-induced swelling of cultured rat astrocytes.

On the other hand, *in vivo* study using anesthetized rats, intracerebroventricular administration of ginsenoside $Rb_1$ but not $Rg_1$ significantly inhibited the magnitude of long term potentiation (LTP) induced by strong tetanus in the dentate gyrus, although ginsenoside $Rb_1$ did not affect the basal synaptic responses evoked by low-frequency test (Abe et al., 1994). Pretreatment of ginsenosides via intrathecal route attenuated NMDA- or substance P- but not glutamate-induced nociceptive behaviors (Yoon et al., 1998; Nah et al., 1999) and pretreatment of ginsenosides via intraperitoneal route also attenuated cell death of hippocampal neurons induced by kainite (Lee et al., 2001).

These results also indicate that ginsenosides might interact with various excitatory neurotransmitter receptor subtypes for their actions and their interactions with excitatory receptors might be coupled to neuroprotection against excitotoxins in nervous systems.

However, the underlying mechanism(s) of ginsenoside $Rg_3$ against excitatory neurotransmitter-induced neurotoxicity are not clearly determined. The NMDA receptor channel complex has a number of regulatory sites that are targets for modulation by endogenous as well as exogenous compounds.

These regulatory sites include a binding site for the endogenous agonist glutamate (and the synthetic NMDA), a co-agonist glycine-binding site, which is different from the chloride-permeable glycine receptor, and sites within the channel lumen where $Mg^{2+}$ and phencyclidines (PCP, MK-801, ketamine, etc.) bind to produce a voltage-dependent open channel block (Lerma et al., 1998).

Kim *et al.* (2004) demonstrated that ginsenoside Rg$_3$ did not compete with NMDA in NMDA receptor-mediated ion current regulations. In addition, they also showed that ginsenoside Rg$_3$ did not interact with Mg$^{2+}$ and phencyclidines (PCP, MK-801, ketamine) binding sites. However, the inhibitory effects of ginsenoside Rg$_3$ on NMDA receptor-mediated ion currents were attenuated by increasing glycine concentrations. Thus, ginsenoside Rg$_3$-mediated inhibition was diminished as the concentration of glycine was increased, showing a possibility that ginsenoside Rg$_3$ seems to be a competitive antagonist at the glycine-binding site, although it was not directly demonstrated using site-directed mutagenesis method. Table 1 provides a brief summary of ginsenosides-mediated regulations of various ion channels and receptors.

### Table 1. Summary of EC$_{50}$ or IC$_{50}$ on ginsenoside-induced inhibitions or stimulations of various voltage-gated ion or ligand-gated ion channel activities

| Voltage-gated ion channels | Ginsenoside | EC$_{50}$ or IC$_{50}$ ($\mu$M) |
|---|---|---|
| Ca$^{2+}$ channels | | |
| L | Rg$_3$ | 39.9 ± 9.5 (Lee et al., 2006) |
| N | Rg$_3$ | 64.4 ± 13.6 (Lee et al., 2006) |
| P/Q | Rg$_3$ | 29.6 ± 11.3 (Lee et al., 2006) |
| R | Rg$_3$ | 57.5 ± 12.5 (Lee et al., 2006) |
| T | Rg$_3$ | 97.3 ± 12.4 (Lee et al., 2006) |
| K$^+$ channels | | |
| Kv1.4 | Rg$_3$ | 32.6 ± 2.2 (Lee et al., 2006) |
| BK$_{Ca}$ | Rg$_3$ | 15.3 ± 3.1 (Choi et al., 2011) |
| hERG | Rg$_3$ | 0.41 ± 0.05 (Choi et al., 2011) |
| KCNQ | Rg$_3$ | 15.2 ± 8.7 (Choi et al., 2010) |
| Na$^+$ channels | | |
| Nav1.2 | Rg$_3$ | 32.0 ± 6.0 (Lee et al., 2005) |
| Nav1.4 | Rg$_3$ | 58.5 ± 6.3 (Lee et al., 2008) |
| Nav1.5 | Rg$_3$ | 16.1 ± 2.8 (Kang et al., 2005) |
| Ligand-gated ion channels | Ginsenoside | EC$_{50}$ or IC$_{50}$ ($\mu$M) |
| GABA$_A$ | Rc | 53.0 ± 12.3 (Choi et al., 2003) |
| Glycine | Rf | 49.8 ± 9.8 (Noh et al., 2003) |
| 5-HT$_3$ | Rg$_3$ | 27.6 ± 4.3 (Lee et al., 2007) |
| Nicotinic acetylcholine | | |
| α3β4 | Rg$_2$ | 60 ± 14 (Choi et al., 2002) |
| α1β1δε | Rg$_2$ | 16 ± 9 (Choi et al., 2002) |
| α7 (L247A mutant) | Rg$_3$ | 33.1 ± 1.3 (Lee et al., 2009) |

EC$_{50}$ (BK$_{Ca}$, hERG, and KCNQ K$^+$ channels and GABA$_A$ and glycine receptors) or IC$_{50}$ (the rest) values was determined in oocytes expressing those ion channels or receptors.

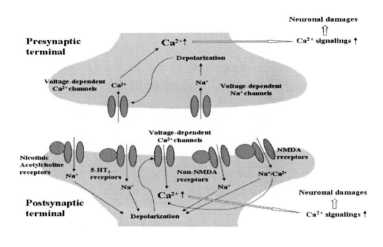

Figure 7. Ginsenosides-induced regulations of $Ca^{2+}$ signalings. (A) This schematic drawings show that cytosolic $Ca^{2+}$ levels are elevated via two different sources from pre- and post-synaptic terminals of nervous systems. The elevation of cytosolic $Ca^{2+}$ levels is either achieved via direct activation of voltage-dependent $Ca^{2+}$ channels or via depolarization caused by voltage-dependent $Na^+$ channel activation at pre-synaptic sites. The second sources of the elevation of cytosolic $Ca^{2+}$ levels are mediated via the activation of 5-$HT_3$, nicotinic acetylcholine, and NMDA/non-NMDA receptors at post-synaptic sites. At pre-synaptic sites, the elevations of intracellular free $Ca^{2+}$ play various important roles for synaptic transmissions including neurotransmitter releases and other $Ca^{2+}$-dependent signalings. At post-synaptic sites the elevations of intracellular free $Ca^{2+}$ also perform various important things such as long-term potentiation and other $Ca^{2+}$-dependent signalings. But the sustained elevations of cytosolic $Ca^{2+}$ level caused by excitatory neurotransmitters or neurotoxins at both sites could induce persistent activations of $Ca^{2+}$-dependent signalings, resulting in neuronal damages such as apoptosis or necrosis. (B) Ginsenosides-induced regulations on ion channels and various ligand-gated in channels attenuate the elevation of cytosolic $Ca^{2+}$ levels mediated by ion channels and ligand-gated ion channels. Thus, the inhibitory effects of ginsenosides on ion channels and ligand-gated ion channels that are directly or indirectly involved in $Ca^{2+}$ signalings could be one of ginsenosides-induced neuroprotective and other beneficial actions in central and peripheral nervous systems.

## V. The Pharmacological Roles of Ginsenoside-Induced Membrane Ion Channel Regulations

In ginsenoside $Rg_3$-mediated ligand-gated ion channel regulations, site-directed mutagenesis experiments and homology docking modeling also allow us to identify ginsenoside $Rg_3$ interaction site(s) with ion channels and ligand-gated ion channels proteins such as 5-$HT_3$ and $\alpha 7$ nicotinic acetylcholine receptors.

The main characteristics of ginsenoside $Rg_3$ interaction site(s) with ligand-gated ion channel proteins are that it could penetrate into channel pore region and interact with amino acids consisting of channel pore, whereas ginsenoside $Rg_3$ interacts with amino acids with channel pore entryway in voltage-gated ion channels, of which sites are shared with channel antagonist and toxin.

In nervous systems, voltage-gated ion channels and ligand-gated ion channels play an important role for depolarization and repolarization, initiation and propagation of action potential, and neurotransmitter release for synaptic transmissions between presynaptic and postsynaptic sites (Hille, 2001). Ginsenoside $Rg_3$ showed a wide range regulatory actions including various ion channels and ligand-gated ion channels involved in synaptic transmission in neuronal or other excitable cells. Ginsenoside $Rg_3$ targets channel pore entrance or channel pore regions, which are common sites for drugs or toxins, for blocking or stimulating ion channels or ligand-gated ion channels. Thus, it is likely that ginsenoside $Rg_3$ attenuates neurotransmitter release from presynaptic sites by inhibiting $Ca^{2+}$ and $Na^+$ channels and also reduces excitatory postsynaptic potentials by inhibiting 5-$HT_3$, nicotinic acetylcholine receptors, NMDA receptor channel activities, whereas ginsenoside $Rg_3$ enhances inhibitory postsynaptic potential by stimulating $GABA_A$ and glycine receptor channel activity (Figure 7).

Ginsenoside $Rg_3$ exhibits dual actions in the regulations of ion channel activity. Taken together, ginsenoside $Rg_3$ might play important roles for the attenuation of over-excitation-induced neurotoxicity and provide neuroprotective actions against various excitatory agents in nervous systems and ginsenoside $Rg_3$ might be clinically applied for neuroprotective agent (Figure 7).

# PART II

## 1. Introduction

Part I has shown that ginsenoside $Rg_3$ regulates various voltage-gated ion channels and ligand-gated ion channels with stereospecific manner and also showed the role of each portion (i.e., carbohydrates or aliphatic side chain) of ginsenoside $Rg_3$-induced ion channel regulations. In addition, Part I showed that ginsenoside $Rg_3$ directly regulates voltage gated-ion channel activity through interaction with channel proteins located at channel pore or channel pore entryway. Part II will manage that ginseng contains another novel ingredient that acts different ways from that of ginsenosides and ginsenoside $Rg_3$, despite ginsenosides and a novel ingredient are co-fractionated after butanol fractionation in crude ginseng total saponin (cGTS) preparation. It appears that a novel ingredient plays as a first messenger, activates membrane G protein-coupled lysophosphatidic acid (LPA) receptors, transfers its extracellular information into cells via second messenger, $Ca^{2+}$, which is produced by signal transduction pathway through PLC and $IP_3$ receptor. As you see below sections, A novel ingredient of ginseng was turned out to be glycolipoproteins, designated gintonin. Gintonin activates $Ca^{2+}$-dependent various ion channels and other various $Ca^{2+}$-dependent biological functions via LPA receptors. This section shows how a ginseng-derived novel ligand, gintonin, was found and identified from cGTS fraction using a research tool of *Xenopus* oocyte gene expression system.

## 2. cGTS-mediated CaCC Activation and Its Signal Transduction Pathway in *Xenopus* Oocytes

Intracellular $Ca^{2+}$, as a second messenger, is a one of key molecules involved in signal transduction pathways in diverse cells. Increases in $Ca^{2+}$ levels in neuronal cells regulate neurotransmitter release, secretion, cell division, growth and differentiation, muscle contraction, and other biological functions (Berridge et al., 1998). Free intracellular $Ca^{2+}$ can be supplied either by $Ca^{2+}$ influx from extracellular fluid or through the release of stored $Ca^{2+}$ from the intracellular compartment, endoplasmic reticulum (Parker and Yao, 1994). In nonexcitable cells, an increase in cytoplasmic free $Ca^{2+}$ for biological response inductions is usually mediated via stimulation of receptors such as G protein coupled receptors (GPCRs), which are coupled to activation of the phospholipase C (PLC) pathway and production of inositol 1,4,5-triphosphate ($IP_3$). $IP_3$ then triggers an increase in the levels of cytosolic free $Ca^{2+}$ from $IP_3$-sensitive or ryanodine-sensitive receptor in endoplasmic reticulum, resulting in depletion of intracellular calcium stores. The other way is $Ca^{2+}$ influx through voltage-gated $Ca^{2+}$ channels in excitable cells.

On the other hand, *Xenopus* oocytes are their large size and easy handling and are a useful model system for investigating the machinery of membrane signal transduction, Moreover, *Xenopus* oocytes have endogenous $Ca^{2+}$-activated $Cl^-$ channels that are well understood (Barish, 1983; Miledi and Parker, 1984), and which have been used for the study of both intracellular $Ca^{2+}$ release (Lechleiter and Clapham, 1002; Callamaras and Parker, 1994; Parker and Yao, 1994). For example, stimulation of oocyte muscarinic receptors by acetylcholine leads to intracellular $Ca^{2+}$ mobilization and activation of $Ca^{2+}$-activated $Cl^-$ channels (Dascal et al., 1984; Berridige and Irvine, 1989; Lechleiter and Clapham, 1992).

In non-excitable cell such as *Xenopus* oocytes, which do not have much voltage-gated ion channels and ligand-gated ion channels as neurons do, crude ginseng total saponin (cGTS) fraction showed the different behaviors from the individual ginsenosides such as ginsenoside $Rg_3$. For example, Choi et al. (2001a) first found that cGTS fraction activates the endogenous $Ca^{2+}$-activated $Cl^-$ channels (CaCC) via PLC activation leading to $Ca^{2+}$ release from the intracellular store by $IP_3$, since PLC inhibitor and $IP_3$ receptor antagonist blocked cGTS-mediated CaCC activations. This process also involved pertussis toxin (PTX)-insensitive G protein via interaction with unknown membrane protein in the cell surface, since pretreatment of PTX had no effects on cGTS action on CaCC activation. The cGTS effect is reversible and transient. Extracellular, but not intracellular, application of cGTS fraction enhanced the $Cl^-$ current in the *Xenopus* oocyte, indicating that cGTS acts outside of oocytes for its action. The current produced by cGTS fraction diminished spontaneously after reaching peak amplitude even in the continued presence of cGTS (Choi et al., 2001a). Thus, the Cl⁻ channels seemed to be desensitized to cGTS. Moreover, the channels showed cross-desensitization to cGTS fraction and acetylcholine [unpublished data]. Stimulation of oocyte muscarinic receptors by acetylcholine activates PLC leading to intracellular $Ca^{2+}$ mobilization and activation of Cl⁻ current (Dascal et al., 1984; Berridge and Irvine, 1989; Lechleiter & Clapham, 1992), suggests that the unknown cGTS binding site(s) on plasma membrane shares a common signaling pathway with muscarinic acetylcholine receptor. Thus, Choi *et al.* (2001) first showed that cGTS fraction can increase $Ca^{2+}$-activated Cl⁻ current in *Xenopus* oocytes which involve interaction with unidentified membrane proteins, PTX-insensitive G protein-coupled PLC activation and $Ca^{2+}$ mobilization from $IP_3$-sensitive intracellular store, which are totally different from those of ginsenoside $Rg_3$ in the regulations of ion channels.

## 3. Involvement of $G\alpha_{q/11}$ Protein Coupled to $G\alpha_{q/11}$, RGS2, and PLCβ3 in cGTS-Mediated CaCC Activation in *Xenopus* Oocytes

In further studies, to identify which the G protein subunit(s) and what PLC isoform(s) mediate the action of cGTS enhancing $Ca^{2+}$-activated Cl⁻ current in *Xenopus* oocytes, Choi et al. (2001b) examined the changes in cGTS effect on the Cl⁻ current after intraoocyte injections of cRNAs coding various G protein subunits, regulator of G protein signaling 2 (RGS2), Gβγ-binding proteins, and PLCβ1–3 antibodies injected into oocytes to block cGTS effect on the Cl⁻ current. Choi et al. (2001) found that the G protein subunits mediating cGTS effect are $G\alpha_q$ and $G\alpha_{11}$. They also showed that intraoocyte injections of $G\alpha_q$ and $G\alpha_{11}$ cRNAs increased the basal $Ca^{2+}$-activated Cl⁻ current and prevented cGTS from enhancing the Cl⁻ current, whereas $G\alpha_{i2}$ and $G\alpha_{oA}$ cRNA injections were without effects.

As the second evidence for the role of $G\alpha_q$ and $G\alpha_{11}$ in cGTS fraction action, Choi et al. (2001b) demonstrated that the injection of RGS2 cRNA led to a profound reduction of cGTS effect on $Ca^{2+}$-activated Cl⁻ current. RGS2, a GTPase-activating protein that reduces the life span of active GTP-Gα complex (Berman et al., 1998), interacts with $G\alpha_{q/11}$ more selectively than any other known RGS isoforms (Ingi et al., 1998). Therefore, the results of the experiments performed with RGS2 cRNA further suggest that $G\alpha_q$ and $G\alpha_{11}$ subunits mediate cGTS fraction effect. The third evidence suggesting a role for these G protein subunits in cGTS fraction signaling comes from the experiments involving injections of cRNAs coding MAS-GRKs, specific Gβγ-binding proteins that inhibit the re-association of Gβγ subunit freed from the Gαβγ complex with active Gα subunit. The results of these experiments indicate that intrinsic gene-derived $G\alpha_q$ and $G\alpha_{11}$ subunits mediates the cGTS effect, although they do not specify the receptor(s) that cGTS interacts.

In an attempt to further identify the PLC isoform(s) involved, Choi et al. (2001b) examined which of the three different antibodies raised against mammalian PLCβ1–3 inhibited cGTS fraction effect. In these experiments, only PLCβ3 antibody, not those of PLC-β1 and PLC-β2, inhibited cGTS fraction action significantly. They also noticed that PLCβ3 antibody reacted most strongly with PLC-βX in an immunoblot analysis carried out later with the same antibodies used in the microinjection experiments. Taken together, these results suggest that, in the *Xenopus* oocyte, mammalian PLCβ3-like enzyme (presumably PLC-βX) participates in cGTS fraction signaling. Furthermore, the results point to the possibility that PLCβ3 may be an isoform involved in cGTS fraction signaling in mammalian cells. Thus,

Choi et al. (2001b) showed that $G\alpha_{q/11}$ coupled to mammalian PLCβ3-like enzyme mediates cGTS fraction effect. This may be one of signaling pathways that underlie cGTS fraction action.

## 4. Involvement of GRK2 and β-arrestin I in a Desensitization of cGTS-Mediated CaCC Activation in *Xenopus* Oocytes

The desensitization of a receptor is defined as the diminished or abolished response to an agonist after repeated stimulation. The desensitizing process of G protein-coupled receptors (GPCRs), which are mainly coupled to $G\alpha_{i/o}$-, $G\alpha_s$-adenylate cyclase, or $G\alpha_{q/11}$-phospholipase C, is well characterized (Kwatra et al., 1993; Appleyard et al., 1999; Oakely et al., 2000). The main specialized regulatory proteins for homologous GPCR desensitization process are G protein-coupled receptor kinases (GRKs) and β-arrestins (Ferguson and Caron, 1998; Pierce and Lefkowitz, 2001). GRKs mediate the phosphorylation of the receptors that are occupied by agonists. The phosphorylated receptors create a binding site for regulatory proteins, β-arrestins, which are involved in the endocytosis of desensitized receptors and bindings of β-arrestins to the phosphorylated receptor facilitate to uncouple it from its target G proteins for termination of effector stimulation (Sasakawa et al., 1994; McConalogue et al., 1998; Sullivan et al., 2002). On the other hand, recent reports showed that $InsP_6$ blocks visual arrestin interaction with phosphorylated rhodopsin by a direct binding to visual arrestin, resulting in elimination of light-induced inactivation of rhodopsin (Paczewski et al., 1992). As described above, Choi et al. (2001a) demonstrated that $Ca^{2+}$-activated $Cl^-$ current produced by cGTS fraction treatment diminished spontaneously after reaching peak amplitude, even in the continued presence of cGTS fraction in *Xenopus laevis* oocytes. Once a loss on cGTS- or acetylcholine-induced $Cl^-$ current responses by short-term and repeated treatment with cGTS fraction or acetylcholine was initiated, the desensitization lasted for up to 8 h before complete recovery. In study on recovery time kinetics from $Cl^-$ channel desensitization in both cGTS fraction and m1 muscarinic acetylcholine receptors in *Xenopus laevis* oocytes. The half-recovery time to control level from desensitization was about 145.8 ± 63 and 619.5 ± 26.9 min for cGTS fraction and m1 muscarinic acetylcholine receptors, respectively.

Lee et al. (2004) further characterized the molecular mechanism(s) underlying cGTS fraction-induced $Ca^{2+}$-activated $Cl^-$ channel desensitization. First, they showed that short- or long-term treatment with cGTS fraction induced a complete loss of cGTS fraction effect on $Cl^-$ current enhancement, whereas preintraoocyte injection of $InsP_6$, which is known to bind β-arrestins and block β-arrestin-dependent receptor trafficking, prevented the desensitization of $Cl^-$ current induced by repeated treatment with cGTS fraction. These results support the concept that the attenuating effect on cGTS fraction-induced $Cl^-$ channel desensitization is specific to $InsP_6$. The potency of the $Cl^-$ channel desensitization-blocking action of $InsP_6$ was very similar to the concentration of $InsP_6$ binding to arrestins (Palczewski et al., 1992). Interestingly, they observed that intraoocyte injection of $InsP_6$ did not restore cGTS fraction or acetylcholine responses on $Ca^{2+}$-activated $Cl^-$ channels after short- or long-term $Cl^-$ channel desensitization caused by cGTS fraction or acetylcholine treatment had already occurred. This study shows further that membrane component(s) or m1 muscarinic acetylcholine receptor that might be interacting with cGTS fraction or acetylcholine could be down-regulated after short- or long-term treatment with cGTS fraction or acetylcholine and that intraoocyte injected-InsP$_6$ was no more helpful for the down-regulated membrane components or m1 muscarinic acetylcholine receptors.

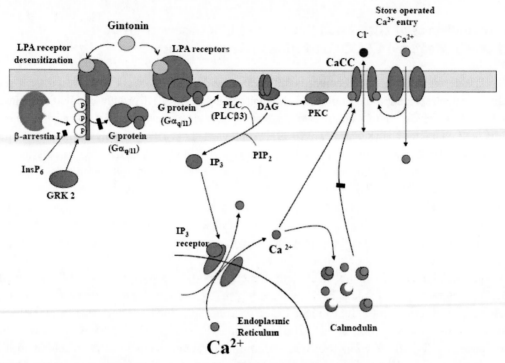

Figure 8. Schematic diagram on gintonin-mediated signal transduction pathways in *Xenopus* oocytes. *Xenopus* oocytes express endogenous LPA1 receptor (Kimura et al., 2001) and gintonin in cGTS induces a transient elevation of $[Ca^{2+}]_i$ and activates CaCC via signaling transduction pathway and repeated treatment of gintonin also induces a desensitization of LPA receptors and CaCC as showin diagram. The detail explanations on gintonin-mediated signaling pathways were shown in text.

As an evidence for the role of β-arrestins in cGTS fraction-induced Cl$^-$ channel desensitization, Lee et al. (2004) also demonstrated that overexpression of β-arrestin I cRNA, but not β-arrestin II cRNA, induced cGTS- or acetylcholine-induced Cl$^-$ channel desensitization in oocytes or in oocytes expressing m1 muscarinic acetylcholine receptors that were preinjected with InsP$_6$ before cGTS fraction or acetylcholine treatment. These results suggest that extra copies of β-arrestin I produced by injection of cRNAs coding β-arrestin I might bind with InsP$_6$ and sequestrate free InsP$_6$ by forming complexes with InsP$_6$ and β-arrestin I. Therefore, the results of the experiments performed with β-arrestin I further suggest that β-arrestin I mediates cGTS fraction- and m1 muscarinic acetylcholine receptor-induced Cl$^-$ channel desensitization.

Lee et al. (2004) further demonstrated that G protein-coupled receptor kinase 2 (GRK2) involvement in cGTS- and m1 muscarinic acetylcholine receptor-induced Cl$^-$ current desensitization comes from the experiments involving injections of cRNAs coding GRK2, which is known to phosphorylate GPCRs after agonist stimulation and facilitate β-arrestin binding to phosphorylated receptors for the receptor down-regulation process. In addition, GRK2 cRNA injection but not by dominant-negative GRK2-K220R, which lacks kinase activity, blocked the cGTS fraction or acetylcholine effect that enhances $Ca^{2+}$-activated $Cl^-$ currents.

These results suggest that the kinase activity of GRK2 is a key role for the inhibitory effect on cGTS fraction- and m1 muscarinic acetylcholine receptor-induced $Cl^-$ current enhancement and that the kinase activity of GRK2 is also involved in signaling pathway of cGTS fraction- or m1 muscarinic acetylcholine receptor-induced $Cl^-$ channel desensitization. Moreover, these results further suggest that phosphorylation of unknown membrane receptors by GRK2 that might interact with cGTS fraction or phosphorylation of m1 muscarinic acetylcholine receptor by GRK2 could be enough for cGTS fraction- or m1 muscarinic acetylcholine receptor-induced $Cl^-$ channel desensitization.

Taken together, using an *Xenopus laevis* oocyte model system for explanation of cGTS fraction signaling pathway that allows various foreign gene expressions, Lee et al. (2004) obtained further results suggesting that GRK2 and β-arrestin I mediate cGTS-induced $Ca^{2+}$-activated $Cl^-$ channel desensitization. This may be one of evidence that cGTS interacts with unidentified membrane protein and repeated treatment of cGTS desensitizes signaling pathways via GRK2 and β-arrestin I (Figure 8).

## 5. Gintonin Is Responsible for cGTS-Mediated Cacc Activation in *Xenopus* Oocytes via PLC-IP₃ Pathway

cGTS fraction comprises about 50% ginsenosides as a main components and the remainder has not been identified. Since the reminder of cGTS was unknown, it was first assumed that certain types of ginsenoside(s) may underlie cGTS action in CaCC activation and desensitization and may interact with unknown plasma membrane proteins coupled to $G\alpha_{q/11}$ protein-coupled receptors (Choi et al., 2001a; Lee et al., 2004). During additional studies with the cGTS fraction, it was unexpectedly discovered that ginsenosides within cGTS do not underlie CaCC activation; ginsenoside enrichment by removing unknown components from the cGTS fraction did not lead to increased CaCC activation [unpublished data]. Thus, the unknown components, and not ginsenosides, in the cGTS function as a unknown $G\alpha_{q/11}$ protein-coupled receptor ligand.

Identification of the novel ingredients in the cGTS fraction began toward the end of the 1990s. However, it was challenging initially to isolate non-saponin, active components from the cGTS fraction for 2 reasons.

First, the unknown active ingredient was co-fractionated with ginsenosides after butanol extraction. Second, the unknown ingredient, like ginsenosides, appeared to be amphiphilic, and it was partially co-eluted with ginsenosides from a silica gel chromatography column that used various organic solvents for ginsenoside isolation from the ginseng butanol fraction. Thus, the unknown ingredient could not be separated from the ginsenosides by using conventional silica gel chromatography, despite their co-fractionation in butanol. Moreover, the unknown active ingredients absorbed into the silica gel easily and some could not be recovered from the silica gel [unpublished data].

After conducting many trials and errors during a period of several years, it was discovered that the unknown ingredients in the cGTS fraction had a negative charge, whereas the ginsenosides did not. Using this characteristic to differentiate between the unknown active components and ginsenosides, the unknown ingredient was finally separated from the ginsenosides by anion exchange chromatography after ginseng butanol extraction (Pyo et al., 2011). The novel non-saponin ingredient was designated as gintonin, an agent that induces transient $[Ca^{2+}]_i$ in cells, where *gin* was derived from *gin*seng, *ton* from the *ton*ic effects of ginseng, and *in* from prote*in*.

In addition, Pyo et al. (2011a) demonstrated that there are six different subtypes of gintonin depending on ionic gradient and that each gintonin induced transient elevation of $[Ca^{2+}]_i$ in mammalian cells and also activated endogenous CaCC in *Xenopus* oocytes with concentration-dependent manner. However, the individual ginsenosides tested did not show any effects on $[Ca^{2+}]_i$ transient in mammalian cells and endogenous CaCC activation in *Xenopus* oocytes.

Pyo et al. (2011a) examined the signaling pathway of gintonin in CaCC activation and found that gintonin utilize the same signaling pathway of cGTS (Pyo et al., 2011a) (Fig. 8). Thus, gintonin but not ginsenosides is responsible for cGTS-induced membrane signaling pathways for intracellular $Ca^{2+}$ mobilization through unidentified membrane proteins.

## 6. Gintonin Composition

Gintonin was found in ginseng stem and leaf as well as root (Pyo et al., 2011b) (Fig. 9). Gintonin comprises about 0.2% of ginseng and its native molecular weight is about 67 kDa. Sodium dodecyl sulfate-polyacrylamide gel electrophoresis, however, results in a broad, not sharp, band of gintonin about 13 kDa in weight (Pyo et al., 2011a), which indicates that gintonin may exist as a multimer of protein and other ingredients.

The staining of gintonin carbohydrates using the periodic acid-Schiff base staining method showed that gintonin may be extensively glycosylated by glucose, rhamnose, mannose, and xylose (Pyo et al., 2011a). In addition, gintonin lipid staining with Sudan black showed that gintonin contains lipids in significant levels, including linoleic acid, palmitic acid, and other fatty acids (Pyo et al., 2011a).

In proteomic analysis, gintonin is shown to contain other proteins, such as ginseng major latex-like protein (GLP) and ginseng ribonuclease-like storage proteins (GSP) (Hwang et al., 2012). GLP belongs to the Bet v1 family of proteins and exhibits similar properties to other members of Bet v1 families (Sun et al., 2010). For example, the molecular weight of GLP is about 17 kDa and that of GSP is in the range of 20–28 kDa. Most latex-like proteins have a secreting function, are used for latex formation, and have ligand-binding sites (Sun et al., 2010).

GLP contains hydrophobic ligand-binding sites, a glycine-rich region that binds to phosphate groups of nucleotides, and 3 *N*-glycosylation sites (Sun et al., 2010). GSP possesses neither ribonuclease activity nor *N*-glycosylation sites, but GSP expression in ginseng root varies seasonally, which indicates that GSP may function as a storage protein used during the vegetative stage of ginseng (Kim et al., 2004). The protein composition of gintonin leads to the notion that the carbohydrate portion of gintonin may be derived from *N*- or *O*-glycosylations of GLP or *O*-glycosylation of GSP. Thus, gintonin is novel glycolipoproteins in ginseng (Fig. 9).

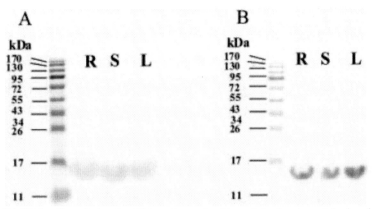

Figure 9. SDS-PAGE (sodium dodecyl sulfate polyacrylamide gel electrophoresis) of each gintonin prepared from ginseng root, stem, and leaf. (A) SDS-PAGE of the crude gintonins obtained from anion exchange chromatography. Coomassie Brilliant blue staining was used to stain protein moieties of gintonins. Crude gintonin prepared from ginseng root (R), stem (S), and leaf (L) in SDS–PAGE showed that the apparent molecular weight of gintonin is about 13 kDa. (B) Periodic acid-Schiff staining demonstrated that crude gintonins contain carbohydrate moiety. Adapted from Pyo et al. (2011b).

## 7. Identification of Active Ligand in Gintonin That Activates G Protein-Coupled Receptor Signaling Pathway

After successfully isolating and analyzing gintonin composition in ginseng root, stem and leaf, one major question remained regarding the specific ingredient(s) that plays an important role in the transient elevation of intracellular $Ca^{2+}$ in mammalian cells and in CaCC activation in *Xenopus* oocytes. The ability of gintonin to activate CaCC was greatly attenuated or abolished after treatment with glycosidase or phospholipase $A_1$, but trypsin did not cause any significant effects (Hwang et al., 2012).

The carbohydrate and lipid portions of gintonin, and not the protein portion, may play key roles in CaCC activation. The attenuating effects of phospholipase $A_1$ on gintonin highlights the importance of position 1 esterification on the fatty acid component, which suggests that gintonin contains phospholipids. Previously, Tigyi and Miledi (1992) demonstrated that LPA bound to serum albumin was sufficient to activate CaCC in *Xenopus* oocytes and digestion with $PLA_1$ prevented activation. Furthermore, they demonstrated LPA dissociation from serum albumin by methanol extraction. Based on this reference, whether gintonin contains LPAs was examined by liquid chromatography-electrospray ionization/multi-stage mass spectrometry (LC-ESI-MS/MS) analysis (Yoon et al., 2003). Surprisingly, gintonin was comprised of 9.5% LPAs, which could be released from other components by methanol extraction. Thus, LPA $C_{18:2}$, LPA $C_{16:0}$, and LPA $C_{18:1}$ (in descending order of importance) were found to be the bioactive components of gintonin (Fig. 10) (Hwang et al., 2012). Thus, gintonin is a unique form of the LPAs in ginseng. Based on the average molecular weight of gintonin (20 kDa), and GLP (17 kDa), and GSP (20–28 kDa), 4 LPA molecules bind 1 molecule of ginseng protein. Further, investigating how LPAs are synthesized and how they form a complex with GLP and GSP in ginseng would be an interesting study.

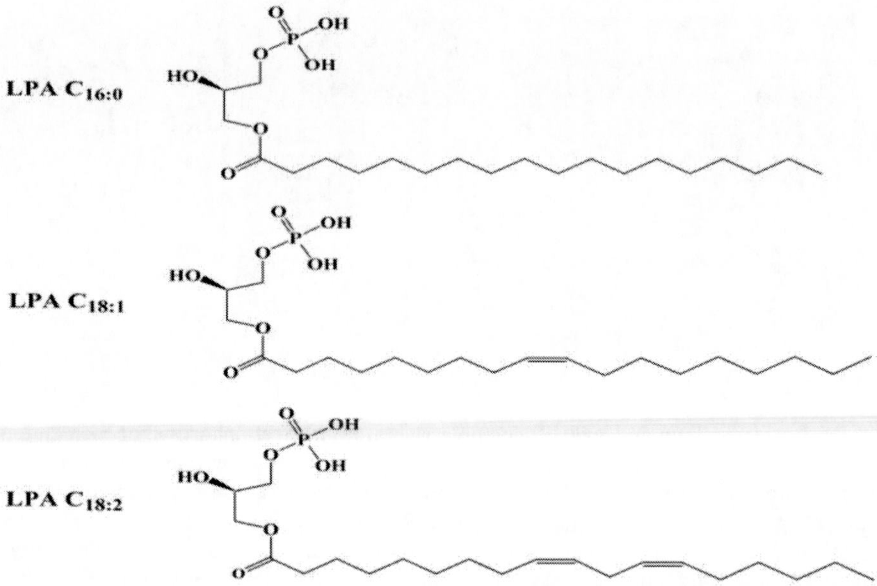

Figure 10. Lysophosphatidic acids (LPAs) in gintonin. The primary LPA in gintonin is LPA $C_{18:2}$.

## 8. Gintonin Activates LPA Receptors

LPAs are the active components of gintonin that induce transient elevation of $[Ca^{2+}]_i$ in mammalian cells and endogenous CaCC activation in *Xenopus* oocytes. Furthermore, Hwang et al. (2012) used oocytes overexpressing the LPA3 receptor to verify that CaCC activation by gintonin is due to the activation of the LPA receptor on the oocyte membrane. On the other hand, the bioactive role of LPA was first discovered in the mid-1980s (LPA; 1-acyl-2-sn-glycerol-3-phosphate). LPA is one of the phospholipid derivatives that functions as a mitogen with hormone- and growth-factor-like activities in most cell types (Moolenaar, 1994). In animals, most LPAs are synthesized with the help of an autotaxin (also called lysophospholipase D), which removes the choline group from lysophosphatidylcholine (Fig. 11). In the mid-1990s, the LPA receptor was first cloned from a developing brain and determined to be a GPCR (Hecht et al., 1996). LPA receptors are distributed widely throughout the body in cells or organs, and their diverse effects become evident when LPA receptors are activated. Currently, at least 6 different subtypes of the LPA receptor (LPA 1–6) are present in neuronal and non-neuronal tissue (Noguchi et al., 2009; Chun et al., 2009). Hwang et al. (2012) demonstrated that gintonin activates LPA receptors—LPA2, LPA5, LPA1, LPA3, and LPA4 (highest to lowest affinity)—with high affinity in mammalian cells. The LPA1/LPA3 receptor antagonist, Ki16425, was shown to block gintonin activity in cells that expressed LPA1 or LPA3 (Hwang et al., 2012). In human umbilical vein endothelial cells (HUVEC), which express endogenous LPA receptors, gintonin also stimulated cell proliferation and migration. Gintonin stimulates ERK1/2 phosphorylation, whereas pertussis toxin (PTX) blocks gintonin-mediated migration and ERK1/2 phosphorylation. Gintonin induces morphological changes that can be blocked by Rho kinase inhibitor Y-27632 (Hwang et al., 2012). The effects of gintonin on cells are consistent with those caused by LPAs, which affect cell proliferation, migration, and morphological changes in neuronal and non-neuronal cells via diverse G proteins such as $G\alpha_{i/o}$, $G\alpha_{12/13}$, and $G\alpha_{q/11}$ (Chun et al., 2009). However, gintonin yielded no effect on cells expressing the $5\text{-}HT_{1C}$ receptor (Dascal et al., 1986) or the muscarinic acetylcholine receptor subtypes (m1, m3, and m5), which are expressed endogenously in *Xenopus* oocytes (Herrera et al., 1994), S1P receptors, short- and long-chain fatty acid receptors, and other lipid-related orphan G protein-coupled receptors, thus indicating that gintonin selectively targets LPA receptors with high affinity (Hwang et al., 2012). In addition, gintonin yielded no effects in animal brain proteins GPR45 and GPR63, which are homologous to the endogenous *Xenopus* oocyte PSP24 (Guo et al., 1996; Kawasawa et al., 2000) or the $P_2Y_1$ receptor (Bucholz et al., 2004).

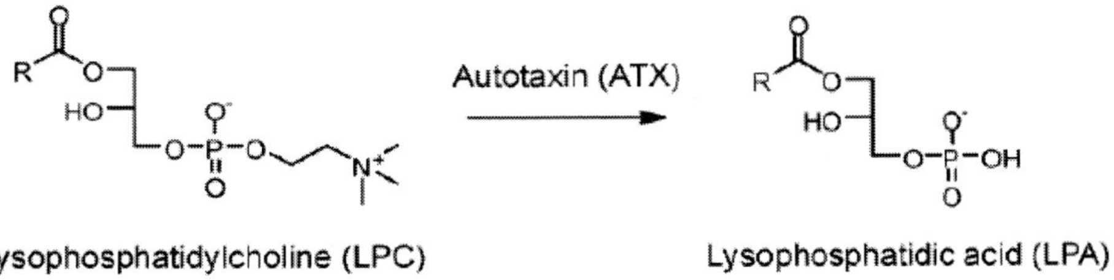

**Lysophosphatidylcholine (LPC)**             **Lysophosphatidic acid (LPA)**

Figure 11. The synthesis of lysophosphatidic acids (LPAs). Most animal LPAs are synthesized in response to autotaxin activity on lysophosphatidylcholine (LPC).

## 9. The Role of Protein Components of Gintonin

The phosphate residues of LPAs are known to be essential to LPA-induced activation of LPA receptors as a functional group; however, free LPAs in biological fluid are very vulnerable to lipid phosphate phosphatases, which hydrolyze the phosphate group (Brindley and Piquil, 2009). The bound form of LPA (to serum albumin) usually is present in animals and activates their LPA receptors. Interestingly, LPAs bound to serum albumin are released by methanol extraction, which indicates that non-covalent bonds, including hydrophobic interaction, bind LPAs to serum albumin (Tigyi and Miledi, 1992). Thus, serum albumin functions as an LPA carrier. Bound to serum albumin, LPAs in gintonin exist as complexes with ginseng proteins, and methanol extraction releases 90% of LPAs from gintonin (Hwang et al., 2012). Thus, the protein components of gintonin may play 3 roles related to LPAs: (1) they may function as LPA-carrier or LPA-storage molecules, (2) they may lessen access of LPA hydrolyzing enzymes, and (3) they may provide a hydrophobic environment that enables efficient delivery of LPAs to their cognate receptors.

## 10. The Pharmacological Actions of Gintonin via LPA Receptors

Gintonin targets LPA receptors on plasma membranes, and gintonin-induced LPA receptor activations are coupled to transient elevation of intracellular $Ca^{2+}$ via diverse G proteins (Hwang et al., 2012). $Ca^{2+}$, a secondary messenger, is involved in a variety of cellular functions, such as the regulation of cell proliferation, synaptic plasticity, neurotransmitter release and hormone secretion, and gene expression and transcription

(Berridge et al., 1998). In addition to the diverse cellular effects it triggers, elevated intracellular $Ca^{2+}$ is coupled to fertilization, muscle contraction, learning and memory, other effects at organ levels, and to biological effects (Berridge et al., 1998). One example of gintonin-mediated LPA receptor activation and the ensuing $Ca^{2+}$-signaling is its anti-Alzheimer's disease (AD) function in AD model cells and in the transgenic mice AD model (Hwang et al., 2012). AD results from amyloid-β protein (Aβ) accumulation via the amyloidogenic pathway. Gintonin hinders the amyloidogenic pathway by activating LPA receptors. Gintonin-induced non-amyloidogenic pathways produce beneficial, soluble APPα (sAPPα) in a concentration- and time-dependent manner. Gintonin also lessens the release of $Aβ_{1-42}$ and attenuates $Aβ_{1-40}$-induced cytotoxicity.

The gintonin activity underlying non-amyloidogenic pathway stimulation was blocked in SH-SY5Y cells by 1,2-bis(o-aminophenoxy)ethane-$N,N,N',N'$-tetraacetic acid (BAPTA; $Ca^{2+}$ chelator), α-secretase inhibitor tumor necrosis factor-alpha protease inhibitor 2 (TAPI-2), and protein-trafficking inhibitor brefeldin. In addition, gintonin has been shown to rescue $Aβ_{1-40}$-induced cognitive dysfunction in mice (Hwang et al., 2012). In a transgenic mouse AD model, long-term oral administration of gintonin effectively attenuated both amyloid plaque deposition and short- and long-term memory impairment (Berridge et al., 1998). Thus, this represents the first biological systems example of AD prevention or therapy coupled to gintonin-mediated cellular elevation of intracellular $Ca^{2+}$ via LPA receptors (Hwang et al., 2012). On the other hand, aberrant LPA pathways are involved in cancer pathophysiology. Melanoma cell lines secrete autotoxin (ATX) to produce LPAs, which facilitate metastasis. ATX was identified initially as an autocrine tumor cell motility factor (Stracke et al., 1992). The ATX-LPA axis has been shown to function as a mitogen and motility factor in various cancers, including neuroblastoma, hepatoma, lung cancer, ovarian cancer, metastatic breast cancer, and melanoma; all of these cancerous processes yield high levels of ATX (Houben et al., 2011). However, a negative feedback mechanism strongly inhibits ATX activity, including its lysolipid products, LPAs, sphingoshine-1-phosphate (S1P), and their analogs. A recent report showed that LPA $C_{18:2}$, which is highly abundant in gintonin, inhibits ATX activity more potently that the other LPAs (Zhang et al., 2009). Gintonin may function as a negative feedback regulator for ATX activity, and potentially may be utilized as a putative anti-metastatic agent.

# PART III

Part III deals with the brief summary on the different properties between ginsenoside and gintonin in their cellular actions and provides some cautions in interpretation of results obtained when crude ginseng extract is used.

# 1. Ginsenoside and Gintonin Exhibit Differential Action Modes, Although They Are Originated from the Same Ginseng Root

Ginsenosides were identified a long time ago and gintonin was recently isolated from ginseng. Both are co-fractionated after butanol extraction. Ginsenosides are one of saponins isolated from the plant kingdoms. The molecular mechanisms of ginsenoside action have not been defined fully because ginsenosides lack their own receptors and act on diverse ion channels with non-selective manner (Nah et al., 2007). However, gintonin is ginseng proteins-LPA complex and exhibits a differential biological mode of action compared to ginsenosides. Gintonin plays a G protein-coupled LPA receptor ligand that selectively activates LPA receptor subtypes through PTX-sensitive and -insensitive G proteins (Hwang et al., 2012). Table 2 provides a brief summary of gintonin and ginsenosides on their chemical characteristics and biological activities.

**Table 2. A brief comparison of ginseng components,
gintonin and ginsenoside**

|  | Gintonin | Ginsenoside |
|---|---|---|
| Molecular Weight (MW) | Native MW: 67 kDa Apparent MW: 13 kDa | 0.6-1.3 kDa |
| Composition | Glycolipoprotein: Carbohydrates (Glucose), lipids (LPA $C_{18:2}$), and ginseng proteins (GLP and GSP) | Dammarane glycosides |
| Content in ginseng | 0.2% | 3-4% (Sum of individual ginsenosides) |
| Target protein on cell membrane and signal cascades | LPA receptors, Transient $[Ca^{2+}]_i$ elevation via PTX-sensitive and -insensitive G proteins coupled PLC pathway | Non-selective interactions with ion channels and receptors, Do not have signal transduction pathway |
| Desensitization after repeated treatment on cells | Induction of rapid desensitization | No desensitization |

# 2. Interpretation of Experimental Results Using cGTS Fraction or Ginseng Total Extract

Ginsenosides was considered as the active ingredients of ginseng for 5 decades. However, from the beginning of ginseng-related efficacy studies many researchers have used the cGTS fraction (butanol fraction), because ginseng contains low percentage of ginsenosides and individual ginsenosides are scarce, not easy to purify, and expensive to purchase compared to other bioactive natural compounds. Although the chemical and physical properties of gintonin differ substantially from those of ginsenosides, both compounds are amphiphilic and difficult to separate without using anion exchange chromatography.

Before gintonin was isolated from the cGTS fraction, similar observations were previously substantiated in a study using cGTS alone to evaluate ginsenoside activity as described in Part II. It appears that gintonin activates G protein-coupled LPA receptors with high affinity to induce transient elevation of intracellular $Ca^{2+}$ (Hwang et al., 2012), which is linked to a variety of cellular or biological effects (Figure 11), whereas the purified ginsenosides did not show evidence that they function as G protein-coupled LPA receptor ligands, instead ginsenoside $Rg_3$ regulates ion channel activities via direct interaction with various channel proteins with low affinities (Figure 12 and Table 1). Further, crude ginsenosides contaminated with even small amounts of gintonin behave like G protein-coupled LPA receptor ligand. In the future, interpretation of biological effects by ginseng saponins needs to be considered with care when less purified ginseng saponin fractions are used.

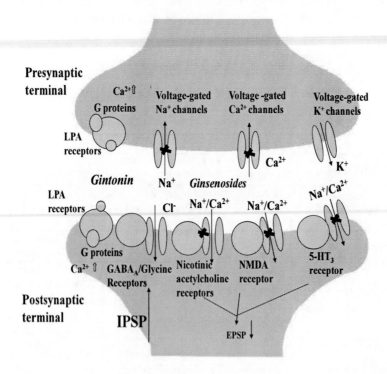

Figure 12. Schematic diagram on ginsenoside and gintonin actions on pre- and post-synpatic sites. Ginsenoside might exert its effects on both ion channels and ligand-gated ion channels present in pre- and post-synaptic sites and inhibit calcium influx and neuronal excitability. In contrast, accumulating evidences show that gintonin induce intracellular calcium elevation through G protein-coupled LPA receptors. If LPA receptors co-exist pre- and post-synaptic sites with voltage-gated ion channels and ligand-gated ion channels and gintonin works together with ginsenosides, it remain unknown what is the neuronal effects induced by both agents. Future study will be needed how gintonin and ginsenoside work together for the regulation of nervous systems. One assumption was briefly described in text.

# IV. PROSPECTS

The understanding on ginseng efficacy has advanced tremendously alongside modern medicine during the last few decades. However, most reports on ginseng efficacy during that period highlighted the role of ginseng extract, cGTS, or individual ginsenosides.

Recent studies revealed that ginseng also contains gintonin, LPA-ginseng protein complexes (as GPCR ligands), which represent a primary area of drug development and many modern drugs are derived from traditional herbal medicines that contain high affinity GPCR ligands (Matsuda et al., 1990; Pert and Synader, 1973). Thus, ginseng contains two bioactive ingredients, ginsenosides and gintonin, with two different faces in their actions. Currently, it is not known whether ginsenosides and gintonin work at the same time in cells and in animal body or how ginsenosides affects on gintonin actions or *vice verse*.

One assumption is that gintonin has a high affinity on LPA receptors and first induces a transient elevation of $[Ca^{2+}]_i$ originated from endoplasmic reticulum or extracellar side and then ginsenosides including ginsenoside $Rg_3$ might exert their action by preventing further $Ca^{2+}$ influx into cells through regulations of various voltage-gated and ligand-gated ion channels. Future studies will be required to elucidate what is meaning of differential actions of ginsenosides and gintonin in pharmacological contribution to ginseng efficacy in biological systems.

## ACKNOWLEDGMENTS

This work was supported by the Basic Science Research Program (2011-0021144) and the Priority Research Centers Program through the National Research Foundation of Korea (NRF), which is funded by the Ministry of Education, Science, and Technology (2012-0006686) and by the BK21 project fund to S.-Y. Nah.

## REFERENCES

Abe, K., Cho, S. I., Kitagawa, I., Nishiyama, N. and Saito, H.: (1994). Differential effects of ginsenoside $Rb_1$ and malonylginsenoside $Rb_1$ on long-term potentiation in the dentate gyrus of rats. *Brain Res.* 649, 7-11.

Alzheimer, C., (2002). $Na^+$ channels and $Ca^{2+}$ channels of the cell membrane as targets of neuroprotective substances. *Adv. Exp. Med. Biol.* 513, 161–181.

Appleyard, S. M., Celver, J., Pineda, V., Kovoor, A., Wayman, G. A., and Chavkin, C. (1999). Agonist-dependent desensitization of the kappa opioid receptor by G protein receptor kinase and beta-arrestin. *J. Biol. Chem.* 274, 23802–23807.

Armstrong C. M., Bezanilla (1977). Inactivation of the sodium channel. II. Gating current experiments. F., *J. Gen. Physiol.*, 70, 567—590.

Attele, A.S., Wu, J.A., Yuan, C.S., (1999). Ginseng pharmacology: multiple constituents and multiple actions. *Biochem Pharmacol.* 58(11):1685-93.

Bai, C.X., Takahashi, K., Masumiya, H., Sawanobori, T., Furukawa, T., (2004). Nitric oxide-dependent modulation of the delayed rectifier $K^+$ current and the L-type $Ca^{2+}$ current by ginsenoside Re, an ingredient of Panax ginseng, in guinea-pig cardiomyocytes. *Br J Pharmacol.* 142(3):567-75.

Barish, M.E. (1983). A transient calcium-dependent chloride current in the immature *Xenopus* oocyte. *J. Physiol. (Lond.),* 342, 309–325.

Berkefeld, H., Sailer, C.A., Bildl, W., Rohde, V., Thumfart, J.O., Eble, S., Klugbauer, N., Reisinger, E., Bischofberger, J., Oliver, D., Knaus, H.G., Schulte, U., and Fakler, B. (2006). $BK_{Ca}$-Cav channel complexes mediate rapid and localized $Ca^{2+}$-activated $K^+$ signaling. *Science 314*, 615-620.

Berman DM, Gilman AG. (1998) Mammalian RGS proteins: barbarians at the gate. *J Biol Chem.* 273(3):1269–1272..

Berridge MJ, Bootman MD, Roderick HL. (1998). Calcium signalling: dynamics, homeostasis and remodelling. *Nat Rev Mol Cell Biol*;4:517-529.

Berridge, M. J., Bootman, M. D. and Lipp, P. (1998). Calcium – a life and death signal. *Nature,* 395, 645-668.

Bertrand D, Devillers-Thiéry A, Revah F, Galzi JL, Hussy N, Mulle C, Bertrand S, Ballivet M, Changeux JP. (1992) Unconventional pharmacology *Proc Natl Acad Sci USA.* 89(4):1261-5.

Bett GC and Rasmusson RL (2004). Inactivation and recovery in Kv1.4 $K^+$ channels: lipophilic interactions at the intracellular mouth of the pore. *J Physiol* 556: 109-120.

Betz H. 1991 Glycine receptors *Trends Neurosci.* 14(10):458-61.

Bhattacharya SK, Mitra SK (1991). Anxiolytic activity of Panax ginseng roots: an experimental study. *J Ethnopharmacol* 34: 87-92.

Bloom FE, Iversen LL (1971). Localizing 3H-GABA in nerve terminals of rat cerebral cortex by electron microscopic autoradiography. *Nature* 229: 628-630.

Brindley DN, Pilquil C. (2009). Lipid phosphate phosphatases and signaling. *J Lipid Res.*; 50 Suppl: S225-230.

Buchholz B, Tauber R, Steffl D. (2004). An inwardly rectifying whole cell current induced by Gq-coupled receptors. *Biochem Biophys Res Commun.*; 322: 177-185.

Callamaras, N. and Parker I. (1994). Inositol 1, 4, 5-triphosphate receptors in *Xenopus laevis* oocyte: localization and modulation by $Ca^{2+}$. *Cell Calc.,* 15, 66–78.

Carroll, R.C., Zukin, R.S., (2002). NMDA-receptor trafficking and targeting: implications for synaptic transmission and plasticity. *Trends. Neurosci.* 25, 571-577.

Catterall, W.A., Cestele, S., Yarov-Yarovoy, V., Yu, F.H., Konoki, K., Scheuer, T., (2007). Voltage-gated ion channels and gating modifier toxins. *Toxicon* 49, 124–141.

Choi S, Rho SH, Jung SY, Nah SY (2001a). A novel activation of $Ca^{2+}$-activated Cl⁻ channel in Xenopus oocytes by Ginseng saponins: evidence for the involvement of phospholipase C and intracellular $Ca^{2+}$ mobilization. *Br J Pharmacol* 132:641-648.

Choi S, Kim HJ, Ko YS, Nah SY (2001b) Galpha(q/11) coupled to mammalian phospholipase C beta 3-like enzyme mediates the ginsenoside effect on $Ca^{2+}$-activated Cl⁻ current in the Xenopus oocyte. *J Biol Chem*; 276:48797-48802.

Choi S, Lee JH, Oh S, Rhim H, Lee SM, Nah SY. (2003) Effects of ginsenoside Rg2 on the 5-$HT_{3A}$ receptor-mediated ion current in Xenopus oocytes. *Mol Cells.* 15(1):108-13.

Choi, D.W., (1992). Excitotoxic cell death. *J. Neurobiol.* 23, 1261-1276.

Choi, S., Jung, S. Y., Kim, C. H., Kim, H. S., Rhim, H., Kim, S. C. and Nah, S. Y. (2001). Effect of ginsenosides on voltage-dependent $Ca^{2+}$ channel subtypes in bovine chromaffin cells. *J. Ethnopharmacol.* 74, 75-81.

Choi S, Jung SY, Lee JH, Sala F, Criado M, Mulet J, Valor LM, Sala S, Engel AG, Nah SY. (2002) Effects of ginsenosides, active components of ginseng *Eur J Pharmacol.* 442(1-2):37-45.

Choi SE, Choi S, Lee JH, Whiting PJ, Lee SM, Nah SY. (2003) Effects of ginsenosides on GABA$_A$ receptor channels expressed in Xenopus oocytes. *Arch Pharm Res*. 26(1):28-33.

Choi, S.H., Lee, J.H., Pyo, M.K., Lee, B.H., Shin, T.J., Hwang, S.H., Kim, B.R., Lee, S.M., Oh, J.W., Kim, H.C., Bae, C.S., Rhim, H., Nah, S.Y., (2009). Mutations of Leu427, Asn428, and Leu431 residues within transmembrane domain-1-segment 6 attenuate ginsenoside-mediated L-type Ca$^{2+}$ channel current inhibitions. *Biol Pharm Bull*. 32, 1224-1230.

Choi, S.H., Shin, T.J., Lee, B.H., Chu, D.H., Choe, H., Pyo, M.K., Hwang, S.H., Kim, B.R., Lee, S.M., Lee, J.H., Kim, H. C., Park, H. Y., Rhim, H., and Nah, S. Y. (2010). Ginsenoside Rg$_3$ activates human KCNQ1 K$^+$ channel currents through interacting with the K318 and V319 residues: A role of KCNE1 subunit. *Eur. J. Pharmacol*. *63*, 138-147.

Choi S.H., Shin T.J., Lee B.H., Hwang S.H., Lee, S.M, Lee B.C., Park C.S., Ha T.S. and Nah, S. Y. (2011a). Ginsenoside Rg$_3$ enhances large conductance Ca$^{2+}$-activated potassium channel currents: a role of Tyr360 residue. *Mol Cells*. 31(2):133-40.

Choi SH, Shin TJ, Hwang SH, Lee BH, Kang J, Kim HJ, Jo SH, Choe H, Nah SY. (2011b) Ginsenoside Rg$_3$ decelerates hERG K$^+$ *Eur J Pharmacol*. 663(1-3):59-67.

Chun, J., Hla, T., Lynch, K.R., Spiegel, S., Moolenaar, W.H., (2010). International Union of Basic and Clinical Pharmacology. LXXVIII. Lysophospholipid receptor nomenclature. *Pharmacol. Rev*. 62, 579-587.

Chung, I. and Kim, N. D. (1999). Ginseng saponins enhance maxi Ca$^{2+}$-activated K$^+$ currents of the rabbit coronary artery smooth muscle cells. *J. Ginseng Res*. 23, 230-234.

Chung, I. and Lee, J. S. (1999). Ginsenoside Rg$_3$ increases the ATP-sensitive K$^+$ channel activity in the smooth muscle of the rabbit coronary artery. *J. Ginseng Res*. 23, 235-238.

Claydon TW, Makary SY, Dibb KM, and Boyett MR (2004). K$^+$ activation of kir3.1/kir3.4 and kv1.4 K$^+$ channels is regulated by extracellular charges. *Biophys J* 87: 2407-2418.

Dascal, N., Yekuel R. and Oron, Y. (1984). Acetylcholine promotes progesterone-induced maturation of Xenopus oocytes. *J. Exp. Zool.*, 230, 131–135.

Dascal N, Ifune C, Hopkins R (1986). Involvement of a GTP-binding protein in mediation of serotonin and acetylcholine responses in Xenopus oocytes injected with rat brain messenger RNA. *Brain Res*;387: 201-209.

Dascal N. (1987). The use of *Xenopus* oocytes for the study of ion channels. CRC Crit Rev Biochem;22:317-387.

Dascal, N. (1997). Signaling via the G prorein-activated K$^+$ channels. *Cell Signal*. 9, 551-573.

Dick, G.M., Hunter, A.C., and Sanders, K.M. (2002). Ethylbromide tamoxifen, a membrane-impermeant antiestrogen, activates smooth muscle calcium-activated large-conductance potassium channels from the extracellular side. *Mol. Pharmacol*. *61*, 1105-1113

Dingledine, R., Borges, K., Bowie, D. and Traynelis, S. F. (1999). Glutamate receptor ion channels. *Pharmacol. Rev*. 51, 7-62.

Duan, Y., Zheng, J., Law, V., Nicholson, R., (2006). Natural products from ginseng inhibit [$^3$H]batrachotoxinin A 20-alpha-benzoate binding to Na$^+$ channels in mammalian brain. *Eur. J. Pharmacol*. 530, 9–14.

Dubin, A.E., Bahnson, T., Weiner, J.A., Fukushima, N., Chun, J., (1999). Lysophosphatidic acid stimulates neurotransmitter-like conductance changes that precede GABA and L-glutamate in early, presumptive cortical neuroblasts. *J. Neurosci*. 19, 1371-1381.

Dubin, A.E., Herr, D.R., Chun, J., (2010). Diversity of lysophosphatidic acid receptor-mediated intracellular calcium signaling in early cortical neurogenesis. *J. Neurosci.* 30, 7300-7309.

Durand, G.M., Bennett, M.V., Zukin, R.S., (1993). Splice variants of the N-methyl-D-aspartate receptor NR1 identify domains involved in regulation by polyamines and protein kinase C. *Proc. Natl. Acad. Sci. USA.* 90, 6731-6735.

Engleman EA, Rodd ZA, Bell RL, Murphy JM. (2008). The role of 5-HT3 receptors in drug abuse and as a target for pharmacotherapy. *CNS Neurol Disord Drug Targets.* 7(5):454-67.

Ferguson, S. S. G., and Caron, M. G. (1998). G protein-coupled receptor adaptation mechanisms. *Cell Dev. Biol.* 9, 119–127.

Furukawa, T., Bai, C.X., Kaihara, A., Ozaki, E., Kawano, T., Nakaya, Y., Awais, M., Sato, M., Umezawa, Y., Kurokawa, J., (2006). Ginsenoside Re, a main phytosterol of Panax ginseng, activates cardiac potassium channels via a nongenomic pathway of sex hormones. *Mol Pharmacol.* 70(6), 1916-24.

Gao, B.Y., Li, X.J., Liu, L., and Zhang, B.H., (1992) Effect of panaxatriol saponins isolated from Panax notoginseng (PTS) on myocardial ischemic arrhythmia in mice and rats. *Yao Xue Xue Bao.* 27, 641-644.

Ghatta, S., Nimmagadda, D., Xu, X., and O'Rourke, S.T. (2006). Large-conductance, calcium-activated potassium channels: structural and functional implications. *Pharmacol. Ther.* 110, 103-116.

Giangiacomo, K.M., Kamassah, A., Harris, G., and McManus, O.B. (1998). Mechanism of maxi-K channel activation by dehydrosoyasaponin-I. *J. Gen. Physiol.* 112, 485-501.

Goldin, A.L., (1995). Voltage-gated $Na^+$ channels. In: North, R.A. (Ed.),Ligand- and voltage-gated ion channels. CRC Press, *Boca Raton*, FL, pp. 73–89.

Gotti C, Clementi F, Fornari A, Gaimarri A, Guiducci S, Manfredi I, Moretti M, Pedrazzi P, Pucci L, Zoli M. (2009). Structural and functional diversity of native brain neuronal nicotinic receptors. *Biochem Pharmacol.*;78(7):703-11.

Guo Z, Liliom K, Fischer DJ. (1996). Molecular cloning of a high-affinity areceptor for the growth factor-like lipid mediator lysophosphatidic acid from Xenopus oocytes. *Proc Natl Acad Sci* USA.;260: 14367-16372.

Ha, T.S., Lim, H.H., Lee, G.E., Kim, Y.C., and Park, C.S. (2006). Electrophysiological characterization of benzofuroindole-induced potentiation of large-conductance $Ca^{2+}$-activated $K^+$ channels. *Mol. Pharmacol.* 69, 1007-1114.

Haralampidis K, Trojanowska M, Osbourn AE. (2002) Biosynthesis of triterpenoid saponins in plants *Adv Biochem Eng Biotechnol.* 2002;75:31-49.

He M, Bodi I, Mikala G, Schwartz A.(1997). Motif III S5 of L-type calcium channels is involved in the dihydropyridine binding site. A combined radioligand binding and electrophysiological study. *J Biol Chem.*;272(5):2629-33.

Hecht J.H., Weiner J.A., Post S.R., and Chun, J. (1996). Ventricular zone gene-1 (vzg-1) encodes a lysophosphatidic acid receptor expressed in neurogenic regions of the developing cerebral cortex. *J Cell Biol*; 135: 1071-1083.

Heginbotham, L., Abramson, T., and Mackinnon R. (1992). A functional conncetion between the pores of distantly related ion channels as revealed by mutant $K^+$ channels. *Science* 258, 1152-1155.

Heginbotham, L., Lu, Z., Abramson, T., and Mackinnon R. (1994). Mutations in the $K^+$ channel signature sequence. *Biophys. J. 66*, 1061-1067.

Heo, J.H., Lee, S.T., Chu, K., Oh, M.J., Park, H.J., Shim, J.Y., Kim, M. (2008). An open-label trial of Korean red ginseng as an adjuvant treatment for cognitive impairment in patients with Alzheimer's disease. *Eur. J. Neurol.* 15, 865-868.

Herrera L, Carvallo P, Antonelli M. (1994). Cloning of a Xenopus laevis muscarinic receptor encoded by an intronless gene. *FEBS Lett*;352: 175-179.

Hille B. (2001). "Ion Channels of Excitable Membranes," Sinauer Associates, Inc., *Sunderland,* MA.

Hollmann, M., Heinemann, S., (1994). Cloned glutamate receptors. Annu. Rev. *Neurosci.* 17, 31-108.

Hoshi T., Zagotta W. N., Aldrich R. W. (1990). Biophysical and molecular mechanisms of Shaker potassium channel inactivation. *Science*, 250(4980):533-8.

Houben AJ, Moolenaar WH. (2011). Autotaxin and LPA receptor signaling in cancer. *Cancer Metastasis* Rev 30:557-565.

Hwang SH, Shin EJ, Shin TJ, Nah SY. (2012) Gintonin, a Ginseng-Derived Lysophosphatidic Acid Receptor Ligand, Attenuates Alzheimer's Disease-Related Neuropathies: Involvement of Non-Amyloidogenic Processing. *J Alzheimers Dis.* 31(1):207-23.

Hwang SH, Shin TJ, Choi SH, Nah SY. (2012). Gintonin, newly identified compounds from ginseng, is novel lysophosphatidic acids-protein complexes and activates G protein-coupled lysophosphatidic acid receptors with high affinity. *Mol Cells*; 33: 151-162.

Imaizumi, Y., Sakamoto, K., Yamada, A., Hotta, A., Ohya, S., Muraki, K., Uchiyama, M., and Ohwada, T. (2002). Molecular basis of pimarane compounds as novel activators of large-conductance $Ca^{2+}$-activated $K^+$ channel α-subunit. Mol. Pharmacol. 62, 836Haralampidis K, Trojanowska M, Osbourn AE. Biosynthesis of triterpenoid saponins in plants. *Adv Biochem Eng Biotechnol.* 75:31-49.

Ingi, T., Krumins, A. M., Chidiac, P., Brothers, G. M., Chung, S., Snow, B. E., Barnes, C. A., Lanahan, A. A., Siderovski, D. P., Ross, E. M., Gilman, A. G., and Worley, P. F. (1998). Dynamic regulation of RGS2 suggests a novel mechanism in G-protein signaling and neuronal plasticity. *J. Neurosci.* 18, 7178–7188.

Jeong, S. M., Lee, J. H., Kim, J. H, Lee, B. H., Yoon, I. S., Lee, J. H., Kim, D. H., Rhim, H., Kim, Y. and Nah, S. Y. (2004): Stereospecificity of ginsenoside $Rg_3$ action on ion channels. *Mol. Cells* 18, 383-389.

Judge SI, Monteiro MJ, Yeh JZ, and Bever CT (1999) Inactivation gating and 4-AP sensitivity in human brain Kv1.4 potassium channel. *Brain Res* 831: 43-54.

Kang DI, Lee JY, Yang JY, Jeong SM, Lee JH, Nah SY, Kim Y. (2005). Evidence that the tertiary structure of 20(S)-ginsenoside Rg(3) with tight hydrophobic packing near the chiral center is important for Na(+) channel regulation. *Biochem Biophys Res Commun.* 333(4):1194-201.

Kawasawa Y, Kume K, Nakade S. (2000). Brain-specific expression of novel G-protein-coupled receptors, with homologies to Xenopus PSP24 and human GPR45. *Biochem Biophys Res Commun*; 276: 952-956.

Kim J.H., Hong Y.H., Lee J.H., Kim D.H., Nam G., Jeong S.M., Lee B.H., Lee S.M., Nah S.Y. (2005a). A role for the carbohydrate portion of ginsenoside $Rg_3$ in $Na^+$ channel inhibition. *Mol Cells.* 19(1):137-42.

Kim J.H., Lee J.H., Jeong S.M., Lee B.H., Yoon I.S., Lee J.H., Choi S.H., Nah S.Y. (2005b). Effect of ginseng saponins on a rat visceral hypersensitivity model. *Biol Pharm Bull.* (11):2120-4.

Kim J.H., Yoon I.S., Lee B.H., Choi S.H., Lee J.H., Lee J.H., Jeong S.M., Kim S.C., Park C.K., Lee SM, Nah SY. (2005c). Effects of Korean red ginseng extract on cisplatin-induced nausea and vomiting. *Arch Pharm Res.* (6):680-4.

Kim JH, Kim S, Yoon IS, Lee JH, Jang BJ, Jeong SM, Lee JH., Lee BH., Han JS., Oh S, Kim HC, Park TK, Rhim H, Nah SY., (2005d). Protective effects of ginseng saponins on 3-nitropropionic acid-induced striatal degeneration in rats. Neuropharmacology 48,743-756.

Kim S, Kim T, Ahn K, Park WK, Nah SY, Rhim H. (2004). Ginsenoside Rg$_3$ antagonizes NMDA receptors through a glycine modulatory site in rat cultured hippocampal neurons. *Biochem Biophys Res Commun.*;323(2):416-24.

Kim T.W., Choi H.J., Kim N.J., Kim D.H. (2009). Anxiolytic-like effects of ginsenoside Rg$_3$ and Rh2 from red ginseng in the elevated plus-maze model. *Planta Med* 75: 836-839.

Kim S, Ahn K, Oh TH, Nah SY. and Rhim H., (2002). Inhibitory effect of ginsenosides on NMDA receptor-mediated signals in rat hippocampal neurons. *Biochem Biophys Res Commun.* 296, 247-254.

Kim, Y. C., Kim, S. R., Markelonis, G. J. and Oh, T. H., (1998). Ginsenosides Rb$_1$ and Rg$_3$ protect cultured rat cortical cells from glutamate-induced neurodegeranation. *J. Neurosci. Res.* 53, 426-432 .

Kimura T, Saunders PA, Kim HS, Rheu HM, Oh KW, Ho IK., (1994). Interactions of ginsenosides with ligand bindings of GABA$_A$ and GABA$_B$ receptors. *Gen Pharmacol* 25: 193-199.

Kimura, Y., Schmitt, A., Fukushima, N., Ishii, I., Kimura, H., Nebreda, A.R., Chun, J., (2001). Two novel Xenopus homologs of mammalian LP(A1)/EDG-2 function as lysophosphatidic acid receptors in Xenopus oocytes and mammalian cells. *J. Biol. Chem.* 276,15208-15.

Kraus R. L., Hering S., Grabner M., Ostler D., Striessinig J., (1998) Molecular mechanism of diltiazem interaction with L-type calcium channels. *J. Biol. Chem.*, 273, 27206—27212.

Kwatra, M. M., Schwinn, D. A., Schreurs J ., Blank, J. L., Kim, C. M., Benovic, J. L., Krause, J. E., Caron, M. G., and Lefkowitz, R. J., (1993). The substance P receptor, which couples to Gq/11, is a substrate of beta-adrenergic receptor kinase 1 and 2. *J. Biol. Chem.* 268, 9161–9164

Lawson, K., (2000). Is there a role for potassium channel openers in neuronal ion channel disorders? *Expert. Opin. Investig. Drugs* 9, 2269-2280.

Lechleiter J.D. and Clahaam, D.E., (1992). Molecular mechanisms of intracellular calcium excitability in Xenopus laevis oocytes. *Cell*, 69, 283–294.

Lee BH, Jeong SM, Lee JH, Kim DH, Kim JH, Kim JI, Shin HC, Lee SM, Nah SY., (2004a) Differential effect of ginsenoside metabolites on the 5-HT$_{3A}$ receptor-mediated ion current in Xenopus oocytes. *Mol. Cells* 17, 51-56 .

Lee BH, Jeong SM, Ha T. S., Park C. S., Lee JH, Kim J. H., Kim D. H., Han J. S., Kim H. C., Ko S..R., Nah SY., (2004b). Ginsenosides regulate ligand-gated ion channels from the outside. *Mol Cells.* 18(1):115-21

Lee BH, Lee JH, Lee SM, Jeong SM, Yoon IS, Lee JH, Choi SH, Pyo MK, Rhim H, Kim HC, Jang CG, Lee BC, Park CS, Nah SY. (2007a). Identification of ginsenoside interaction sites in 5-HT$_{3A}$ receptors. *Neuropharmacology* 2(4):1139-50.

Lee BH, Lee JH, Yoon IS, Lee JH, Choi SH, Shin TJ, Pyo MK, Choi WS, Lee SM, Lim Y, Rhim H, Nah SY., (2007b). Mutations of arginine 222 in pre-transmembrane domain I of mouse 5-HT(3A) receptor abolish 20(R)- but not 20(S)-ginsenoside Rg(3) inhibition of 5-HT-mediated ion currents. *Biol Pharm Bull.* 30(9):1721-6.

Lee BH, Choi SH, Pyo MK, Shin TJ, Hwang SH, Kim BR, Lee SM, Lee JH, Lee JH, Lee HS, Choe H, Han KH, Kim HC, Rhim H, Yong JH, Nah SY (2009) A role for Leu247 residue within transmembrane domain 2 in ginsenoside-mediated alpha7 nicotinic acetylcholine *Mol Cells.* 27(5):591-9.

Lee JH, Kim SH, Kim D, Hong HN, Nah SY., (2001) Protective effect of ginsenosides, active ingredients of Panax ginseng, on kainate-induced neurotoxicity in rat hippocampus. *Neurosci. Lett.* 325, 129-133.

Lee JH, Jeong SM, Lee BH, Noh HS, Kim BK, Kim JI, Rhim H, Kim HC, Kim KM, Nah SY. (2004). Prevention of ginsenoside-induced desensitization of Ca$^{2+}$-activated Cl$^-$ current by microinjection of inositol hexakisphosphate in Xenopus laevis oocytes: involvement of GRK2 and beta-arrestin I. *J Biol Chem.* 279(11):9912-21.

Lee JH, Jeong SM, Kim JH, Lee BH, Yoon IS, Lee JH, Choi SH, Kim DH, Rhim H, Kim SS, Kim JI, Jang CG, Song JH, Nah SY. (2005) Characteristics of ginsenoside Rg$_3$-mediated brain Na$^+$ current inhibition. *Mol Pharmacol.* 68(4):1114-26.

Lee JH, Jeong SM, Kim JH, Lee BH, Yoon IS, Lee JH, Choi SH, Lee SM, Park YS, Lee JH, Kim SS, Kim HC, Lee BY, Nah SY., (2006) Effects of ginsenosides and their metabolites on voltage-dependent Ca$^{2+}$ channel subtypes. *Mol Cells.* 21(1):52-62.

Lee JH, Lee BH, Choi SH, Yoon IS, Pyo MK, Shin TJ, Choi WS, Lim Y, Rhim H, Won KH, Lim YW, Choe H, Kim DH, Kim YI, Nah SY. (2008a) Ginsenoside Rg$_3$ inhibits human *Mol Pharmacol.* 73(3):619-26.

Lee JH, Lee BH, Choi SH, Yoon IS, Shin TJ, Pyo MK, Lee SM, Kim HC, Nah SY., (2008b) Involvement of batrachotoxin binding sites in ginsenoside-mediated voltage-gated Na$^+$ channel regulation. *Brain Res.* 1203:61-7.

Lee JH, Choi SH, Lee BH, Yoon IS, Shin TJ, Pyo MK, Lee SM, Rhim H, Park MH, Park TY, Nah SY. (2008c) Modifications of aliphatic side chain of 20(S)-ginsenoside Rg$_3$ cause an enhancement or loss of brain Na$^+$ channel current inhibitions. *Biol Pharm Bull.* 31(3):480-6.

Lisman, J., Yasuda, R., Raghavachari, S., (2012). Mechanisms of CaMKII action in long-term potentiation. *Nat. Rev. Neurosci.* 13, 169-82.

Liu XW, Sok DE, Yook HS, Sohn CB, Chung YJ, Kim MR., (2007) Inhibition of lysophospholipase D activity by unsaturated lysophosphatidic acids or seed extracts containing 1-linoleoyl and oleoyl lysophosphatidic acid. *J Agric Food Chem* 55:8717-8722.

Liu D, Li B, Liu Y, Attele AS, Kyle JW, Yuan CS., (2001) Voltage-dependent inhibition of brain Na$^+$ channels by American ginseng. *Eur. J. Pharmacol.* 413, 47-54.

Lyford LK, Sproul AD, Eddins D, McLaughlin JT, Rosenberg RL. (2003) Agonist-induced conformational changes in the extracellular domain of alpha 7 nicotinic acetylcholine *Mol Pharmacol.* 64(3):650-8.

Macdonald RL, Olsen RW., (1994). GABA$_A$ receptor channels. *Ann Res Neurosci* 17: 569-602.

MacDonald JF, Jackson MF, Beazely MA., (2006). Hippocampal long-term synaptic plasticity and signal amplification of NMDA receptors. *Crit. Rev. Neurobiol.* 18, 71-84.

Maricq, A. V., Peterson, A. S., Brake, A. J., Myers, R. M. and Julius, D., (1991) Primary structure and functional expression of the 5-HT$_3$ receptor, a serotonin-gated ion channel. Science, 254, 432-437 .

Matsuda LA, Lolait SJ, Brownstein MJ, Young AC, Bonner TI., (1990). Structure of a cannabinoid receptor and functional expression of the cloned cDNA. *Nature* ;346: 561-564.

McCabe RT, Wamsley JK., (1986). Autoradiographic localization of subcomponents of the macromolecular GABA receptor complex. *Life Sci* 39: 1937-1945.

McConalogue, K., Corvera, C. U., Gamp, P. D., Grady, E. F., and Bunnet, N. W., (1998). Desensitization of the neurokinin-1 receptor (NK1-R) in neurons: effects of substance P on the distribution of NK1-R, Galphaq/11, G-protein receptor kinase-2/3, and beta-arrestin-1/2. *Mol. Biol. Cell* 9, 2305–2324.

Miledi R and Parker I., (1984). Chloride current induced by injection of calcium into Xenopus oocytes. *J. Physiol.* (Lond.), 357, 173–183.

Miller, R. J., (2001). Rocking and rolling with Ca$^{2+}$ channels. *Trends in Neurosci.* 24, 445-449.

Miyazawa A, Fujiyoshi Y, Unwin N. (2003) Structure and gating mechanism of the acetylcholine *Nature* 423(6943):949-55.

Moolenaar WH., (1994). LPA: a novel lipid mediator with diverse biological actions. *Trends Cell Biol* ;4: 213-219.

Moriyoshi, K., Masu, M., Ishii, T., Shigemoto, R., Mizuno, N., Nakanishi, S., ( 1991). Molecular cloning and characterization of the rat NMDA receptor. *Nature* 354, 31-37.

Nah SY, Kim DH, Rhim H., (2007). Ginsenosides: are any of them candidates for drugs acting on the central nervous system? *CNS Drug Rev.* 13(4):381-404.

Nah SY., Park, H. J. and McCleskey, E.W. (1995) A trace component of ginseng that inhibit Ca$^{2+}$ channels through a pertussis toxin-sensitive G protein. *Proc Natl Acad Sci* USA 92, 8739-8743.

Noguchi K, Herr D, Mutoh T. (2009) Lysophosphatidic acid (LPA) and its receptors. *Curr Opin Pharmacol* 2009;9: 15-23.

Noh JH, Choi S, Lee JH, Betz H, Kim JI, Park CS, Lee SM, Nah SY. (2003). Effects of ginsenosides on glycine receptor alpha1 channels expressed in Xenopus oocytes. *Mol Cells.* 15(1):34-9.

Oakely, R. H., Laporte, S. A., Holt, J. A., Caron, M. G., and Barak, L. S. (2000) Differential affinities of visual arrestin, beta arrestin1, and beta arrestin2 for G protein-coupled receptors delineate two major classes of receptors. *J. Biol. Chem.* 275, 17201–17210.

Palczewski, K., Rispoli, G., and Detwiler, P. B., (1992). The influence of arrestin (48K protein) and rhodopsin kinase on visual transduction. *Neuron* 8, 117–126.

Palma E, Mileo AM, Eusebi F, Miledi R. (2006) Threonine-for-leucine *Proc Natl Acad Sci* U S A. 93(20):11231-5.

Panicker S, Cruz H, Arrabit C, Slesinger PA. (2002). Evidence for a centrally located gate in the pore of a serotonin-gated ion channel. *J Neurosci.* 22(5):1629-39.

Pardo LA, Heinemann SH, Terlau H, Ludewig U, Lorra C, Pongs O, and Stuhmer W., (1992). Extracellular $K^+$ specifically modulates a rat brain $K^+$ channel. *Proc Natl Acad Sci U S A* 89: 2466-2470.

Park JH, Cha HY, Seo JJ, Hong JT, Han K, Oh KW., (2005). Anxiolytic-like effects of ginseng in the elevated plus-maze model: comparison of red ginseng and sun ginseng. *Prog Neuropsychopharmacol Biol Psychiatry* 29: 895-900.

Parker, Yao., (1994). Relation between intracellular $Ca^{2+}$ signals and $Ca^{2+}$-activated Cl⁻ current in Xenopus oocytes. *Cell Calc.*, 15, 276–288.

Pert CB, and Snyder SH. Opiate receptor: demonstration in nervous tissue. *Science* 1973;179: 1011-1014.

Pierce, K., L., and Lefkowitz, R. J. (2001) Classical and new roles of beta-arrestins in the regulation of G-protein-coupled receptors. *Nat. Rev.* 2, 727–733.

Pyo MK, Shin TJ, Choi SH, Cho HJ, Lee BH, Pyo MK, Lee JH, Kang J, Kim HJ, Park CW, Shin HC, Nah SY. (2011a). Novel glycoproteins from ginseng. *J Ginseng Res* 2011;35: 92-103.

Pyo MK, Choi SH., Shin TJ, Hwang SH, Lee BH, Kang J, Kim HJ, Lee SH, Nah SY (2011b) A Simple Method for the Preparation of Crude Gintonin from Ginseng Root, Stem, and Leaf. *J. Ginseng Res.* 35, 209-218.

Qian, X., Nimigean, C.M., Niu, X., Moss, B.L., and Magleby, K.L., (2002). Slo1 tail domains, but not the $Ca^{2+}$ bowl, are required for the beta 1 subunit to increase the apparent $Ca^{2+}$ sensitivity of BK channels. *J. Gen. Physiol.* 120, 829-843.

Qian, T., Cai, Z., Wong, R. N. S., Mak, N. K., and Jiang, Z. H., (2005). In vivo rat metabolism and pharmacokinetic studies of ginsenoside Rg₃. J. Chromatograph. B., 816, 223-232.

Rajendra S, Lynch JW, Schofield PR. (1997). The glycine receptor. *Pharmacol Ther.*; 73(2):121-46.

Reeves DC, Goren EN, Akabas MH, Lummis SC., (2001). Structural and electrostatic properties of the 5-HT3 receptor pore revealed by substituted cysteine accessibility mutagenesis. *J Biol Chem.* 276(45):42035-42.

Revah F, Bertrand D, Galzi JL, Devillers-Thiéry A, Mulle C, Hussy N, Bertrand S, Ballivet M, Changeux JP. (1991) Mutations in the channel domain alter desensitization *Nature* 353(6347):846-9.

Rhim H., Kim H., Lee DY., Oh TH, Nah SY., (2002). Ginseng and ginsenoside Rg₃, a newly identified active ingredient of ginseng, modulate $Ca^{2+}$ channel currents in rat sensory neurons. *Eur. J. Pharmacol.* 436, 151-158.

Robbins, J., (2001). KCNQ potassium channels: physiology, pathophysiology, and pharmacology. *Pharmacol Ther.* 90(1), 1-19.

Rudolph U, Knoflach F., (2011). Beyond classical benzodiazepines: novel therapeutic potential of GABAₐ receptor subtypes. *Nat Rev Drug Discov* 10: 685-697.

Sala, F., Mulet, J., Choi, S., Jung, S. Y., Nah SY., Rhim H., Valor, L. M., Criado, M. and Sala, S., (2002). Effects of ginsenoside Rg₂ on human neuronal nicotinic acetylcholine receptors. *J. Pharm. Exp. Ther.* 301, 1052-1059.

Salkoff, L., Butler ,A., Ferreira, G., Santi, C., and Wei, A. (2006). High-conductance potassium channels of the SLO family. *Nat. Rev. Neurosci.* 7, 921-31.

Sanguinetti, M.C., Curran, M.E., Zou, A., Shen, J., Spector, P.S., Atkinson, D.L., Keating, M.T., (1996). Coassembly of K(V)LQT1 and minK (IsK) proteins to form cardiac I(Ks) potassium channel. *Nature* 7, 384(6604):80-3.

Sargent, P. B., (1993). The diversity of neuronal nicotinic acetylcholine receptor. *Ann. Rev. Neurosci.* 16, 403-443.

Sasakawa, N., Ferguson, J. E., Sharif, M., and Hanley, M. R. (1994) .Attenuation of agonist-induced desensitization of the rat substance P receptor by microinjection of inositol pentakis-and hexakisphosphates in Xenopus laevis oocytes. *Mol. Pharmacol.* 46, 380–385.

Schreiber, M., and Salkoff, L., (1997). A novel calcium-sensing domain in the BK channel. *Biophys. J.* 73, 1355-1363.

Schreiber, M., Yuan, A., and Salkoff, L., (1999). Transplantable sites confer calcium sensitivity to BK channels. *Nat. Neurosci.* 2, 416-421.

Seong, Y. H., Shin, C. S., Kim, H. S. and Baba, A., (1995). Inhibitory effect of ginseng total saponins on glutamate-induced swelling of cultured atrocytes. *Biol. Pharm. Bull.* 18, 1776-1778.

Stracke ML, Krutzsch HC, Unsworth EJ, Arestad A, Cioce V, Schiffmann E, Liotta LA., (1992). Identification, purification, and partial sequence analysis of autotaxin, a novel motility-stimulating protein. *J Biol Chem* ;267:2524-2529.

Sullivan Hanley, N. R., and Hensler, J. G., (2002). Mechanisms of ligand-induced desensitization of the 5-hydroxytryptamine(2A) receptor. *J. Pharmacol. Exp. Ther.* 300, 468–477.

Sun H, Kim MK, Pulla RK, Kim YJ, Yang DC., (2010) Isolation and expression analysis of a novel major latex-like protein (MLP151) gene from Panax ginseng. *Mol Biol Rep.* ;37: 2215-2222.

Tachikawa E, Kudo K, Nunokawa M, Kashimoto T, Takahashi E, Kitagawa S., (2001). Characterization of ginseng saponin ginsenoside-Rg(3) inhibition of catecholamine secretion in bovine adrenal chromaffin cells. *Biochem Pharmacol.* Oct 1;62(7):943-51.

Tigyi G, and Miledi R., (1992). Lysophosphatidates bound to serum albumin activate membrane currents in Xenopus oocytes and neurite retraction in PC12 pheochromocytoma cells. *J Biol Chem*; 267: 21360-21367.

Timofeeva, O.A., Levin, E.D., (2011). Glutamate and nicotinic receptor interactions in working memory: importance for the cognitive impairment of schizophrenia. *Neuroscience* 195, 21-36.

Toro, L., Wallner, M., Meera, P., and Tanaka, Y., (1998). Maxi-$K_{Ca}$, a unique member of the voltage-gated $K^+$ channel superfamily. *News Physiol. Sci.* 13, 112-117.

Trigg ME, Higa GM., (2010). Chemotherapy-induced nausea and vomiting: antiemetic trials that impacted clinical practice. *J Oncol Pharm Pract.* 16(4):233-44.

Tristani-Firouzi M, Sanguinetti MC. (2003) Structural determinants and biophysical properties of HERG and KCNQ1 channel gating. J Mol Cell Cardiol. 35(1):27-35.

Tyler, V. E., (1995). Herbal remedies. *J Pharm Technol* 11, 214-220.

Uchiyama A, Mukai M, Fujiwara Y, Kobayashi S, Kawai N, Murofushi H, Inoue M, Enoki S, Tanaka Y, Niki T, Kobayashi T, Tigyi G, Murakami-Murofushi K., (2007). Inhibition of transcellular tumor cell migration and metastasis by novel carba-derivatives of cyclic phosphatidic acid. *Biochim Biophys Acta;*1771:103-112.

Unwin N. (2005) Refined structure *J Mol Biol.* 2005 Mar 4;346(4):967-89.

Valverde, M.A., Rojas, P., Amigo, J., Cosmelli, D., Orio, P., Bahamonde, M.I., Mann, G.E., Vergara, C., and Latorre, R., (1999). Acute activation of Maxi-K channels (hSlo) by estradiol binding to the beta subunit. *Science* (Wash DC) 285, 1929-1931.

Vergara, C., Latorre, R., Marrion, N.V., Adelman, J.P., (1998). Calcium-activated potassium channels. *Curr. Opin. Neurobiol.* 8, 321-329.

Wang, S.Y., Wang, G.K., (1998). Point mutations in segment I-S6 render voltage-gated $Na^+$ channels resistant to batrachotoxin. *Proc. Natl. Acad. Sci. USA.* 95, 2653–2658.

Wanner, S.G., Koch, R.O., Koschak, A., Trieb, M., Garcia, M.L., Kaczorowski, G.J., and Knaus, H.G., (1999). High-conductance calcium-activated potassium channels in rat brain: pharmacology, distribution, and subunit composition. *Biochemistry* 38, 5392-400.

Watanabe I, Zhu J, Recio-Pinto E, and Thornhill WB., (2004). Glycosylation affects the protein stability and cell surface expression of Kv1.4 but Not Kv1.1 potassium channels. A pore region determinant dictates the effect of glycosylation on trafficking. *J Biol Chem* 279: 8879-8885.

Wei, A., Solaro, C., Lingle, C., and Salkoff, L., (1994). Calcium sensitivity of BK-type KCa channels determined by a separable domain. *Neuron* 13, 671-681.

Weiger, T.M., Hermann, A., and Levitan, I.B., (2002). Modulation of calcium-activated potassium channels. *J. Comp. Physiol. A. Neuroethol. Sens. Neural. Behav. Physiol.* 188, 79-87.

Whiting PJ, McKernan RM, Wafford KA., (1995). Structure and pharmacology of vertebrate GABA-A receptor subtypes. *Int Res Neurobiol* 38: 95-138.

Yamaguchi S., Zhorov B. S., Yoshioka K., Nagao T., Ichijo H., Adachi-Akahane S. (2003). Key roles of Phe1112 and Ser1115 in the pore-forming IIIS5-S6 linker of L-type $Ca^{2+}$ channel alpha1C subunit (CaV 1.2) in binding of dihydropyridines and action of $Ca^{2+}$ channel agonists. *Mol. Pharmacol.*, 64(2):235-48.

Yang, Y., He, K., Wu, T., Li, Q., Zhang, J.S., and Fu, Z.G., (1999) Effects of ginsenosides on myocardial reperfusion arrhythmia and lipid superoxidation in high cholesterol diet rats. *Shi Yan Sheng Wu Xue Bao.* 32, 349-352.

Yoon HR, Kim H, and Cho, SH. (2003). Quantitative analysis of acyl-lysophosphatidic acid in plasma using negative ionization tandem mass spectrometry. *J Chromatogr B Analyt Technol Biomed Life Sci* 788: 85-92.

Yoon, S. R., Nah, J. J., Shin, Y. H., Kim, S. K., Nam, K. Y., Choi, H. S., Nah SY.:, (1998). Ginsenosides induce differential antinocicepion and inhibit substance P induced-nociceptive response in mice. *Life Sci.* 62, PL319-PL325.

Zhang H, Xu X, Gajewiak J, Tsukahara R, Fujiwara Y, Liu J, Fells JI, Perygin D, Parrill AL, Tigyi G, Prestwich GD., (2009). Dual activity lysophosphatidic acid receptor pan-antagonist/autotaxin inhibitor reduces breast cancer cell migration in vitro and causes tumor regression in vivo. *Cancer Res* ;69:5441-5449.

In: Recent Advances in Ginseng and Glycosides Research        ISBN: 978-1-62417-765-1
Editor: Claude J. Hopkins                                      © 2013 Nova Science Publishers, Inc.

*Chapter 2*

# THE MEDITERRANEAN MEDICINAL PLANTS: A REVIEW OF GLYCOSIDES AND THEIR PHARMACOLOGICAL EFFECTS

## *Ludmila Yarmolinsky[1,2], Arie Budovsky[1], Jonathan Gorelick[1], Amir Kitron[1] and Shimon Ben-Shabat[2]\**

[1]Judea Regional Research and Development Center, Carmel, Israel
[2]Department of Pharmacology, Faculty of Health Sciences,
Ben-Gurion University of the Negev, Beer-Sheva, Israel

## ABSTRACT

Medicinal plants from the Mediterranean region have been used in medicine since ancient times and are well known for their successful therapeutic activity. Many glycosides isolated from these plants showed various medicinal properties. The purpose of this review is to provide the verified data on the anti-viral, anti-microbial, anti-cancer, anti-inflammatory, anti-aging, anti-oxidant and anti-diabetic activities of the glycosides extracted from the medicinal plants of the Mediterranean flora and to discuss the various mechanisms of their actions.

## 1. INTRODUCTION

The medicinal application of plants from the Mediterranean region have been widely acknowledged since ancient times (Gonzales-Tejero et al., 2008). The Mediterranean medicinal plants were quoted in the Bible and other historical sources.

Hippocrates (in the late fifth century B.C.) mentioned 300 to 400 medicinal plants (Cowan, 1999, Katsambas and Marketos, 2007). In the first century A.D., Dioscorides wrote

\* Corresponding author: Dr. Shimon Ben-Shabat. Tel: +972-8- 6479354; Fax: +972-8-6472984; E-mail: sbs@bgu.ac.il.

De Materia Medica, a medicinal plant catalog which became the prototype for modern pharmacopoeias.

The Mediterranean region is home to over 25.000 species of higher plants, many of which are endemic (Greuter, 1991). Recently, in the framework of the project RUBIA which was undertaken from 2003 to 2005 (Gonzales-Tejero et al., 2008), a total of 985 species from the Mediterranean region were catalogued, including 406 species having medicinal uses.

A wide variety of bioactive constituents of different structures stands behind the therapeutic activity of the Mediterranean plants. These compounds, identified from medicinal plants, include flavonoids, terpenoids, lignans, sulphides, polyphenolics, coumarins, saponins, furils, alkaloids, polyines, thiophenes, different sugars, proteins, peptides and etc. (Jassim and Naji, 2003, Saladino et al., 2008, Haque et al., 2011).

In particular, conjugates of sugars with small organic molecules called glycosides are a source for drug discovery given their structural diversity and wide variety of biological activities which include anti-bacterial, anti-tumor, anti-viral, anti-inflammatory, neuro-protective, anti-oxidant, hepatoprotective, and immunomodulatory actions (Fu et al., 2008).

Glycosides can be classified by the glycone groups, types of glycosidic bonds, and by the aglycone groups. A classification by the aglycone group is the most useful, there are several approaches to this classification ( Dembitsky, 2004a, Dembitsky 2004b, Dembitsky, 2005a, Dembitsky, 2005b, Dembitsky, 2005c, Dembitsky, 2005d, Dembitsky, 2006, Lindhorst, 2007).

In this review we consider the anti-viral, anti-microbial, anti-cancer, anti-inflammatory, anti-aging, anti-oxidant and anti-diabetic activities of the glycosides extracted from the medicinal plants of the Mediterranean flora and discuss the various mechanisms of their actions.

## 2. ANTI-VIRAL AND ANTI-MICROBIAL ACTIVITIES OF THE GLYCOSIDES EXTRACTED FROM THE MEDICINAL PLANTS OF THE MEDITERRANEAN FLORA

Resistance to antimicrobial and antiviral agents is an ongoing challenge (Prabaker and Weinstein, 2011). Mechanisms of this resistance include activation of ATP-binding cassette transporters; activation of cytochrome p450 oxidases; and activation of glutathione transferases (Wink et al., 2012). While we live in an era of wide spread use of antibiotics (Dryden et al., 2011), many known antimicrobial and antiviral agents are very toxic (Thompson and Townsend, 2011). Thus, there is an urgent need for new anti-microbial and antiviral drugs with higher efficacy and lower toxicity. Glycosides found in the plants could be a promising source for new generation of these drugs.

Many antimicrobial glycosides isolated and identified from plants of the Mediterranean flora are very active against both gram-positive and gram-negative bacteria (Table 1).

In some cases, herbal glycosides are also effective against antibiotic resistant strains. For instance, kaempherol 3-O-alphaL-(2",4"-di-E-p-coumaroyl)-rhamnoside (C2) and Kaempherol 3-O-alphaL-(2"-Z -p-coumaroyl)-rhamnoside (C3), isolated from extracts of *Laurus nobilis* , showed strong activity against methicillin resistant *Staphyloccoccus aureus* and vancomycin resistant enterococci (Otsuka et al., 2008, Liu et al., 2009).

**Table 1. Antimicrobial activities of glycosides found in the Mediterranean plants**

| Plant | Glycosides | Pathogens | References |
|---|---|---|---|
| *Ricinus communis* | 3-O-[β -D-glucoronopyranosyl-(1→ 3)-α –L-rhamnopyranosyl-(1→ 2)β-D-glucopyranosyl]-4α,20α-hydroxy methyl olean-12-ene-28-oic acid | *Escherichia coli* and *Staphylococcus aureus* | Khan et al., 2010 |
| *Cephalaria elmallensis* | Macranthoidin A, dipsocoside B, 3-O-α-L-ramnopyranosyl-(1→ 2)-α –L-arabinopyranosyl hederagenin 28-O-β-D-glucopyranosyl ester, 3-O-β- D-glucopyranosyl-(1→3)-α-L-rhamnopyranosyl-(1→2)-α-L-arabinopyranosyl hederagenin 28-O-β-D-glucopyranosyl ester, α-hederin, sapindoside B, macranthoside A, tiliroside, luteolin-7-O-β-D-glycoside, elmalienoside | *Escherichia coli, Pseudomonas aeruginosa, Salmonella typhimurium, Kliebsiella pneumpniea, Staphylococcus aureus, Staphylococcus epidermidis, Bacillus cereus, Enterococcus faecalis* | Sarikahya and Kirmizigul, 2012 |
| *Laurus nobilis* | Kaempherol 3-O-alphaL-(2",4"-di-E-p-coumaroyl)-rhamnoside (C2) and Kaempherol 3-O-alphaL-(2"-Z -p-coumaroyl)-rhamnoside (C3) | *Streptococcus pneumoniea, Pseudomonas aeruginosa , Ser*ratia marcessens | Otsuka et al., 2008, Liu et al., 2009 |
| *Marrubium globossum* | Quercetin 3-O-beta –D-rubinoside and naringenin 7-O-beta-D-glucoside | *Enterococcus faecalis, Staphyloccoccus epidermidis, Staphyloccoccus aureus, Bacillus subtilis, Enterobacter aerogenes, Enterobacter cloacae, Eisheriella coli, Klebsiella pneumoniea, Proteus mirabilis, Proteus vulgaris, Pseudomonas aeruginosa, Salmonella typhi* | Rigano et al., 2007 |
| *Centaurium pulchellum* | Secoiridoid glycosides | Many pathogenic bacteria | Siler et al., 2010 |
| *Momordica balsamina* | Cucurbitane-type triterpenoids: balsaminol F and balsaminoside B ; glycosylated cucurbitacins: cucurbita-5,24-diene-3β,23(R)-diol-7-O-β-D-glucopyranoside and kuguaglycoside A | *Staphylococcus aureus and Enterococcus faecalis* | Ramalhete et al., 2010, Ramalhete et al., 2011. |
| *Gkycyrthiza glabra* | Glycyrrhizin | *Pseudomonas aeruginosa* | Yashida et al., 2010 |

**Table 1. (Continued)**

| Plant | Glycosides | Pathogens | References |
|---|---|---|---|
| *Senecio aegiptius* | Rutin and quercetin-3-O-glycoside7-O-rutinoside | *Klebsiella pneumoniea* | Hassan et al., 2012 |
| *Plant* | Glycosides | *Pathogens* | References |
| *Galium fissurence, Viscum album, Cirsium hypoleucum* | Rutin, 5,7-dimethoxyflavanone-4'-O-beta-D-glucopyranoside , 5,7,3'-trihydroxy-flavanone-4'-O-beta-D-glucopyranoside , 5,7-dimethoxyflavanone-4'-O-[2"-O-(5"'-O-trans-cinnamoyl)-beta-D-apiofuranosyl]-beta-D-glucopyranoside | *Escherichia coli, Pseudomonas aeruginosa, Proteus mirabilis, Klebsiella pneumoniae, Acinetobacter baumannii, Staphylococcus aureus, Enterococcus faecalis, Bacillus subtilis* | Orhan et al., 2010 |

It is important to stress that there are innumerable potentially useful medicinal plants of the Mediterranean flora waiting to be evaluated and exploited for therapeutic applications against different microorganisms. For example, although many Senecio species, including *Senecio flavus, S. glaucys, S. vernalis, S. vulgaris* have anti-viral and anti-microbal folkloric reputation, scientifically their active phytochemicals have not been yet identified except in case of *S. aegiptius* (Table 1).

As seen from Table 1 many antimicrobial glycosides are flavonoids. Several anti-bacterial mechanisms of flavonoids are known and include inhibition of nucleic acid synthesis via interference in bacterial type II topoisomerases (DNA gyrase and topoisomerase IV) activity (Pommier et al., 2010); inhibition of cytoplasmic membrane function (Pommier et al., 2010); inhibition of energy metabolism (Pommier et al., 2010); inhibition of cell wall synthesis (Pommier et al., 2010), inhibition of efflux pumps in bacteria (Ramalhete et al., 2010, Holler et al., 2012), and inhibition of cell membrane synthesis (Cushnie, Lamb, 2011).

Antiviral properties of flavonoids are also acknowledged. For example, three flavone glycosides quercetin 3-O-rutinoside, kaempferol 3-O-rutinoside and kaempferol 3-O-robinobioside (Figure 1) from *Ficus benjamina* were found by us to be highly effective against HSV-1 and HSV-2 viruses (Yarmolinsky et al., 2012). Rutin, 5,7-dimethoxyflavanone-4'-O-beta-D-glucopyranoside and 5,7,3'-trihydroxy-flavanone-4'-O-beta-D-glucopyranoside isolated from extracts of *Galium fissurence, Viscum album* and *Cirsium hypoleucum* were active against Parainfluenza-3 virus (Orhan et al., 2010). Skyrin-8-O-beta-D-glucopyranoside from *Hypericum triquetrifolium* was highly effective against HSV-1 (Naithani et al., 2008). Glycyrrhizin or glycyrrhizic acid isolated from extracts of G*kycyrthiza glabra* (Figure 2) was used for treatment of viral respiratory tract infection and hepatitis (Fiore et al., 2008). It proved to be effective against *Pseudomonas aeruginosa* (Yashida et al., 2010, table 1) and many viruses *in vitro*: Epstein-Barr virus (EBV) (Lin, 2003), HSV-1 (Pompei et al., 1979), Hepatitis A virus (HAV) (Crance et al., 1990), Hepatitis B virus (HBV) (Takahara et al., 1994, Sato et al., 1996), Hepatitis C virus (HCV) (Van Rosum et al., 1998), Human cytomegavirus (CMV) (Numazaki et al., 1994), Human immunodeficiency virus (HIV) (Ito et al., 1988), Influenza virus (Utsunomiya et al., 1997), SARS coronavirus (Cinatl et al., 2003), and Varicella-zoster virus (VZV) (Baba and Shigeta, 1987). *In vivo* testing of this glycoside was performed for HBV (Sato et al., 1996) and Influenza virus (Utsunomiya et al., 1997). For many of the above-mentioned viruses, the antiviral action of glycyrrhizin is still poorly understood.

Kaempferol ;  R = H

kaempferol 3-O-rutinoside ;  R = Glu-Rha

kaempferol 3-O-robinobioside ;  R = Gala-Rha

Quercetin  ;  R = H

quercetin 3-O-rutinoside;  R = Glu-Rha

Glu- glucose  ; Gala-galactose ; Rha-Rhamnose

Figure 1. Chemical Structures of three flavone glycosides: quercetin 3-O-rutinoside, kaempferol 3-O-rutinoside and (3) kaempferol 3-O-robinobioside) of *Ficus benjamina* and their aglycons, quercetine and kaempferol.

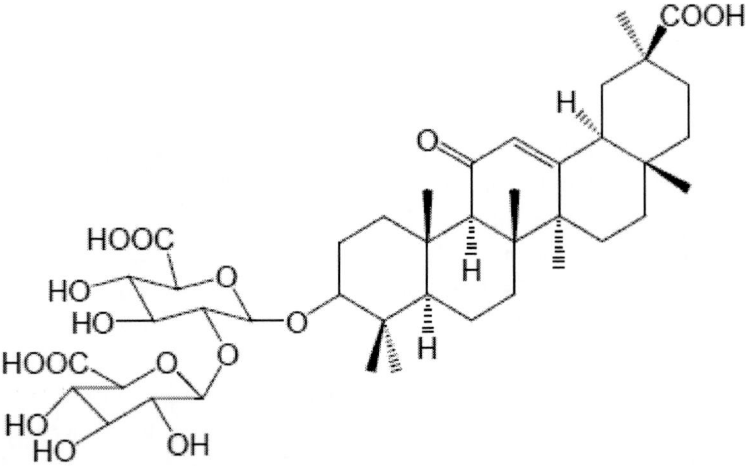

Figure 2. Glycyrrhizin or glycyrrhizic acid isolated from extracts of *Gkycyrthiza glabra*.

Nevertheless, it was investigated for EBV. Time of addition experiments suggested that glycyrrhizin interferes with an early step of EBV replication cycle (possibly penetration) but does not influence viral adsorption (Lin, 2003). It was also found that Glycyrrhizin inhibits HIV replication through interfering in virus–cell binding (Ito et al., 1988). Glycyrrhizin was also able to inhibit HIV replication in peripheral blood mononuclear cells cultures by inducing the production of beta-chemokines (Sasaki et al., 2002).

In summary, the antiviral mechanisms of flavone glycosides include antioxidant activities, scavenging capacities, inhibition of DNA and RNA synthesis, inhibition of the viral entry, inhibition of the viral reproduction, etc. (Naithani et al., 2008; Bertol et al., 2011).

## 3. Anti-Inflammatory Action of Glycosides from the Mediterranean Plants

Chronic inflammation is the basis and the linking bridge between various human polygenic pathologies such as aging, cancer, atherosclerosis, Alzheimer's disease, diabetes, obesity, and others (Franceschi et al., 2000; Curtis et al., 2005; Chung et al., 2009). Therefore, drug therapies aimed against inflammation are also important in decreasing the severity of the above mentioned ailments. While the major anti-inflammatory drugs of synthetic origin (both steroidal and nonsteroidal anti-inflammatory agents) have a long standing history of human use (Rainsford, 2007), almost 90% of them produce drug related toxicities, iatrogenic reactions, and adverse effects complicating the treatment process (Lanas, 2009). Hence, a shift in the area of anti-inflammatory treatment has been observed from the use of synthetics to natural, less toxic herbal therapies (Bent and Ko, 2004). The search for new plant-based anti-inflammatory agents has given rise to several varieties of beneficial compounds belonging to various classes of phytopharmaceuticals (reviewed by Beg et al., 2011).

In particular, glycosides in small amounts proved to be potent anti-inflammatory agents (Beg et al., 2011). For example, glycosides found in the aerial parts of the widely spread Mediterranean herbs *Hypericum perforatum* and *Hypericum reflexum* significantly reduced the TPA-induced ear oedema in mice (Sánchez-Mateo et al., 2006). Application of a triterpenoid saponin glycoside, aescin (extracted from the *Aesculushippo castanum* – a large deciduous tree growing in the Balkans) to human vascular endothelial cells relived CoCl2 induced inflammation (Montopoli et al., 2007). Apigenin, luteolin, and their corresponding glycosides, found in another plant growing in Balkans- *Sideritis scardica*, proved to have anti-inflammatory and gastroprotective activity (Tadic et al., 2012). Extract from leaves of *Rhododendron ponticum*, a small shrub growing in the South of Europe, containing mixture of flavonol glycosides as active compounds was found to be effective against carrageenan-induced edema in mice (Erdemoglu et al., 2008). Oleanane-type triterpene saponins isolated from the methanolic extract of the aerial parts of *Bupleurum rotundifolium* proved to be effective in the mouse model of skin chronic inflammation (Navvaro et al., 2001). Iridoid glucosides from *Veronica anagallis* such as verproside and catalposide (Figure 3) possessed an inhibitory activity against carrageenan-induced paw edema in mice (Kupeli et al., 2005).

Glycosides found in the Mediterranean plants exert their anti-inflammatory action through various mechanisms. For example, glycosides found in the flowers of *Verbascum pterocalycinum* (ilwensisaponin A and C, ajugol and picroside IV) diminish the cyclooxygenase activitiy (Akkol et al., 2007).

Three phenylpropanoid glycosides (salidroside, syringin and coniferin) and one lignan (phillyrin) isolated from the leaves of *Phillyrea latifolia* inhibited enzymes of the arachidonate cascade (Diaz Lanza et al., 2001). Such an activity was also demonstrated in case of acetophenone glucosides isolated from extracts of *Helichrysum italicum* (Sala et al., 2001).

On the other hand, apiin glycoside from *Apium graveolens* inhibited inducible nitric oxide synthase (iNOS) and exerted anti-inflammatory activity in-vivo (Mencherini et al., 2007). A glycoside called acteoside from *Cistanche tubulosa* inhibited histamine release, reduced TNF- $\alpha$, and IL-4 production in a dose-dependent manner, and delayed basophilic cell-derived immediate-type and delayed-type allergic reactions (Yamada et al., 2010).

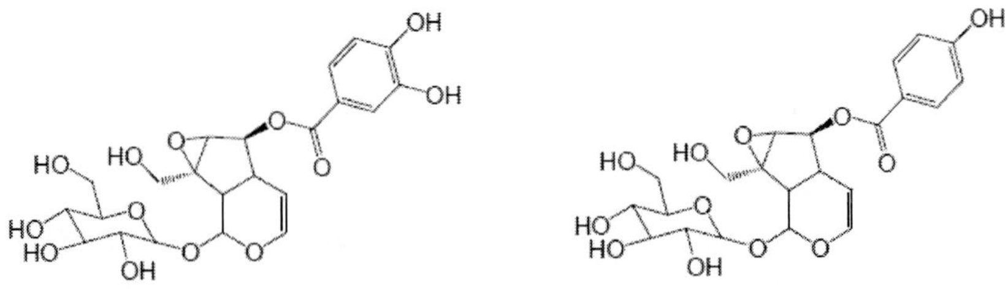

verproside

catalposide

Figure 3. Iridoid glucosides from *Veronica anagallis*: verproside and catalposide.

C-glycosylflavones from the aerial parts of *Eleusine indica* inhibited LPS-induced mouse lung inflammation by reducing induction of pro-inflammatory cytokines (De Meio et al., 2005). Phenolic substances from *Phagnalon rupestre* such as 2-isoprenylhydroquinone-1-glucoside, 3,5-dicaffeoylquinic acid, and 3,5-dicaffeoylquinic acid methyl ester reduced the expression of pro-inflammatory cytokines and hypersensitivity response in mice (Giner et al., 2011). It was also found that some glycosides such as Oenothein B, produced by *Epilobium hirsutum*, inhibited myeloperoxidase (MPO) release from stimulated neutrophils and thus reduced their inflammatory burst (Kiss et al., 2011).

## 4. THE ANTI-AGING EFFECTS OF THE HERBAL GLYCOSIDES

Combination of antioxidant/anti-inflammatory polyphenols, including the glycosidic derivatives, has showed some efficacy in slowing down aging (Joseph et al., 2005). Among them is resveratrol, a polyphenol found in red wine, for which anti-cancer, anti-inflammatory, blood sugar-lowering, beneficial cardiovascular effects and lifespan extension in lower organisms have been reported (reviewed by Baur and Sinclair, 2006). Other dietary flavonoids, such as quercetin and blueberry polyphenols, have been shown to increase both the lifespan and the stress resistance in simple model organisms (Saul et al., 2008; Wilson et al., 2006).

While the studies on the anti-aging/pro-longevity effects of herbal glycosides have been quite limited so far, Canuelo et al. (2012) have recently demonstrated that the major glycoside found in the olive oil called tyrosol prolonged the lifespan, and increased the stress resistance of the nematode worm *Caenorhabditis elegans*.

In particular, treatment with a moderate concentration of tyrosol induced hermetic response through mobilization of the heat shock proteins and modulation of the insulin signaling.

Other glycosides kaempferol and fisetin, found in a variety of the Mediterranean plants, increased the survival of *C. elegans*, reduced the intracellular ROS accumulation at lethal thermal stress, and diminished the extent of induced oxidative stress with kaempferol having a stronger impact (Kampkotter et al., 2007). Kaempferol but not fisetin attenuated the accumulation of the aging marker lipofuscin suggesting a life prolonging activity of this agent.

# 5. ANTI-CANCER PLANT GLYCOSIDES

Several glycosides possessing anti-cancer activity have been found in the Mediterranean plants. Salicin and its derivatives isolated from different species of willows from the Mediterranean region inhibit tumor growth by promoting apoptosis, inducing of DNA damage, affecting cell membranes and evoking of protein denaturation (El-Shemy et al., 2007). Lauroside B, a megastigmane glycoside, isolated from extracts of *Laurus nobilis* suppressed the proliferation of three human melanoma cell lines: A 375, WM 115 and SK-Mel-28 by inducing apoptosis (Panza et al., 2011).

Many glycosides of various structures with anticancer properties were isolated from crude extracts of *Nerium oleander*. Two flavonaidal glycosides and one pentacyclic triterpene demonstrated some anti-tumor activities against 57 human cancer cell lines (Siddiqui et al., 2012).

Many cardenolide glycosides had anticancer properties, the most active compounds possessing the 3β, 14β-dihydroxy-5β-card-20(22)-enolide structure with or without an acetoxy group at C-16; the cytotoxic effects were induced by inhibition of the plasma membrane bound Na(+)/K(+)-ATPase (Rashan et al., 2011, Zhao et al., 2011, Siddiqui et al., 2012). Oleandrin, one of the cardenolide glycosides, also had an excellent activity against a variety of human tumor cells (Pathak et al., 2000, Smith et al., 2001, Zhong et al., 2004). It was shown that oleandrin induced apoptosis produced a sustained increase in calcium dependent release of cytochrome C and activated caspase-dependent pathways (Lin et al., 2008).

Hamed et al. (2006) isolated three new cardenolide glycosides from roots of *Pergulatia tomentosa:* 3'-O-beta D-glucopyranosylcalactin; 12-dehydroxyghalaktinoside and 6'-dehydroxyghalaktinoside. These compounds along with known ghalaktinoside and calactin caused apoptotic death of Kaposi's sarcoma cells.

Glycyrrhizin, a glycoside already mentioned as antiviral agent in the previous section (Figure 2) was shown to induce apoptosis in various cancer cells including human stomach cancer cells, promielotic leukemia HL-60 cells, hepatoma cells (Hibasami et al., 2005, Hibasami et al., 2006), and ovarian carcinoma cells (Lee et al., 2010). It was shown that glycyrrhizic acid triggered the pro-apoptic pathway by inducing mithochondrial permeability transition (Salvi et al., 2003, Fiore et al., 2004).

Steroidal saponins with significant anti-carcinogenic activity were isolated from *Balanites aegtptiaca*. Among them, SAP-1016 (3β-O-β-D-xylopyranosyl-(1-3)-β-D-glucopyranosyl-(1-4)-[α-L-rhamnopyranosyl-(1-2)]-β-D-glucopyranoside) (Figure 4), was shown to have potent anti-proliferative activity against human MCF-7 breast cancer and HT-29 colon cancer cells through ROS (reactive oxygen species)-dependent mechanism (Beit-Yannai et al., 2011).

Two new furostanol saponins, terrestroside A, 3-O-{beta-D-xylopyranosyl-(1-->3)-[beta-D-xylopyranosyl(1-->2)]-beta-D-glucopyranosyl(1-->4)-[alpha-L-rhamnopyranosyl(1-->2)]-beta-D-galactopyranosy}-26-O-beta-D-glucopyranosyl-L-5a-furost-20(22)-en-(25R)-3beta,26-diol (1) and terrestroside B, 3-O-{beta-D-xylopyran-osyl(1-->3)-[beta-D-xylopyranosyl(1-->2)]-beta-D-glucopyranosyl(1-->4)-[alpha-L-rhamnopyranosyl-(1-->2)]-beta-D-galactopyranosy}-26-O-beta-D-glucopyranosyl-5a-furostan-12-one-(25R)-22-methoxy-3beta,26-diol (2), together with three known compounds, chloromaloside E (3), terrestrinin B (4) and terrestroneoside A (5) were isolated from the dry fruits of *Tribulus terrestris*. Furthermore, the inhibitory effects of the compounds on tumour cells were evaluated, and compounds 1-5 showed potential anti-tumour activity (Wang et al., 2009).

Terpenoids, cardiac glycosides can interfere ABC transporters in cancer cells (Wink et al., 2012). Some glycosides (for example,saponins) may inhibit P—gp, multiple resistance-associated protein 1 (Patel, Miltra, 2001). More polar glycosides (containing phenolic acids, flavonoids, catechins, chalcones, xanthones, stilbenes, anthocyanins, tannins, anthraquinones, and naphthoquinones) directly inhibit proteins forming several hydrogen and ionic bonds and thus disturbing the 3D structure of the transporters (Wink et al., 2012). Flavonoids can inhibit enzymes such as prostaglandin synthase, hypoxygenase and cyclooxygenase, closely related to tumorigenesis (Miesan, Mohamed, 2001).

Ten novel saponins,were elucidated in the plant Aesculus pavia: 3-O-[β-D-xylopyranosyl (1 → 2)] [-β-d-glucopyranosyl (1 → 4)]-β-D-glucopyranosiduronic acid 21-tigloyl-22-acetyl barringtogenol C , 3-O-[β-D-xylopyranosyl (1 → 2)] [-β-D-glucopyranosyl (1 → 4)]-β-D-glucopyranosiduronic acid 21-angeloyl-22-acetyl barringtogenol C (1b), 3-O-[β-D-xylopyranosyl (1 → 2)] [-β-D-galactopyranosyl (1 → 4)-β-D-glucopyranosiduronic acid 21-tigloyl-22-acetyl barringtogenol C , 3-O-[β-D-xylopyranosyl (1 → 2)] [-β-D-galactopyranosyl (1 → 4)]-β-D-glucopyranosiduronic acid 21-angeloyl-22-acetyl barringtogenol C , 3-O-[β-D-xylopyranosyl (1 → 2)] [-β-D-xylopyranosyl (1 → 4)]-β-D-glucopyranosiduronic acid 21-tigloyl-22-acetyl barringtogenol C , 3-O-[β-D-xylopyranosyl (1 → 2)] [-β-D-xylopyranosyl (1 → 4)]-β-d-glucopyranosiduronic acid 21-angeloyl-22-acetyl barringtogenol C , 3-O-[β-D-xylopyranosyl (1 → 2)] [-β-D-xylopyranosyl (1 → 4)]-β-D-glucopyranosiduronic acid 21-tigloyl-22-acetyl protoaescigenin (4a), and 3-O-[β-D-xylopyranosyl (1 → 2)] [-β-D-xylopyranosyl (1 → 4)]-β-D-glucopyranosiduronic acid 21-angeloyl-22-acetyl protoaescigenin (Lanzotti et al., 2012), and new saponins (Sun et al., 2011) (Figure 5). The compounds identified by Lanzotti et al., 2012 showed cytotoxic activity on J-774, murine monocyte/macrophage, and WEHI-164, murine fibrosarcoma, cell lines.

Structure-activity relationship studies indicated the positive effect on the activity of xylose unit in the place of glucose, while a little detrimental effect is observed when glucose is substituted by galactose.

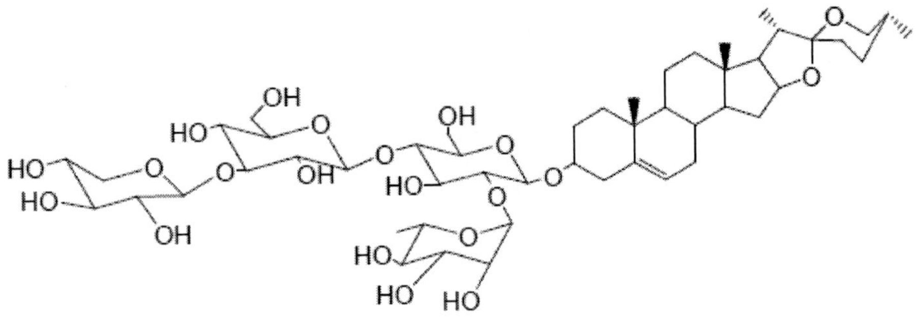

**SAP-1016**

Figure 4. A steroidal saponins with significant anticarcinogenic activity isolated from *Balanites aegtptiaca*, a compound SAP-1016 (3β-O-β-D-xylopyranosyl-(1-3)-β-D-glucopyranosyl-(1-4)-[α-L-rhamnopyranosyl-(1-2)]-β-D-glucopyranoside).

The aglycone structure and the presence of a tigloyl or an angeloyl group at C-21 do not affect significantly the inhibitory activity on both tested cell lines (Lanzotti et al., 2012). The isolated furostanol saponins were evaluated for cytotoxic activity against human normal amniotic and human lung carcinoma cell lines using neutral red and MTT assays (Sun et al., 2011). Many plant glycosides have certain cancer-prevention and anti-cancer activities because these compounds have an ability to block nuclear factor-kappa B activation, induce apoptosis, inhibit signal transducer, and activate transcription and angiogenesis (Efferth, 2012).

# 6. GLYCOSIDES FROM MEDITERRANEAN PLANTS WITH ANTI-DIABETIC ACTIVITY

With the increasing prevalence of diabetes worldwide (Beckman et al., 2002), there is an ever increasing demand for effective treatments. As traditional medicine has not adequately dealt with this disease, more and more attention is being placed on herbal treatments.

In particular, plant glycosides have shown some promising activity in the treatment of diabetes (Bedekar et al., 2010). Among them, some glycoside containing Mediterranean plants have displayed anti-diabetic effects.

*Scrophularia deserti* Del. (Scrophulariaceae), is used traditionally to treat diabetes, in addition to kidney disease, and inflammation (Perry and Metzger, 1980). Chemical analysis of *S. deserti* revealed 3 iridoid glycosides with anti-diabetic activity: harpagoside-B, scropolioside-D, koelzioside, and 8-O-acetyl-harpagide (Ahmed et al., 2003).

All compounds significantly reduced blood glucose levels in alloxan induced diabetic mice 1 h after treatment. Structural Activity Relationship (SAR) analysis revealed the importance of cinnamoyl and acetyl moieties at the C-3 and C-4 positions. Although the mechanism of action of these glycosides is not known, scropoliosides have been shown to reduce the production of a host of inflammatory compounds including prostaglandin E2, nitric oxide, and many interleukins (Bas et al., 2007).

*Cleome droserifolia* (Forssk.) Del. is used traditionally by Bedouins for the treatment of diabetes (Yaniv et al., 1987; Abdel-Hady et al., 1998). The anti-diabetic activity of *C. droserifolia* was validated in tetracycline induced diabetic rats, where treatment with the plant extract significantly reduced blood glucose levels (Nicola et al., 1996). Three flavanol glycosides: isorhamnetin-3-O-β-D-glucoside, quercetin-3'-methoxy-3-O-(4"-acetylrhamnoside)-7-O-α-rhamnoside, and kaempferol-4'-methoxy-3,7-O-dirhamnoside were identified which significantly increased glucose uptake in skeletal muscle cells and enhanced adipogenesis in adipocytes (Motaal et al., 2011; Ezzat and Motaal, 2012).

*Zizyphus spina-christ* L. is also traditionally used in the treatment of diabetes. Multiple glycosides were identified with biological activity including the flavonoid glycoside, quercetin-3-O-[β-xylosyl-(1-2)-α-rhamnoside]4'-O-α-rhamnoside (Shahat et al., 2001) as well as multiple saponin glycosides: 3-O-[α-L-fucopyranosyl (1 → 2)-β-D-glucopyranosyl(1 → 3)-α-L-arabinopyranosyl]jujubogenin (Christinin A), 3-O-[alpha-D-fucopyranosyl(1 → 2)-β-D-β-pyranosyl-4-sulphate(1 → 3)-α-L-arabinopyranosyl] jujubogenin, β-glucopyranosyl(1 → 2)-α-L-rhamnopyranosyl (1 → 3)-α- L-arabinopyranosyl]jujubogenin, and 3-O-[α-L-fucopyranosyl(1 → 2) -β-D-arabinopyranosyl(1 → 3)-β-D-glucopyranosyl(1 → 3)α-L-arabinopyranosy] jujubogenin (Mahran, et al., 1996).

Pretreatment with its major saponin glycoside, christinin A, significantly improved oral glucose tolerance and glucose induced insulin secretion as well as decreased liver phosphorylase and glucose-6-phosphatase activities in streptozotocin induced diabetic rats (Glombitza et al., 1994; Abdel-Zaher et al., 2005).

*Artocarpus heterophyllus* (Lam.) in the Moraceae family, is also used to treated diabetes (Marles and Farnsworth, 1995). Known as Jackfruit, *A. heterophyllus* is native to India, but current distribution has spread to much of Asia and Africa. Aqueous and ethyl acetate extracts from the *A. heterophyllus* leaves were shown to have hypoglycemic activities in streptozotocin-induced diabetic rats (Chackrewarthy et al., 2010) and diabetic human patients (Fernando et al., 1991).

This activity was at least partially attributed to the flavonoid glycoside, isoquercitrin, isolated from *A. heterophyllus* (Omar et al., 2011).

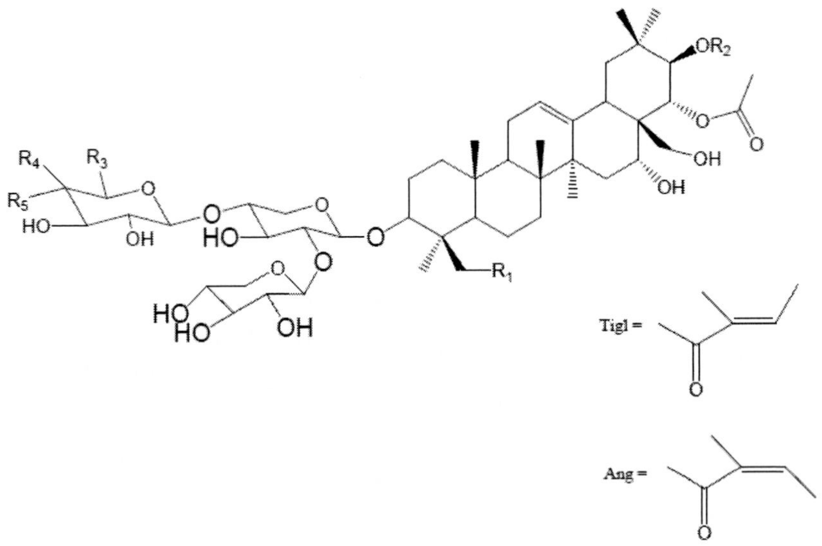

| | | | | |
|---|---|---|---|---|
| **Pavioside A** | $R_1$ =H | $R_2$=Tigl | $R_3$ =CH$_2$OH | $R_4$ =H | $R_5$ =OH |
| **Pavioside B** | $R_1$ =H | $R_2$=Ang | $R_3$ =CH$_2$OH | $R_4$ =H | $R_5$ =OH |
| **Pavioside C** | $R_1$ =H | $R_2$=Tigl | $R_3$ =CH$_2$OH | $R_4$ =OH | $R_5$ =H |
| **Pavioside D** | $R_1$ =H | $R_2$=Ang | $R_3$ =CH$_2$OH | $R_4$ =OH | $R_5$ =H |
| **Pavioside E** | $R_1$ =H | $R_2$=Tigl | $R_3$ =H | $R_4$ =H | $R_5$ =OH |
| **Pavioside F** | $R_1$ =H | $R_2$=Ang | $R_3$ =H | $R_4$ =H | $R_5$ =OH |
| **Pavioside G** | $R_1$ =OH | $R_2$=Tigl | $R_3$ =H | $R_4$ =H | $R_5$ =OH |
| **Pavioside H** | $R_1$ =OH | $R_2$=Ang | $R_3$ =H | $R_4$ =H | $R_5$ =OH |

Figure 5. Chemical structure of saponins of *Aesculus pavia*.

Treatment with isoquercitrin, or 2-(3,4-dihydroxyphenyl) -3- (β-D- glucofuranosyloxy) - 5,7-dihydroxy-4H-1-benzopyran-4-one, ameliorated alloxan induced hyperglycemia in rats (Panda and Kar, 2007). The hypoglycemic activities of isoquercitrin have been linked to alpha-glucosidase inhibition (Li et al., 2009) as well as inhibition of the intestinal glucose transporter GLUT2 (Kwon et al., 2007).

Tiliroside, (kaempferol 3-O-(6"-O-p-coumaroyl)-β-D-glucopyranoside) a glycosidic flavonoid that can be found in many Mediterranean plants such as *Rubus ulmifolius* Schott (Rosaceae) (Panizzi et al., 2002), has been shown to possess anti-diabetic activities. In streptozotocin induced diabetic rats, tiliroside decreased blood glucose as well as total and LDL cholesterol (Qiao et al., 2011).

It was subsequently shown that tiliroside's beneficial effects on many of the obesity induced-metabolic syndrome related parameters including reduced serum insulin, triglyceride, and free fatty acid levels may be due to improved adiponectin signaling (Goto et al., 2012b) as well as inhibition of the glucose transporters GLUT2 and SGLT1 (Goto et al., 2012a). Although the findings support the role of AMPK and PPAR α activation in the anti-diabetic activity of tiliroside, further research is needed to fully elucidate the mechanism of action.

*Glycyrhizia glabra* L. (Papilionceae), found throughout the Mediterranean is widely used for the treatment of diabetes. The major bioactive constituent of *G. glabra* roots is the previously mentioned triterpenoid saponin, glycyrrhizic acid (Figure 2), which produces a wide range of pharmacological effects (Asl and Hosseinzadeh, 2008).

Glycyrrhizic acid, or glycyrrhizin, significantly reduced serum glucose in streptozotocin induced diabetic rats (Sen et al., 2011) as well as in the genetic non-insulin dependent diabetic model, KK-Ay (Takii et al., 2001). This effect was later associated with a decrease in the activities of gluconeogenesis enzymes including PEPCK, H6PDH, and 11β-HSD1 (Chia et al., 2012). Although the mode of action of glycosides' anti-diabetic activity has been partially revealed, the picture is far from clear due to the likely possibility that multiple mechanisms may exist.

Some glycoside activity has been linked to the inhibition of digestive enzymes such as alpha-amylase and glucosidase. In addition, the inhibition of glucose transporters such as GLUT2 and SGLT1 has been implicated. Modulation of the gluconeogenesis pathway has also been suggested. However, there is still much that remains to be elucidated before the anti-diabetic activity of glycosides can be thoroughly understood.

## CONCLUSION

With its cultural heritage and rich biodiversity, the Mediterranean region has promising therapeutic potentials, especially in the case of herbal glycosides. The current collected data on their anti-viral, anti-microbial, anti-cancer, anti-inflammatory, anti-aging, anti-oxidant and anti-diabetic activities suggest a bright future for these compounds as potential prophylactic and therapeutic agents.

More in vivo studies are warranted in order to establish their effectiveness in the treatment of chronic diseases.

# REFERENCES

Abdel-Hady, N. M. (1998). Pharmacognostical investigation and biological verification of some recipes and preparations of natural origin for the treatment of diabetes. *MS Thesis, Faculty of Pharmacy* (Girls), Al-Azhar University, Cairo, Egypt.

Abdel-Zaher, A. O., Salim, S. Y., Assaf, M. H., Abdel-Hady, R. H. (2005). Antidiabetic activity and toxicity of Zizyphus spina-christi leaves. *J. Ethnopharmacol.* 101,129-138.

Ahmed, B., Al-Rehaily, A. J., Al-Howiriny, T. A., El-Sayed, K. A., Ahmad, M. S. (2003). Scropolioside-D2 and harpagoside-B: two new iridoid glycosides from Scrophularia deserti and their antidiabetic and antiinflammatory activity. *Biol. Pharm. Bull.* 26, 462-467.

Akkol, E. K., Tatli, I. I., Akdemir, Z. S. (2007). Antinociceptive and anti-inflammatory effects of saponin and iridoid glycosides from Verbascum pterocalycinum var. mutense Hub.-Mor. *Z Naturforsch. C.* 62, 813-820.

Ashfag, U. A., Masoud, M. S., Nawaz, Z., Riazuddin, S. (2011). Glycyrrhizin, an antiviral agent against Hepatitis C virus. *J. of Translational Medicine.* 9, 112-118.

Asl, M. N., Hosseinzadeh, H. (2008). Review of pharmacological effects of Glycyrrhiza sp. and its bioactive compounds. *Phytother. Res.* 22, 709-724.

Baba, M., Shigeta, S. (1987). Antiviral activity of glycyrrhizin against varicella-zoster virus in vitro. *Antiviral Res.* 7, 99-107.

Bas, E., Recio, M. C., Máñez, S., Giner, R. M., Escandell, J. M., López-Ginés, C., Ríos J. L. (2006). New insight into the inhibition of the inflammatory response to experimental delayed-type hypersensitivity reactions in mice by scropolioside A. *Eur. J. Pharmacol.* 555, 199-210.

Baur, J. A., Sinclair, D. A. (2006). Therapeutic potential of resveratrol: the in vivo evidence. *Nat. Rev. Drug Discov.* 5, 493-506.

Beckman, J. A., Creager, M. A., Libby, P. (2002). Diabetes and Atherosclerosis Epidemiology, Pathophysiology, and Management. *JAMA.* 287, 2570-2581.

Bedekar, A., Shah, K., Koffas, M. (2010). Natural products for type II diabetes treatment. *Adv. Appl. Microbiol.* 71, 21-73.

Beg, S., Swain, S., Hasan, H., Barkat, M. A., Hussain, M. S. (2011). Systematic review of herbals as potential anti-inflammatory agents: Recent advances, current clinical status and future perspectives. *Pharmacogn. Rev.* 5, 120-37.

Beit-Yannai, E., Ben-Shabat, S., Goldschmidt, N., Chapagain, B. P., Liu, R. H., Wiesman, Z. (2011). Antiproliferative activity of steroidal saponins from *Balanites aegtptiaca* – An *in vitro* study. *Phytochemistry Letters.* 4, 43-47.

Bent, S., and Ko, R. (2004). Commonly used herbal medicines in the United States: a review. *Am. J. Med.* 1, 478-485.

Bertol, J. W., Rigotto, C., de Pádua, R. M., Kreis, W., Barardi, C. R., Braga, F. C., Simões, C. M. (2011). Antiherpes activity of glucoevatromonoside, a cardenolide isolated from a Brazilian cultivar of Digitalis lanata *Antiviral Res.* 92, 73-80.

Cañuelo, A., Gilbert-López, B., Pacheco-Liñán, P., Martínez-Lara, E., Siles, E., Miranda-Vizuete, A. (2012). Tyrosol, a main phenol present in extra virgin olive oil, increases lifespan and stress resistance in Caenorhabditis elegans. *Mech. Ageing Dev.* 21, 563-574.

Chackrewarthy, S., Thabrew, M. I., Weerasuriya, M. K., Jayasekera, S. (2010) Evaluation of the hypoglycemic and hypolipidemic effects of an ethyl acetate fraction of Artocarpus heterophyllus (jak) leaves in streptozotocin-induced diabetic rats. *Pharmacogn. Mag.* 6,186-190.

Chia, Y. Y., Liong, S. Y., Ton, S. H., Kadir, K. B. (2012) Amelioration of glucose homeostasis by glycyrrhizic acid through gluconeogenesis rate-limiting enzymes. *Eur. J. Pharmacol.* 677, 197-202.

Chung, H. Y., Cesari, M., Anton, S., Marzetti, E., Giovannini, S., Seo, A. Y., Carter, C., Yu, B. P., Leeuwenburgh, C. (2009). Molecular inflammation: underpinnings of aging and age-related diseases. *Ageing Res. Rev.* 8, 18-30.

Cinatl, J., Morgenstern, B., Bauer, G., Chandra, P., Rabenau, H., Doerr, H. W. (2003). Glycyrrhizin, an active component of licorise roots, and replication of SARS-associated coronavirus. *Lancet.* 361, 2045-2046.

Cowan, M. M. (1999). Plant products as antimicrobial agents, *Clin. Microbiol. Rev.* 12, 564-582.

Crance, J. M., Biziagos, E., Passagot, J., Van cuyck-Gandre, H., Deloince, R. (1990). Inhibition of hepatitis A virus replication in vitro by antiviral compounds. *J. Med. Virol.*, 31: 155-160.

Curtis, R., Geesaman, B. J., DiStefano, P. S. (2005). Ageing and metabolism: drug discovery opportunities. *Nat. Rev. Drug Discov.* 4, 569-580.

Cushnie, T. P., Lamb, A. J. (2011). Recent advances in understanding the antibacterial properties of flavonoids. *J. Antimicrob. Agents.* 38, 99-107.

Dembitsky, V. M. (2004). a Chemistry and biodiversity of the biologically active natural glycosides. *Chemistry and biodiversity.* 1, 673-778.

Dembitsky, V. M. (2004). b Astonishing diversity of natural surfactants: 1. Glycosides of fatty acids and alcohols. *Lipids.* 39, 933-953.

Dembitsky, V. M. (2005). a Astonishing diversity of natural surfactants: 2. Polyether glycosidic ionophores and macrocyclic glycosides. *Lipids.* 40, 219-248

Dembitsky, V. M. (2005). b Astonishing diversity of natural surfactants: 3. Carotenoid glycosides, and isoprenoid glycosides. *Lipids.* 40, 535-557.

Dembitsky, V. M. (2005). c Astonishing diversity of natural surfactants: 4. Fatty acid amide glycosides, their analogs and derivatives. *Lipids.* 40, 1-27.

Dembitsky, V. M. (2005). d Astonishing diversity of natural surfactants: 5. Biologically active glycosides of aromatic metabolites. *Lipids.* 40, 641-660.

Dembitsky, V. M. (2006). Astonishing diversity of natural surfactants: 7. Biologically active hemi- and monoterpenoid glycosides. *Lipids.* 41, 869-900.

Díaz Lanza, A. M., Abad Martínez, M. J., Fernández Matellano, L., Recuero Carretero, C., Villaescusa Castillo, L., Silván Sen, A. M., Bermejo Benito, P. (2001). Lignan and phenylpropanoid glycosides from *Phillyrea latifolia* and their in vitro anti-inflammatory activity. *Planta Med.* 67, 219-223.

De Melo, G. O., Muzitano, M. F., Legora-Machado, A., Almeida, T. A., De Oliveira, D. B., Kaiser, C. R., Koatz, V. L., Costa, S. S. (2005). C-glycosylflavones from the aerial parts of Eleusine indica inhibit LPS-induced mouse lung inflammation. *Planta Med.* 71, 362-363.

Dryden, M., Johnson, A. P., Ashiru-Oredope, D., Sharland, M. ( 2011). Using antibiotics responsibly: right drug, right time, right dose, right duration. *J. Antimicrob. Chemother.* 66, 2441-2443

Efferth, T. (2012). Stem cells, cancer stem-like cells and natural products. *Planta Med.* 78, 915-942.

El-Shemy, H. A., Aboul-Enein, A. M., Aboul-Enein, K. M., Fujita, K. (2007). Willow leaves extracts contain anti-tumor agents against three cell types. *PloS One.* 2, 178-180.

Erdemoglu, N., Akkol, E. K., Yesilada, E., Caliş, I. (2008). Bioassay-guided isolation of anti-inflammatory and antinociceptive principles from a folk remedy, Rhododendron ponticum L. leaves. *J. Ethnopharmacol.* 2, 172-178.

Ezzat, S. M., Abdel Motaal, A. (2012). Isolation of new cytotoxic metabolites from Cleome droserifolia growing in Egypt. *Z Naturforsch C.* 67(5-6), 266-274.

Fernando, M. R., Wickremasinghe, S. M., Thabrew, M. I., Ariyananda, P., Karunanayake, E. H. (1991) Effect of Artocarpus heterophyllus andAsteracanthus longifolia on glucose tolerance in normal human subjects and in maturity onset diabetic patients. *J. Ethanopharmacol.;* 31, 277-282

Fiore, C., Salvi, M., Palermo, M., Sinigagllab, G., Armanini, D., Toninello, A. (2004). On the mechanism of mitochondrial permeability by transition induction by glycyrrhemic acid. *Biochim. Biophys. Acta.* 1658, 195-201.

Fiore, C., Eisenhut, M., Keausse, R., Ragazzi, E., Pellati, D., Armanini, D., Bielenberg, J. (2008). Antiviral effects of *Gkycyrthiza* species. *Phytother. Res.,* 22, 141-148.

Franceschi, C., Bonafè, M., Valensin, S., Olivieri, F., De Luca, M., Ottaviani, E., De Benedictis, G. (2000). Inflamm-aging. An evolutionary perspective on immunosenescence. *Ann. N Y Acad. Sci.;*908, 244-254.

Fu, G., Pang, H., Wong, Y. H. (200 ). Naturally occurring phenylethanoid glycosides: potential leads for new therapeutics. *Curr. Med. Chem.* 15, 2592-2613.

Giner, E., El Alami, M., Máñez, S, Recio, M. C., Ríos, J. L., Giner, R. M. (2011). Phenolic substances from Phagnalon rupestre protect against 2,4,6-trinitrochlorobenzene-induced contact hypersensitivity. *J. Nat. Prod.* 27, 1079-1084.

Glombitza, K. W., Mahran, G. H., Mirhom,Y. M., Michel, C. G., Motawi, T. K. (1994). Hypoglycemic and antihyperglycemic effects of Zizyphus spina-christi in rats. *Planta Medica* 60, 244–247.

Gonzales-Tejero, M. R., Casares-Porcel, M., Sanches-Rojas, C. P., Ramiro-Gutierrez, J. M., Molero-Mesa, J., Pieroni, A., Giusti, H. E., Censorii, E., Pasquale, Cde., Della, A., Paraskeva-Hadijchambi, D., Hadjichambis, A., Houmani, Z.,El- Demerdash, M., El-Zayat, M., Hmamouchi, M., Eljohrig, S. (2008). Medicinal plants in the Mediterranean area: Synthesis of the results of the project Rubia. *Journal of Ethnopharmacology,* 116, 341-357.

Goto, T., Horita, M., Nagatomo, A., Nishida, N., Matsuura, Y., Nagaoka, S. (2012).a Tiliroside, a glycosidic flavonoid, inhibits carbohydrate digestion and glucose absorption in the gastrointestinal tract. *Mol. Nutr. Food Res.* 56, 435-445.

Goto, T., Teraminami, A., Lee, J. L., Ohyama, K., Funakoshi, K., Kim, Y. I., Hirai, S., Uemura, T., Yu, R., Takahashi, N., Kawada, T. (2012). b. Tiliroside, a glycosidic flavonoid, ameliorates obesity-induced metabolic disorders via activation of adiponectin signaling followed by enhancement of fatty acid oxidation in liver and skeletal muscle in obese–diabetic mice. *J. Nutri. Biochem.* 23, 768-776.

Greuter, W. (1991). Botanical diversity , endemism, rarity and extinction in the The Mediterranean area: an analysis based on the published volumes of Med-Checklist. *Botanika Chronika*, 10, 63-79.

Hamed, A. L., Plaza, A., Balestrieri, M. L., Mahalel, U. A., Sprinquel, I. V., Oleszek, W., Pizza, C., Piacente, S. (2006). Cardenolide glycosides from *Pergulatia tomentosa* and their propoptotic activity in Kaposi's sarcoma cells. *J. Nat. Prod.* 69, 1319-1322.

Haque, N., Salma, U., Nurrunhabi, T. R., Uddin, M. J., Jahanqir, M. F., Islam, S. M., Kamruzzaman, M. (2011). Management of type 2 diabetes mellitus by lifestyle, diet and medicinal plants. *Pak. J. Biol. Sci.* 14, 13-24.

Hassan, W., Al-Gendy, A., Al-Youssef, H., El-Shazely, A. (2012). Chemical constituents and biological activities of *Senecio aegiptius* var. discoideus Boiss. *Z. Naturforsch, C, 67*, 144-150.

Hibasami, H., Iwase, H., Yoshioka, K., Takahashi, H., (2005). Glycyrrhizin induces apoptosis in human cancer KATO III and human promielotic leukemia HL-60 cells. *Int. J. Mol. Med.* 16, 233-236.

Hibasami, H., Iwase, H., Yoshioka, K., Takahashi, H. (2006). Glycyrrhemic acid ( a metabolic substance and aglycon of glycyrrhizin) induces apoptosis in human hepatoma, promielotic leukemia and stomack cancer cells. *Int. J. Mol. Med.* 17, 215-219.

Holler, J. C., Christen, S. B., Slotved, H. C., Rassmussen, H. B., Guzman, A., Olsen, C. E., Petersen, B., Malgaard, P. M. (2012). Novel inhibitory activity of the *Staphylococcus aureus* Nor A efflux pump by a kaempherol rhamnoside isolated from *Persea lingue Nees. J. of Antinicrobal Chemotherapy.* 6, 1138-1144.

Ito, M., Sato, A., Hirabayashi, K., Tanabe, F., Shigeta, S., Baba, M., De Clerq, E. (1988). Mechanism of inhibitory effect of glycyrrhizin on replication of human immunodeficiency virus (HIV*). Antiviral Res.* 10, 289-298.

Jassim, S. A., Naji, M. A. (2003). Novel antiviral agents: a medicinal plant perspective. *Journal of Applied Microbiology.* 95, 412-427.

Joseph, J. A., Shukitt-Hale, B., Casadesus, G. (2005). Reversing the deleterious effects of aging on neuronal communication and behavior: beneficial properties of fruit polyphenolic compounds. *Am. J. Clin. Nutr.* 81, 313-316.

Kampkötter, A., Gombitang Nkwonkam, C., Zurawski, R. F., Timpel, C., Chovolou, Y., Wätjen, W., Kahl, R. (2007). Effects of the flavonoids kaempferol and fisetin on thermotolerance, oxidative stress and FoxO transcription factor DAF-16 in the model organism Caenorhabditis elegans. *Arch. Toxicol.;* 81, 849-858.

Katsambas, A., Marketos, S. G. (2007). Hippocratic messages for modern medicine (the vindication of Hippocrates). *Journal of the European Academy of Dermatology and Veneorology.* 21, 859-862.

Khan, N. A., Dubey, C., Srivastava, A. (2010). A triterpenoid saponin from seeds of *Ricinus communis. 14th International Electronic Conference on Synthetic Organic Chemistry, 1-30 November* 2010.

Kiss, A. K., Bazylko, A., Filipek, A., Granica, S., Jaszewska, E., Kiarszys, U., Kośmider, A., Piwowarski, J. (2011). Oenothein B's contribution to the anti-inflammatory and antioxidant activity of Epilobium sp. *Phytomedicine.* 18, 557-560.

Küpeli, E., Harput, U. S., Varel, M., Yesilada, E., Saracoglu, I. (2005). Bioassay-guided isolation of iridoid glucosides with antinociceptive and anti-inflammatory activities from Veronica anagallis-aquatica L. *J. Ethnopharmacol.* 102, 170-176.

Kwon, O., Eck, P., Chen, S., Corpe, C. P., Lee, J. H., Kruhlak, M., Levine, M. (2007). Inhibition of the intestinal glucose transporter GLUT2 by flavonoids. *FASEB J.* 21, 366-377.

Lanas, A. (2009). Nonsteroidal antiinflammatory drugs and cyclooxygenase inhibition in the gastrointestinal tract: a trip from peptic ulcer to colon cancer. *Am. J. Med. Sci.* 338, 96-106.

Lanzotti, V., Termolino, P., Dolci, M., Curir, P. (2012). Paviosides A-H, eight new oleane type saponins from *Aesculus pavia* with cytotoxic activity. *Bioorg. Med. Chem.* 20, 3280-3286.

Lee, C. S., Yang, J. C., Kim, Y. J., Jang, E. R., Kim, W., Myung, S. C. (2010). 18 β-glycyrrhetinic acid potentiates apoptotic effect of trichostatin A on human epithelial ovarian carcinoma cell lines. *Eur. J. Pharmacol.* 649, 354-361.

Li, Y. Q., Zhou, F. C., Gao, F., Bian, J. S., Shan, F. (2009) Comparative evaluation of quercetin, isoquercetin and rutin as inhibitors of alpha-glucosidase. *J. Agric. Food Chem.* 57, 11463-11468.

Lin, J. C. (2003). Mechanism of action of glycyrrhizic acid in inhibition of Epstein-Barr virus replication in vitro. *Antiviral Res.,* 59, 41-47.

Lin, Y., Dubinsky, W. P., Ho, D. H., Felix, E., Newman, R. A. (2008). Determinants of human and mouse melanoma cell sensititivities to oleandrin. *J. Exp. Ther. Oncol.,* 7, 195-205.

Lindhorst, T. K. (2007). Essentials of Carbohydrate Chemistry and Biochemistry. Wiley-VCH, 5-26.

Liu, M. H., Otsuka, N., Noyori, K., Shiota, S., Oqawa. W., Kuroda, T., Hatano, T., Tsuchiya, T. (2009). Synergistic effect of kaempherol glycosides purified from *Laurus nobilis* and fluoroquinolones on methicillin -resistant *Staphyloccoccus aureus*. *Bio. Pharm. Bull.* 32, 489-492.

Mahran, G., Glombitza, K. W., Mirhom, Y. W., Hartmann, R., Michel, C. G. (1996) Novel Saponins from Zizyphus spina-christi growing in Egypt. *Planta Med.* 62, 163-165.

Marles, R., Farnsworth, N. (1995) Antidiabetic plants and their active constituents. *Phytomedicine* 2, 137–189.

Mencherini, T., Cau, A., Bianco, G., Della Loggia, R., Aquino, R. P., Autore, G. (2007). An extract of Apium graveolens var. dulce leaves: structure of the major constituent, apiin, and its anti-inflammatory properties. *J. Pharm. Pharmacol.* 59, 891-897.

Miesan, K. H., Mohamed, S. (2001). Flavonoid (myricetin, quercetin, kaempferol, luteolin and apigenin ) content of edible tropical plants. *J. Agric. Food. Chem,* 49, 3106-3112.

Montopoli, M., Froldi, G., Comelli, M. C., Prosdocimi, M., Caparrotta, L. (2007). Aescin protection of human vascular endothelial cells exposed to cobalt chloride mimicked hypoxia and inflammatory stimuli. *Planta Med.* 73, 285-288.

Motaal, A. A., Ezzat, S. M., Haddad, P. S. (2011). Determination of bioactive markers in Cleome droserifolia using cell-based bioassays for antidiabetic activity and isolation of two novel active compounds. *Phytomedicine.* 15, 38-41.

Naithani, R., Huma, L. C., Holland, L. E., Shukla, D., McCormick, D. L., Mehta, R. G., Moriarty, R. M. (2008). Antiviral activity of phytochemicals: A comprehensive Review. *Mini-Reviews in Medicinal Chemistry.* 8, 1106-1133.

Navarro, P., Giner, R. M., Recio, M. C., Máñez, S., Cerdá-Nicolás, M., Ríos, J. L. (2001). In vivo anti-inflammatory activity of saponins from Bupleurum rotundifolium. *Life Sci.* 68, 1199-1206.

Nicola, W. G., Ibrahim, K. M., Mikhail, T. H., Girgis, R. B., Khadr, M. E. (1996). Role of the hypoglycemic plant extract cleome droserifolia in improving glucose and lipid metabolism and its relation to insulin resistance in fatty liver. *Boll Chim. Farm.* 135,507-517.

Numazaki, K., Umetsu, M., Chiba, S. (1994). Effects of glycyrrhizin in children with liver dysfunction associated with cytomegavirus infection. *Tohoku J. Exp. Med.* 172, 147-153.

Omar, H. S., El-Beshbishy, H. A., Moussa, Z., Taha, K. F., Singab, A. N. (2011) Antioxidant Activity of Artocarpus heterophyllus Lam. (Jack Fruit) Leaf Extracts: Remarkable Attenuations of Hyperglycemia and Hyperlipidemia in Streptozotocin-Diabetic Rats *The Scientific World Journal* 11, 788–800.

Orhan, D. D., Ozçelik, B., Ozgen, S., Ergun, F. (2010). Antibacterial, antifungal, and antiviral activities of some flavonoids. *Microbiological Research.* 165, 496-504.

Otsuka, N., Liu, M. H., Shiota, S., Oqawa. W., Kuroda, T., Hatano, T., Tsuchiya, T. (2008). Anti- methicillin resistant *Staphyloccoccus aureus* (MRSA) compounds isolated from *Laurus nobilis. Bio. Pharm. Bull.* 31, 1794-1797.

Panda, S., Kar, A. (2007). Antidiabetic and antioxidative effects of Annona squamosa leaves are possibly mediated through quercetin-3-O-glucoside. *Biofactors.* 31, 201-210.

Panizzi, L., Caponi, C., Catalano, S., Cioni, P. L., Morelli, I. (2002). In vitro antimicrobial activity of extracts and isolated constituents of Rubus ulmifolius. *J. Ethnopharmacol.* 79,165-168.

Panza, E., Tersigni, M., Iorizzi, M., Zollo, F., De Marino, S., Festa, C., Napolitano, M., Castwello, G., Lalenti, A., Ianaro, A. (2011). Lauroside B, a megastigmane glycoside from *Laurus nobilis* (bay laurel) leaves, induces apoptosis in human melanoma cell lines by inhibiting NF-κB activation. *J. Nat. Prod.* 74, 228-233.

Patel, J., Miltra, A. K. (2001). Strategies to overcome simultaneous P-glycoprotein mediated efflux and CYP3A4 mediated metabolism of drugs. *Pharmacogenomics.* 2, 401-415.

Pathak, S., Mulyani, A. S, Narayan, S., Kumar, V., Newman, R. A. (2000). Arvirzel[TM], an extract of *Nerium oleander* induces cell death in human but not murine cancer cells. *Anti-cancer Drugs.* 11, 455-463.

Perry, L. M. and Metzger, J. (1980). *Medicinal Plants of Southeast Asia* MIT Press, Cambridge, MA and London, UK.

Pommier, Y., Leo, E., Zhang, H., Marchand, C. (2010). DNA topoisomerases and their poisoning by anticancer and antibacterial drugs. *Chem. Biol.* 17, 421-433.

Pompei, R., Flore, O., Marciallis, M. A., Pani, A, Loddo, B. (1979). Glycyrrhizic acid in inhibits virus growth and inactivates virus particles. *Nature,* 281, 689-690.

Prabaker, K., Weinstein, R. A. (2011). Trends in antimicrobial resistance in intensive care units in the United States. *Curr. Opin. Crit. Care.* 17, 472-479.

Qiao, W., Zhao, C., Qin, N., Zhai, H. Y., Duan, H. Q. (2011). Identification of trans-tiliroside as active principle with anti-hyperglycemic, anti-hyperlipidemic and antioxidant effects from Potentilla chinesis. *J. Ethnopharmacol.* 135, 515-521.

Rainsford, K. D. (2007). Anti-inflammatory drugs in the 21st century. *Subcell Biochem.* 42, 3-27.

Ramalhete, C., Spengler, G., Martins, A., Martins, M., Viveiros, M., Mulhovo, S., Ferreira, M. J., Amaral, L. (2010). Inhibition of efflux pumps in methicillin-resistant *Staphylococcus aureus* and *Enterococcus faecalis* resistant strains by triterpenoids from *Momordica balsamina*. *Int. J. Antimicrob Agents.* 37, 70-74.

Ramalhete, C., da Cruz, F. P, Lopes, D., Mulhovo, S., Rosário, V. E., Prudêncio, M., Ferreira, M. J. (2011). Triterpenoids as inhibitors of erythrocytic and liver stages of Plasmodium infections. *Bioorg. Med. Chem.* 19, 7474-7481.

Rashan, L. J., Franke, K., Khine, M. M., Kelter, G., Fiebig, H. H., Neumann, J., Wessjohann, L. A. (2011). Characterization of the anticancer properties of monoglycosidic cardenolides isolated from *Nerium oleander* and *Streptocaulon tomentosum*. *J. Ethnopharmacol.* 134: 781-788.

Rigano, D., Formissano, C., Bassille, A., Lavitola, A., Senatore, F., Rosselli, S., Bruno, M. (2007). Antibacterial activity of flavonoids and phenylpropanoids from *Marrubium globossum* ssp. *Libonoticum*. *Phytother. Res,* 21, 395-397.

Sala, A., Recio, M. C., Giner, R. M., Máñez, S., Ríos, J. L. (2001). New acetophenone glucosidesisolated from extracts of Helichrysum italicum with antiinflammatory activity. *J. Nat. Prod.* 64, 1360-1362.

Saladino, R., Gualandi, G., Farina, A., Crestini, C., Nencioni, L., Palamara, A. T. (2008). Advances and challenges in the synthesis of highly oxidised natural phenols with antiviral, antioxidant and cytotoxic activities. *Cur. Med. Chem.* 15,1500-1519.

Salvi, M., Fiore, C., Armanini, D., Toninello, A. ( 2003). Glycyrrhemic acid – induced permeability transition in rat liver mitochondria. *Biochem. Pharmacol.* 66, 2375-2379.

Sánchez-Mateo, C. C., Bonkanka, C. X., Hernández-Pérez, M., Rabanal, R. M. (2006). Evaluation of the analgesic and topical anti-inflammatory effects of *Hypericum reflexum* L. fil. *J. Ethnopharmacol.* 107, 1-6.

Sarikahya, N. B., Kirmizigul, S. (2012). Antimicrobially active heteragenin glycosides from *Cephalaria elmallensis*, *Planta Med.* 78, 828-833.

Sasaki, H., Takei, M., Kobayashi, M, Pollard, R. B., Suzuki, F. (2002). Effect of glycyrrhizin, an active component of licorice roots, on HIV replication in cultures of peripheral blood mononuclear cells from HIV-seropositive patients. *Pathobiology.* 70,:229-236.

Sato, H., Goto, W., Yamamura, J., Kurokawa, M., Kageyama, S., Takahara, T., Watanabe, A., Shiraki, K. (1996). Therapeutic basis of glycyrrhizin on chronic hepatitis B. *Antiviral Res.*30, 171-177.

Saul, N., Pietsch, K, Menzel, R., Steinberg, C. E. (2008). Quercetin-mediated longevity in *Caenorhabditis elegans*: is DAF-16 involved? *Mech. Ageing Dev.* 129, 611-613.

Sen, S., Roy, M., Chakraborti, A. S. (2011) Ameliorative effects of glycyrrhizin on streptozotocin-induced diabetes in rats. *J. Pharm. Pharmacol.* 63, 287-296.

Shahat, A. A., Pieters, L., Apers, S., Nazeif, N. M., Abdel-Azim, N. S., Berghe, D. V., Vlietinck, A. J. (2001). Chemical and biological investigations on Zizyphus spina-christi L. *Phytother. Res.* 15,593-597.

Shibata, S. ( 2000). A drug over the millennia: pharmacognosy, chemistry and pharmacology of licorise. *Yakugaku Zasshi.* 120, 849-862.

Siddiqui, B. S., Khatoon, N., Begum, S., Farooq, A. D., Qamar, K., Bhatti, H. A., Ali, S. K. (2012). Flavonoid and cardenolide glycosides and a pentacyclic triterpene from the leaves of *Nerium oleander* and evaluation of cytotoxicity. *Phytochemistry.* 77, 238-244.

Siler, B., Misic, D., Nestorovic, J., Banjanac, J., Glamoclija, J., Sokovic, M., Ciric, A. (2010). Antibacterial and antifungal screening of *Centaurium pulchellum* crude extracts and main secoiridoid compounds. *Nat. Prod. Commun.* 10, 1525-1530.

Smith, J. A., Madden, T., Vijjesvarapu, M., Newman, B. A. (2001). Inhibition of export of fibroblast growth factor-2 (FGF-2) from the prostate cancer cell lines PC3 and DU 145 by Anvirzel and its cardiac glycoside component, oleandrin. *Biochem. Pharmacol.* 62, 469-472.

Sun, Z. L., Zhang, M., Wu, Y., Wan, A. H., Zhang, R. (2011). Bioactive saponins from the fruits of *Aesculus pavia* L. *Fitoterapia.* 82, 1106-1109.

Tadić, V. M., Jeremic, I., Dobric, S., Isakovic, A., Markovic, I., Trajkovic, V., Bojovic, D., Arsic, I. (2012). Anti-inflammatory, gastroprotective, and cytotoxic effects of Sideritis scardica extracts. *Planta Med.* 78, 415-427.

Takahara, T., Watanabe, A., Shiraki, K. (1994). Effects of glycyrrhizin on hepatitis B surface antigen: a biochemical and morphological study. *J. Hepatol.* 21, 601-609.

Takii, H., Kometani, T., Nishimura, T., Nakae, T., Okada, S., Fushiki, T. (2001) Antidiabetic effect of glycyrrhizin in genetically diabetic KK-Ay mice. *Biol. Pharm. Bull.* 24, 484-487.

Thompson, S., Townsend, R. (2011). Pharmacological agents for soft tissue and bone infected with MRSA: which agent and for how long? *Injury,* 42, 7-10.

Utsunomiya, T., Kobayashi, M., Pollard, R. B., Suzuki, F. (1997). Glycyrrhizin, an active component of licorise roots reduces morbidity and mortality of mice infected with lethal doses of influenza virus. *Antimicrob. Agents Chemother.* 41, 551-556.

Van Rosum, T. G. J., Vulto, A. G., De Man, R. A., Brouwer, J. T., Schalam, S. W. (1998). Review article: Glycyrrhizin as potential treatment for chronic hepatitis C. *Aliment. Pharmacol. Ther.* 12, 199-205.

Wang, J., Zu, X., Jiang, Y. (2009). Five furostanol saponins from fruits of Tribulus terrestris and their cytotoxic activities. *Nat. Prod. Res.* 23, 1435-1439.

Wilson, M. A., Shukitt-Hale, B., Kalt, W., Ingram, D. K., Joseph, J. A., Wolkow, C. A. (2006). Blueberry polyphenols increase lifespan and thermotolerance in Caenorhabditis elegans. *Aging Cell.* 5, 59-68.

Wink, M., Ashour, M. L., El-Readi, M. Z. (2012). Secondary metabolites from Plants Inhibiting ABC Transporters and Reversing Resistance of Cancer Cells and Microbes to Cytotoxic and Antimicrobial Agents. *Front Microbiol.* 3, 130-134.

Yamada, P., Iijima, R., Han, J., Shigemori, H., Yokota, S., Isoda, H. (2010). Inhibitory effect of acteoside isolated from Cistanche tubulosa on chemical mediator release and inflammatory cytokine production by RBL-2H3 and KU812 cells. *Planta Med.* 14, 1512-8.

Yaniv, Z., Dafni, A., Friedman, J., Palevitch, D. (1987) Plants used for the treatment of diabetes in Israel. *J. Ethnopharmacol.* 19, 145-151.

Yarmolinsky, L., Huleihel, M., Zaccai, M., Ben-Shabat, S. (2012). Potent antiviral flavone glycosides from *Ficus benjamina* leaves. *Fitoterapia.* 83, 362-367.

Yashida, T., Yashida, S., Kobayashi, M., Herndon, D. N., Suzuki, F. (2010). Pivotal Advance: Glycyrrhizin restores the impaired production of β-defensins in tissues surrounding the burn area and improves the resistance of burn mice to Pseudomonas aeruginosa wound infection. *J. of Leucocyte Biology.* 87, 35-41.

Zhao, M., Bai, L., Toki, A., Hasegawa, R., Sakai, J., Hasegawa, T., Ogura, H., Kataoka, T., Bai Y., Ando, M., Hirose, K., Ando, M. (2011). The structure of a new cardenolide diglycoside and the biological activities of eleven cardenolide diglycosides from *Nerium oleander*. *Chem. Pharm. Bull. (Tokyo)*. 59, 371-377.

Zhong, Z., Kotova, O., Davidescu, A., Ehren, I., Ekberg, K., Jornvall, H., Wahren, J., Ghibalin, A. V. (2004). C-peptide stimulates $Na^+$, $K^+$-ATPase via activation of ERK ½ Map kinases in human renal tabular cells. *Cell. Mol. Life Sci.* 62, 2782-2790.

In: Recent Advances in Ginseng and Glycosides Research    ISBN: 978-1-62417-765-1
Editor: Claude J. Hopkins    © 2013 Nova Science Publishers, Inc.

*Chapter 3*

# SYNTHESIS AND PHYSICO-CHEMICAL PROPERTIES OF BENZIMIDAZOLONE DERIVATIVES WITH N-BOUND GLYCOSIDIC UNITS

*Brahim Lakhrissi*[*1], *Loubna Lakhrissi*[†2],
*Essassi El Mokhtar*[‡2], *Mohamed Massoui*[§3]
*and Carlos Rodriguez-Abreu*[‖4]

[1]Laboratoire d'Agroressources et Génie des Procédés, Université Ibn Tofaïl,
Faculté des Sciences, Kénitra, Morocco
[2]Laboratoire de Chimie Organique Hétérocyclique,
Université Mohammed V – Agda, Faculté des Sciences, Rabat, Morocco
[3]Pôle de Compétences Pharmacochimie, Université Mohammed V - Agdal,
Faculté des Sciences, Rabat, Morocco
[4]International Iberian Nanotechnology Laboratory, Braga, Portugal

## ABSTRACT

New water-soluble benzimidazolone derivatives bearing a glucosyl unit were synthesized using an efficient glycosylation method. Also a series of new non-ionic amphiphiles based on bis-galactobenzimidazolones have been synthesized by grafting alkyl bis-benzimidazolone units as hydrophobic tails on glucopyranose and on hydroxypropyloxygalactopyranose moieties as hydrophilic heads. Their surface and self-aggregation properties in water were investigated. The new amphiphiles show characteristic UV-Vis absorption and fluorescence emission bands associated with the benzimidazolone moiety. The fluorescence emission is quenched with a certain degree of selectivity by cations, due to their strong affinity towards the benzimidazolone group, which shows ion complexation properties.

[*] E-mail: b_lakhrissi@yahoo.fr.
[†] E-mail: lo.lakhrissi@yahoo.fr.
[‡] E-mail: emessassi@yahoo.fr; m.essassi@mascir.com
[§] E-mail: massoui@yahoo.fr.
[‖] E-mail: crodriguez@inl.int.

Reaction of 1,5-benzodiazepine-2,4-dione with 3-O-substituted-5,6-anhydro-1,2–isopropyli-dene-α-D-glucofuranose gave the unexpected N,N'-di-glucofuranosyl benzimidazol-2-one by a novel rearrangement and ring closure reaction. A mechanism is proposed.

**Keywords:** Benzimidazolone - D-glucose - D-galactose - Surfactant synthesis - Self aggregation - Surface properties - Fluorescence probe spectroscopy – unexpected rearrangement

# 1. INTRODUCTION

Benzimidazolone is well known for its large range of biological activities (Yu et al., 2006; Li et al., 2005; Baragatti et al., 2000; Zhang et al., 2001; Biagi et al., 2001) and industrial applications (Torres et al., 2003, Sarri et al., 2003) Thus, some benzimidazolone derivatives such as 1-ethyl-2-benzimidazolone (Devor et al., 1996; Anderson et al., 2006) have created a great deal of interest because of the direct activation of the potassium ($K^+$) cation channels. Benzimidazolone are also important for their complexant properties for metallic ions such as $Mg^{2+}$ and $Ca^{2+}$ (Htay and Meth-Cohn, 1976; Meth-Cohn and Smith, 1982; Cignitti et al., 1995). And show a characteristic UV absorption band and fluorescence emission (Lazar et al., 2003; Benali et al., 2006). Hence, they can act as intrinsic chemosensor molecules in which the donor atoms for substrate complexation are a part of the fluorophore (Mancin et al., 2006; El Majzoub et al., 2009); the interaction between the bound substrate and the fluorophore leads directly to the modification of its emission properties. However, the low solubility in water is a drawback, therefore designing benzimidazolone-based hydrosoluble chemosensors is an interesting goal (Pina et al., 2000). They could attract an additional interest if they would have amphiphilic nature and therefore form self assemblies in solution or on substrates (Mancin et al., 2006).

If a benzimidazolone moiety could be attached to an amphiphilic molecule, it would add peculiar functionalities with applications in fields such as pharmaceuticals, separation processes and corrosion inhibition. On the other hand Sugar-based surfactants, with their low toxicity and excellent biodegradability, i.e. reduced environmental impact, offer an attractive alternative to more conventional non-ionic surfactants such as poly(ethyleneoxide) alkyl ethers (Rodrıguez-Abreu et al., 2005). Moreover, they show performance properties which are exploited in microbiology and biotechnology (Rauter et al., 2005; Van Hamme et al., 2006; Singh et al, 2007), and have potential pharmaceutical and biomedical applications (Rozycka-Roszak et al., 2007; Ren et al., 2009; Jiao, 2008).

Sugar surfactants are made from renewable resources and are increasingly used in washing agents (Tracy et al., 1999), cosmetics (Bais et al., 2005; Ahsan et al., 2003), and drug carriers (Uchegbu and Vyas, 1998; Wu et al., 2009). The influence of structural changes on the physical properties of this family of surfactants has been studied in several reports (Rodrıguez-Abreu et al., 2005; Nakamura et al., 1999; Stradner et al., 1999; Castro et al., 1999).

This preamble showed the large number of benzimidazolone derivatives applications in different areas. The purpose of this paper is to review recent research into the synthesis of some new non-ionic amphiphiles compounds based on glycobenzimidazolones (Lakhrissi et al., 2008, 2010, 2011 and 2012) (Figure 1).

Their surface and aggregation properties in water were investigate by several techniques such as surface tension, fluorescent probe spectroscopy, polarized]) optical microscopy and Small Angle X-ray Scattering (SAXS). The ion complexing properties of some of these compounds have been also investigated by UV–Vis and fluorescence spectroscopy.

## 2. RESULTS AND DISCUSSION

### 2.1. Synthesis

#### 2.1.1 Synthesis of Benzimidazolone Derivatives 1-3

The starting benzimidazolones *1-3* (Scheme 1) were prepared according to the method described by (Townsend et al., 1995). *o*-Phenylenediamine was reacted with 1 equiv of urea in dry n-butanol at 120°C during 10 h. Benzimidazolones derivatives *1–3* were obtained by the filtration of the crude product in 80–94% yield.

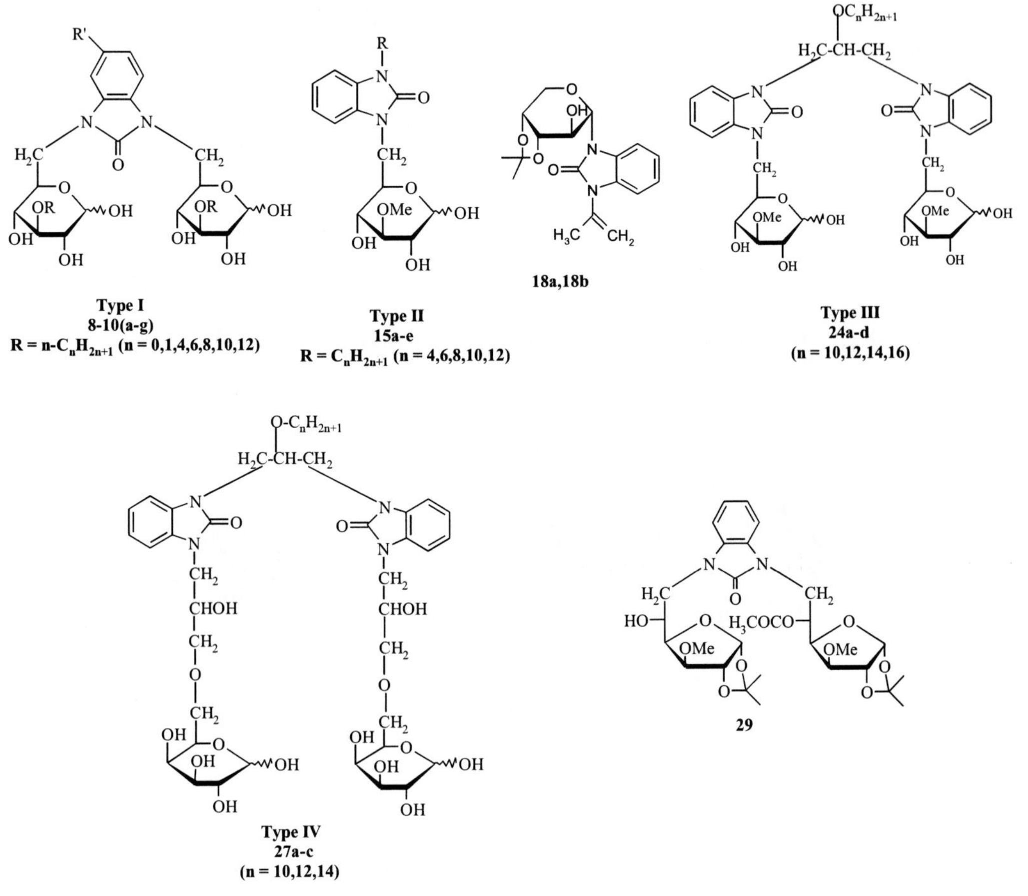

Figure 1. Structures of synthesis glycobenzimidazolones.

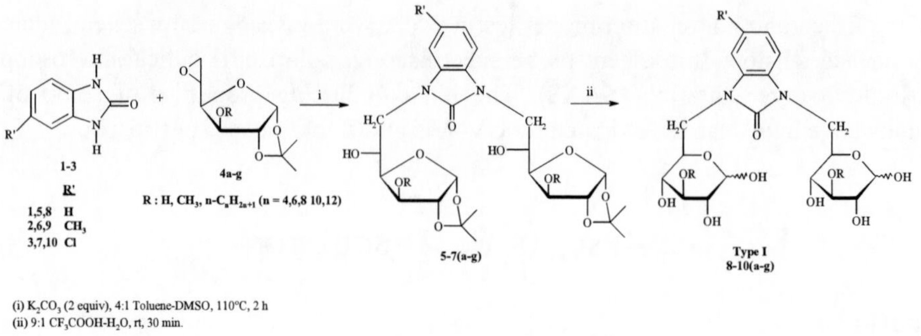

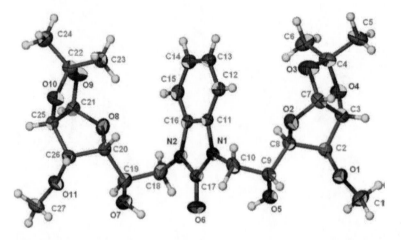

(i) K$_2$CO$_3$ (2 equiv), 4:1 Toluene-DMSO, 110°C, 2 h
(ii) 9:1 CF$_3$COOH-H$_2$O, rt, 30 min.

Scheme 1. Synthesis of *N,N'*-bis-(3-*O*-alkyl-6-desoxy-D-glucopyranos-6-yl)-benzimidazol-2-one *8-10(a-g)*.

### 2.1.2. Synthesis of 1,3-N,N'-bis-(6-deoxy-D-glucopyranos-6-yl)benzimidazol-2-one and 1,3-N,N'-bis-(6-deoxy-3-O-alkyl-D-glucopyranos-6-yl)benzimidazol-2-one derivatives 8-10(b-g) (Type I)

The glucopyranosyl benzimidazolone derivatives *5-7* (Scheme 1) were obtained by the regiospecific condensation of benzimidazolones *1-3* on the anhydroglucosyl substrates *4a-g* (Goueth et al., 1994; Lakhrissi et al., 2004) in the presence of K$_2$CO$_3$ at 110 °C, and by using 4:1 toluene-DMSO as solvent. Under these conditions we obtained the desired products *5–7* with 70–93% yield. Taking advantage of the convergent synthesis and with the aim of modulating hydrophilic–lipophilic balance, we replaced *4a* by homologues 5,6-anhydro-3-*O*-alkyl-1,2-*O*-isopropylidene-α-D-glucofuran-ose *4b-g* (R = n-C$_n$H$_{2n+1}$; n = 1, 4, 6, 8, 10 and 12). Deprotection of the isopropylidene groups with 9:1 CF$_3$CO$_2$H-H$_2$O (Christensen and Goodman, 1968) afforded the expected glucopyranosylbenzimidazolone derivatives *8-10(a-g)* (*Type I*) in good yields (70-95%).

Physico-chemical constants for some compounds are given in Tables *1* and *2*.

Figure 2. Thermal ellipsoid plot of C$_{27}$H$_{38}$N$_2$O$_{11}$ (*5a*) at the 30% probability level; hydrogen atoms are drawn as spheres of arbitrary radius.

The compound *5a* was characterized by X-Ray analysis (Lakhrissi et al., 2012) (Figure 2). The result show that in the title benzimidazolone, C$_{27}$H$_{38}$N$_2$O$_{11}$, which has N-bound glycosidic units, all five-membered O-heterocyclic rings adopt envelope conformations [for the outer rings, the C atom with the dimethyl groups represents the flap atom]. The two glycosidic units are related by a non-crystallographic twofold rotation axis that passes through the carbonyl portion. In the molecular structure, the hydroxy groups are hydrogen-bond donors to the carbonyl O atom. Weak intermolecular C—H----O hydrogen bonding is present in the crystal structure.

**Table 1. Physico-chemical constants of compounds 5-7(b) and their precursors 8-10(b)**

| Compound | Yield (%) | Mp (°C) | $[\alpha]_D^{27}$ (c = 0.6) | α/β |
|---|---|---|---|---|
| 5b (n=1, R'= H) | 78 | 159–161 | 93.1* | - |
| 6b (n=1, R'= CH₃) | 70 | 190–192 | 104.0* | - |
| 7b (n=1, R'= Cl) | 76 | 191–193 | 119.9* | - |
| 8b (n=1, R'= H) | 81 | 124–126 | 48.5–50.2** | 4/3 |
| 9b (n=1, R'= CH₃) | 80 | 116-118 | 52.3–53.8** | 9/5 |
| 10b(n=1, R'= Cl) | 70 | 143-146 | 44.8–45.8** | 5/3 |

\* In CHCl₃.
\*\* In fresh MeOH and after 3 days.

### 2.1.3. Synthesis of 3-N-alkyl-1-N-(6-deoxy-3-O-alkyl-D-glucopyranos-6-yl)benzimidazol-2-one Derivatives 15a-e (Type II)

The glucobenzimidazolone series (*Type II*) was synthesized as is shown in Scheme 2. The strategy followed in this part was to partially protect the benzimidazolone unit leaving only one NH group available for an alkylation reaction with an alkyl bromide (step ii). For this purpose, the first step was performed by using the Meth-Cohen's method. (Meth-Cohen and Smith, 1982). To modulate the HLB, an alkyl chain (R = n-$C_nH_{2n+1}$; n=1, 4, 6, 8, 10 and 12) was introduced (step i, 90–95% yield), and the protecting isopropenyl group was then removed by using 1:1 water–$H_2SO_4$ at room temperature. Addition of the glucose derivative *4b* to benzimidazolones *13a-e* using the same procedure as previously reported (Goueth et al., 1994; Lakhrissi et al., 2004) for *5–7* mainly provided the desired 3-N-alkyl-1-N-(6-deoxy-1,2-O-isopropylidene-3-O-methyl-α-D-glucofuranos-6-yl)-benzimidazol-2-one derivatives *14a-e* (step iii, 93–97% yield). Subsequent deprotection of *14a-e* was performed by using Amberlyst-15 (H⁺) in 4:1 dioxane-water to lead benzimidazolone derivatives *15a–e* in 72–89% yield (step iv).

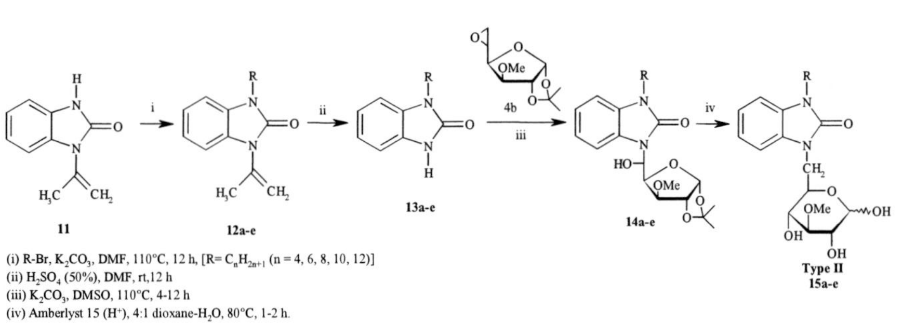

(i) R-Br, K₂CO₃, DMF, 110°C, 12 h, [R= CₙH₂ₙ₊₁ (n = 4, 6, 8, 10, 12)]
(ii) H₂SO₄ (50%), DMF, rt,12 h
(iii) K₂CO₃, DMSO, 110°C, 4-12 h
(iv) Amberlyst 15 (H⁺), 4:1 dioxane-H₂O, 80°C, 1-2 h.

Scheme 2. Synthesis of N-alkyl-N-(6-desoxy-3-O-methyl-D-glucopyranos-6-yl)-benzimidazol-2-one *15a-e*.

Physico-chemical constants are given in Tables 3 and 4.

**Table 2. NMR spectroscopic data of compound 5b in CDCl₃ and its precursor 8b in DMSO-d₆**

| Compound | Glucosyl moiety | Oxo-benzimidazolyl moiety |
|---|---|---|
| 5b (n=1, R'= H) | $H^1$:5.90(d, 2H, $J_{1,2}$ = 3.6 Hz) $H^2$:4.51(d, 2H, $J_{2,3}$ = 0.0 Hz) $H^3$:3.84(d, 2H, $J_{3,4}$ = 3.0 Hz) $H^4$:3.96(dd, 2H, $J_{4,5}$ = 8.5 Hz) $H^5$:4.19(m, 2H, $J_{5,6a}$ =2.5 Hz) $H^{6a}$:4.27(dd, 4H $J_{6a,6b}$ = 14.4 Hz ) $H^{6b}$:4.05(dd, 4H, $J_{5,6b}$= 5.8 Hz) OCH₃:3.45 (s, 6H) CH₃iso :1.49-1.22 (4s,12H) | $H_{arom}$:7.47-7.05 (m,8H) |
| 5b (n=1, R'= H) | $C^1$:104.9 $C^2$: 82.1 $C^3$: 83.0 $C^4$:81.5 $C^5$:68.9 $C^6$:45.4 OCH₃:58.4 (CH₃)₂:26.8-26.5 $C_{iso}$:111.6 | C=O:157.3 C-8,C-9:129.7 C-5,C-6:121.8 C-4,C-7:108.6 |
| 8b (n=1, R'= H) | $C^{1\alpha}$ :92.2 $C^{1\beta}$:96.7 $C^3$:82.8, 85,6 $C^2$,$C^4$,$C^5$:74,1-69,5 C-6:42.7 OCH₃:59.8 | C=O:153.8 C-8,C-9:129.6 C-5,C-6:120.7 C-4,C-7:108.7;108.4 |

**Table 3. Physico-chemical constants of compounds 14a-e and their precursors 15a-e**

| Compound | Yield (%) | Mp (°C) | $[\alpha]_D^{26}$ (c=1.0) | α/β |
|---|---|---|---|---|
| 14a (n = 4) | 97 | 100-102 | 76.9* | - |
| 14b (n = 6) | 96 | 96-98 | 68.4* | - |
| 14c (n = 8) | 95 | 70-72 | 68.0* | - |
| 14d (n = 10) | 93 | 53-55 | 62.1 | - |
| 14e (n = 12) | 91 | 50-52 | 59.6 | - |
| 15a (n = 4) | 83 | 67-69 | 34.9-40.6** | 4:3 |
| 15b (n = 6) | 89 | 64-66 | 35.5-39.2** | 9:7 |
| 15c (n = 8) | 84 | 54-56 | 33.3-38.8** | 4:3 |
| 15d (n = 10) | 93 | 51-53 | 29.3-35.5** | 5:3 |
| 15e (n = 12) | 72 | 44-46 | 25.5-32.1** | 1:1 |

\* In CHCl₃.

\** In fresh MeOH and after 3 days.

## 2.1.4. Synthesis of 1-N-isopropenyl-3-N-(3,5,6-tri-O-benzyl-1-deoxy-β-D-glucofuranos-1-yl)benzimidazol-2-one (18a) and [1-N-(1-Deoxy-3,4-O-isopropylidene-α-D-arabinopyra-nos-1-yl)-3-N-isopropenylbenzimidazol-2-one (18b)

The glycosylation conditions were applied to benzimidazolone *11* and studied with 3,4,6-tri-*O*-benzyl-1,2-*O*-sulfinyl-α-D-glucofuranose *17a* and 3,4-*O*-isopropylidene-1,2-*O*-sulfinyl-β-D-arabinopyranose *17b* (Scheme 3) (Benksim et al., 2004).

These latter compounds were obtained from 1,2- diols *16a* and *16b*, respectively, by sulfinylation reaction with *N,N'*-sulfinyldiimidazole (Benksim et al., 2004; El Meslouti et al., 1994).

The nucleophilic opening of the cyclic sulfites was realized by the potassium form of the benzimidazolinone anion, preliminary formed with $K_2CO_3$ in DMF. The 1,2-trans compounds *18a* and *18b* were obtained in 61% and 62% yields, respectively. The latter compounds were characterized by NMR spectroscopy showing the anomeric protons at 5.82 ppm with a coupling constant $J_{1,2}$ 0 Hz for the glucofuranosyl compound *18a* and 5.25 ppm with $J_{1,2}$ 9.8 Hz for the arabinopyranoside *18b*.

**Table 4. NMR spectroscopic data of compounds 14a in CDCl₃ and its precurseur 15a in DMSO-d₆**

| Compound | Glucose moiety | Benzimidazolone moiety |
|---|---|---|
| **14a (n = 4)** | $H^1$:5.93(d, 2H, $J_{1,2}$ = 3.7 Hz)<br>$H^2$:4.52(d, 2H, $J_{2,3}$ = 0.0 Hz)<br>$H^5$:4.15(m, 2H, $J_{5,6a}$ = 2.7 Hz, $J_{5,6b}$ = 5.7 Hz)<br>$H^6$:4.28, 4.05 (2dd, 2H $J_{6a,6b}$ = 14.6 Hz )<br>$H^4$: 3.95 (dd, H $J_{4,5}$ = 8.6 Hz )<br>$H^4$: 3.89 (dd, H $J_{3,4}$ = 3.4 Hz)<br>$OCH_3$:3.40 (s, 6H)<br>$CH_{3iso}$:1.35 -1.23 (2s, 6H) | $H_{arom}$:7.47-7.05 (m, 4H)<br>$N\text{-}CH_2^\alpha$ : 3.85 (t, 2H)<br>$CH_2^\beta$ : 1.71 (m, 2H)<br>$CH_2^\gamma$ : 1.30 (m, 2H)<br>$CH_2^\omega$ : 0.95 (t, 2H) |
| **14a (n = 4)** | $C^1$:105.1<br>$C^2$: 81.8<br>$C^3$: 83.6<br>$C^4$:80.1<br>$C^5$:68.8<br>$C^6$:45.6<br>$OCH_3$:58.2<br>$CH_{3iso}$:26.6;26.2<br>$C_{iso}$:111.6 | C=O : 156.0<br>C-8,C-9:129.7, 129.3<br>C-5,C-6:121.5, 121.3<br>C-4,C-7:108.7, 107.7<br>$N\text{-}CH_2^\alpha$ : 41.0<br>$CH_2^\beta$ : 30.4<br>$CH_2^\gamma$ : 20.0<br>$CH_2^\omega$ : 13.7 |
| **15a (n = 4)** | $C^{1\alpha}$ : 92.2<br>$C^{1\beta}$: 96.7<br>C: 85.9-82.8<br>$C^2,C^4,C^5$:74,1-69,5<br>C-6: 42.6<br>$OCH_3$: 59.8 | C=O: 153.6<br>C-8,C-9: 129.7, 127.8<br>C-5,C-6: 120.6<br>C-4,C-7: 108.7, 107.5<br>$N\text{-}CH_2^\alpha$ : 40.5<br>$CH_2^\beta$ : 29.9<br>$CH_2^\gamma$ : 19.3<br>$CH_2^\omega$ : 13.5 |

**Table 5. Physico-chemical constants of compounds 24a-d and their precursors 23a-d**

| Compound | Yield (%) | Mp (°C) | $[\alpha]_D^{26}$ (c=1.0) | α/β |
|---|---|---|---|---|
| 23a (n = 10) | 95 | 78-80 | - 53.0* | - |
| 23b (n = 12) | 93 | 70-72 | - 49.5* | - |
| 23c (n = 14) | 93 | 66-68 | - 51.6* | - |
| 23d (n = 16) | 92 | 62-64 | - 47.7* | - |
| 24b (n = 10) | 83 | 119-121 | 31.8 - 38.1** | 6/5 |
| 24b (n = 12) | 80 | 116-118 | 32,6 - 35,1** | 4/3 |
| 24b (n = 14) | 79 | 112-114 | 34,1 - 35,9** | 6/5 |
| 24b (n = 16) | 78 | 100-102 | 35,5 - 31,1** | 4/3 |

* In CHCl$_3$.
** In fresh MeOH and after 3 days.

**Table 6. NMR spectroscopic data of compound 23a in CDCl$_3$ and its precursor 24a in DMSO-d$_6$**

| Compound | Galactosyl moiety | Oxo-benzimidazolyl moiety | Alkyl chain moiety | Propyloxy moiety |
|---|---|---|---|---|
| 23a (n = 10) | H$^1$:5.85(d, 2H, J$_{1,2}$ = 3.3 Hz)<br>H$^2$:4.55(d,2H, J$_{2,3}$ = 0.0 Hz)<br>H$^3$:3.85(d, 2H, J$_{3,4}$ = 3.0 Hz)<br>H$^4$:3.90(dd, 2H, J$_{4,5}$ = 7.1 Hz)<br>H$^5$:4.15(m, 2H, J$_{5,6a}$ =14.5 Hz)<br>H$^{6a}$:4.30(dd, 4H J$_{6,6}$ = 6.4 Hz)<br>H$^{6b}$:4.05(dd, 4H, J$_{5,6b}$=2.7 Hz)<br>OCH$_3$:3.40 (s, 6H)<br>CH$_{3iso}$ :1.25 -1.28 (4s,12 Hz)<br>OH:2.12 (s, 2H) | H$_{arom}$:7.00-7.20(m,8H) | CH$_3^\omega$:0.80 (t, 3H)<br>CH$_2^{\omega-1}$:1.03(sext, 2H)<br>7CH$_2$:1.15-1.40(m, 14H)<br>OCH$_2^\alpha$ :3.30(t,2H)<br><br>J$_{\omega,\omega-1}$ = 7,2<br>J$_{\alpha,\beta}$ = 6,4 | OCH:4.10(m,1H)<br>NCH$_2$:3.95(m,4H)<br><br>J$_{1,2}$ = 5.5 |
| 23a (n = 10) | C$^1$:105.1<br>C$^3$: 83.5<br>C$^2$: 81.8<br>C$^4$:80.3<br>C$^5$:68.3<br>C$^6$:45.5<br>OCH$_3$:58.2<br>(CH$_{3iso}$)$_2$:26.2;26.5<br>C$_{iso}$:111.7 | C$^{2\alpha}$=O:155.9<br>C$^{2\beta}$=O:155.8<br>C-8,C-9:129.4;129.6<br>C-5,C-6:121.4;121.6<br>C-4,C-7:108.5;108.6 | CH$_3^\omega$:14.0<br>CH$_2^{\omega-1}$ : 22.6<br>CH$_2^\gamma$:25.7<br>5CH$_2$:29.3-31.8<br>CH$_2^\beta$:29.6<br>OCH$_2^\alpha$:71.4 | NCH$_2$:43.6<br>OCH:76.4 |
| 24a (n = 10) | C$^{1\alpha}$ :92.2<br>C$^{1\beta}$:96.7<br>C$^{3\alpha}$:82.8<br>C$^{3\beta}$:85,9<br>C$^{2\alpha}$,C$^{4\alpha}$,C$^{5\alpha}$:71,7;71,3;69,3<br>C$^{2\beta}$,C$^{4\beta}$,C$^{5\beta}$:74,2;73,8;73,6<br>C-6:43.0<br>OCH$_3$:59.8 | C$^{2\alpha}$=O:153.7<br>C$^{2\beta}$=O:153.8<br>C-8,C-9:129.3;129.7<br>C-5,C-6:120.6<br>C-4,C-7:108.2;108.6 | CH$_3^\omega$:13.8<br>CH$_2^{\omega-1}$:22.0<br>CH$_2^\gamma$:25.0<br>5CH$_2$:28.5-31.2<br>CH$_2^\beta$:29.1<br>OCH$_2^\alpha$:69.9 | NCH$_2$: 42.6<br>OCH: 75.4 |

### 2.1.5. Synthesis of N,N'-1,3-bis-[N-3-(6-deoxy-3-O-methyl-D-glucopyranose-6-yl)-2-oxo-benzimidazol-1-yl)]-2-alkyloxypropanes 24a-d (Type III)

Bis-benzimidazolone derivatives of glucose (*Type III*) were synthesized by grafting the 6-deoxy-3-*O*-methyl-D-glucopyranose-6-yl group on the *N-3* nitrogen atom of two benzimidazolone units that are linked by an alkyloxypropylene group, as described earlier

(Lakhrissi et al., 2000) (Lakhrissi et al., 2000). *N,N'*-1,3-bis-[*N*-3-(6-deoxy-3-*O*-methyl-D-glucopyranose-6-yl)-2-oxobenzimidazol-1-yl)]-2-alkyloxypropanes *24a-d* was synthetized following Scheme 4. The junction of the two *N*-isopropenylbenzimidazolone units (Meth-Cohen and Smith, 1982) (step a) was performed by condensing the 1-*N*-isopropenylbenzimidazolone 1 with epichlorohydrin in DMF in the presence of $K_2CO_3$ (Lakhrissi et al., 2000 and 2004). Subsequent alkylation of the free OH group by *n*-bromoalkanes (Lakhrissi et al., 2000 and 2004) (step b), *N*-3 deprotection (step c), glucose derivative *6* (Goueth et al., 1994; Lakhrissi et al., 2004) condensation (Lakhrissi et al., 2000) (step d), and final deacetylation (step e), gave the compounds *24a-d*.

Physico-chemical constants are given in Tables 5 and 6.

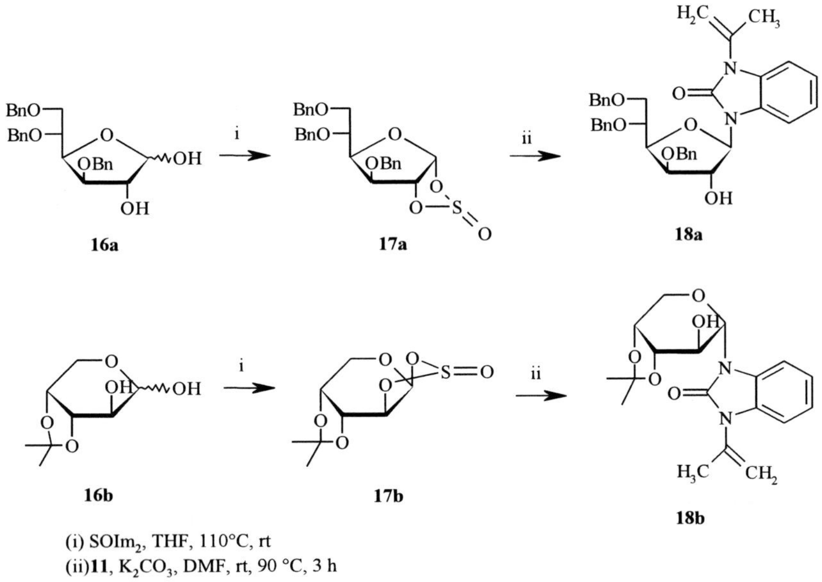

(i) SOIm$_2$, THF, 110°C, rt
(ii)11, K$_2$CO$_3$, DMF, rt, 90 °C, 3 h

Scheme 3. Synthesis of 1-*N*-isopropenyl-3-*N*-(3,5,6-tri-*O*-benzyl-1-deoxy-β-D-glucofuranos-1-yl)benzimidazol-2-one *18a* and 1-*N*-(1-Deoxy-3,4-*O*-isopropylidene-α-D-arabinopyranos-1-yl)-3-*N*-isopropenylbenzimidazol-2-one *18b*.

## 2.1.6. Synthesis of N,N'-1,3-bis-[N-3-(6-(2'-hydroxypropyloxy)-D-galactopyranos-6-yl)-2-oxobenzimidazol-1-yl)]-2-alkyloxypropanes 27a-c (Type IV)

*N,N'*-1,3-bis-[*N*-3-(6-(2'-hydroxypropyloxy)-1,2:3,4-di-*O*-isopropylidene-α-D-galactopyran-os-6-yl)-2-oxobenzimidazol-1-yl)]-2-alkyloxypropanes *27a-c (Type IV)* were synthesized following Scheme 5, by condensing the 1,3-*N,N'*-bis-[2-oxobenzimidazol-1-yl]-2-alkyloxy-propanes *22a-c* (Lakhrissi et al., 2010) units with 6-*O*-[2,3-epoxypropyl]-1,2:3,4-di-*O*-isopropylidene-α-D-galactopyranose *25* (Köll et al., 1994) in the presence of potassium carbonate and in pure DMSO as solvent ((Lakhrissi et al., 2000 and 2010). In order to give a hydrophilic character to the molecules obtained *26a-c,* they were treated with a mixture of trifluoroacetic acid-water (9:1, v/v) at room temperature (Goueth et al., 1994; Lakhrissi et al., 2004 and 2010). The precipitates obtained were purified by chromatography with a mixture of acetone-methanol (1:1, v/v) to give *N,N'*-1,3-bis-[*N*-3-(6-(2'-hydroxypropyloxy)-D-galacto-pyranos-6-yl)-2-oxobenzimidazol-1-yl)]-2-alkyloxypropanes *27a-c* as white solids.

Physico-chemical constants are given in Tables 7 and 8.

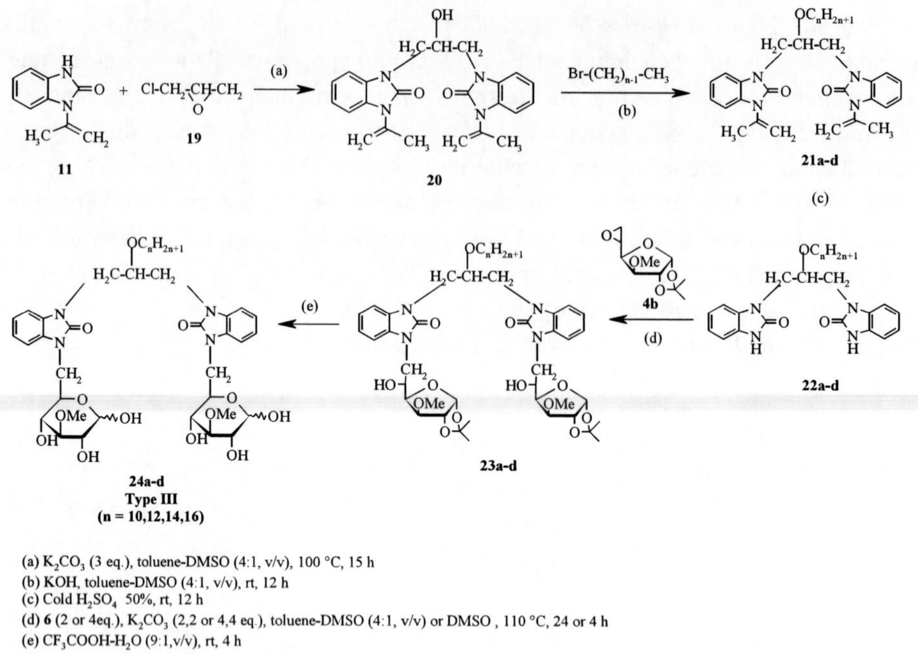

(a) K$_2$CO$_3$ (3 eq.), toluene-DMSO (4:1, v/v), 100 °C, 15 h
(b) KOH, toluene-DMSO (4:1, v/v), rt, 12 h
(c) Cold H$_2$SO$_4$ 50%, rt, 12 h
(d) **6** (2 or 4eq.), K$_2$CO$_3$ (2,2 or 4,4 eq.), toluene-DMSO (4:1, v/v) or DMSO , 110 °C, 24 or 4 h
(e) CF$_3$COOH-H$_2$O (9:1,v/v), rt, 4 h

Scheme 4. Synthesis of *N,N'*-1,3-bis-[*N*-3-(6-deoxy-3-*O*-methyl-D-glucopyranos-6-yl)-2-oxobenzimidazol-1-yl)]-2-alkyloxypropanes *24a–d.*.

**Table 7. Physico-chemical constants of compounds 27a-c and their precursors 26a-c**

| Compound | Yield (%) | Mp (°C) | $[\alpha]_D^{26}$ (c = 1.0) | α/β |
|---|---|---|---|---|
| **26a (n = 10)** | 88 | 68-78 | - 60.2°* | - |
| **26b (n = 12)** | 84 | 62-64 | - 60.3°* | - |
| **26c (n = 14)** | 79 | 58-60 | - 59.6°* | - |
| **27a (n = 10)** | 90 | 120-122 | 20.4°** | 3/4 |
| **27b (n = 12)** | 88 | 116-118 | 20.2°** | 5/6 |
| **27c (n = 14)** | 86 | 96-98 | 20,8°** | 3/4 |

* In CHCl$_3$.
** In CH$_3$OH.

### 2.1.7. Synthesis of 1-N-(6-deoxy-5-O-acetyl-1,2-O-isopropylidene-3-O-methyl-α-D-glucofuranos-6-yl)-3-N-6-deoxy-1,2-O-isopropylidene-3-O-methyl-α-D-glucofuranos-6- yl]-benzimidazol-2-one 29 from 1,5-benzodiazepine-2,4-dione 28

The glucobenzimidazolone *29* was synthesized as is shown in Scheme 6. The starting material, 1,5-benzodiazepine-2,4-dione *28* was prepared by condensing malonic acid with *o*-phenylenediamine in hydrochloric acid (Essassi et al., 1991).

Refluxing compound *28* with 3-*O*-methyl-5,6-anhydro-1,2-*O*-isopropylidene-α-D-glucofuranose (*4b*) for 2 hours in the presence of K$_2$CO$_3$ in 4:1 toluene-DMSO gave exclusively the unexpected product *29* [1-*N*-(6-deoxy-5-*O*-acetyl-1,2-*O*-isopropylidene-3-*O*-methyl-α-D-glucofuranos-6-yl)-3-*N*-6-deoxy-1,2-*O*-isopropylidene-3-*O*-methyl-α-D-glucofuranos-6-yl]-benzimidazol-2-one as white crystals) in 51% yield (mp 156-158 °C, $[\alpha]_D^{26}$ (c = 0.6, CHCl$_3$) : - 94.7°, EIMS [M]$^+$ m/z 608).

**Table 8. NMR spectroscopic data of compound 26a in CDCl₃ and its precursor 27a in DMSO-d₆**

| Compound | Galactosyl moiety | Oxo-benzimidazolyl moiety | Alkyl chain moiety | Propyloxy moiety | Hydroxypropyl moiety |
|---|---|---|---|---|---|
| **26a (n = 10)** | $H^1$: 5.45 (d, 2H, $J_{1,2}$ = 5.00) <br> $H^2$: 4.32 (dd, 2H, $J_{2,3}$ = 2.40) <br> $H^3$: 4.60 (dd, 2H, $J_{3,4}$ = 8.00) <br> $H^4$: 4.24 (dd, 2H, $J_{4,5}$ = 1.70) <br> $H^5$: 3.96 (m, 2H, $J_{5,6a}$ = 6.60) <br> $H^{6a}$: 3.68 (dd, 4H $J_{6,6}$ = 10.10) <br> $H^{6b}$: 3.54 (dd, 4H, $J_{5,6b}$ = 4.20) <br> CH$_{3iso}$: 1.24 -1.46 (4s, 12H) <br> OH: 2.12 (s, 2H) | Harom : 7.00-7.28 (m, 8H) | $CH_3^\omega$ : 0.87(t, 3H) <br> $CH_2^{\omega-1}$ : 1.03 (sext, 2H) <br> $7CH_2$ : 1.05-1.55(m, 14H) <br> $OCH_2^\alpha$ : 3.35 (t, 2H) <br><br> $J_{\omega,\omega-1}$ = 7.2 <br> $J_{\alpha,\beta}$ = 6.4 | OCH: 4.10 (m,1H) <br> NCH$_2$: 3.95 (m, 4H) <br><br> $J_{1,2}$ = 5.5 | OCH$_2$: 3.44 (m, 2H) <br> CHOH: 4.25 (m, 2H) <br> NCH$_2$: 3.95(dd, 1H) 4.30 (dd, 1H) |
| **26a (n = 10)** | $C^1$: 96.2 <br> $C^2$: 70.4 <br> $C^3$: 70.6 <br> $C^4$: 71.1 <br> $C^5$: 66.7, 66.7 <br> $C^6$: 71.4 <br> (CH$_{3iso}$)$_2$: 26.2, 26.5 <br> C$_{iso}$: 111.7 | $C^2$=O: 155.1 <br> $C^8$,$C^9$:129.5, 129.8 <br> $C^5$,$C^6$:121.3, 121.5 <br> $C^4$,$C^7$:108.4, 108.5, 108.6, 109.3 | $CH_3^\omega$: 14.1 <br> $CH_2^{\omega-1}$: 22.6 <br> $CH_2^\gamma$ : 25.7 <br> $5CH_2$ : 29.3-31.8 <br> $CH_2^\beta$ : 29.6 <br> $OCH_2^\alpha$ : 71.3 | NCH$_2$: 43.6 <br> OCH: 76.5 | OCH$_2$: 72.3, 72.5 <br> CHOH: 69.0, 69.2 <br> NCH$_2$: 44.3, 44.4 |
| **27a (n = 10)** | $C^{1\alpha}$ : 92.7 <br> $C^{1\beta}$: 97.4 <br> $C^2$, $C^3$, $C^4$, $C^5$ : 68.4 – 83.1 <br> C-6 : 70.1 | $C^{2\alpha}$=O: 153.8 <br> $C^{2\beta}$=O: 153.9 <br> $C^8$,$C^9$:129.4, 129.5 129.7, 129.8 <br> $C^5$,$C^6$:120.6, 120.8 <br> $C^4$,$C^7$:108.2;108.5 | $CH_3^\omega$: 13.9 <br> $CH_2^{\omega-1}$: 22.1 <br> $CH_2^\gamma$ : 25.0 <br> $5CH_2$ : 28.6 - 31.2 <br> $CH_2^\beta$: 29.2 <br> $OCH_2^\alpha$ : 70.8 | NCH$_2$: 43.1 <br> OCH: 76.1 | OCH$_2$: 72.8, 72.9 <br> CHOH:69.2, 69.3 <br> NCH$_2$: 44.3, 44.4 |

¹H and ¹³C NMR data are given in Table 9.(Lakhrissi et al.,2004).

This reaction may have proceeded by *N,N'*-disubstitution of compound *28* with subsequent rearrangement and ring contraction from a 1,5-diazepine-2,4-dione to 1,3-imidazol-2-one. A plausible mechanism is presented in Scheme 7.

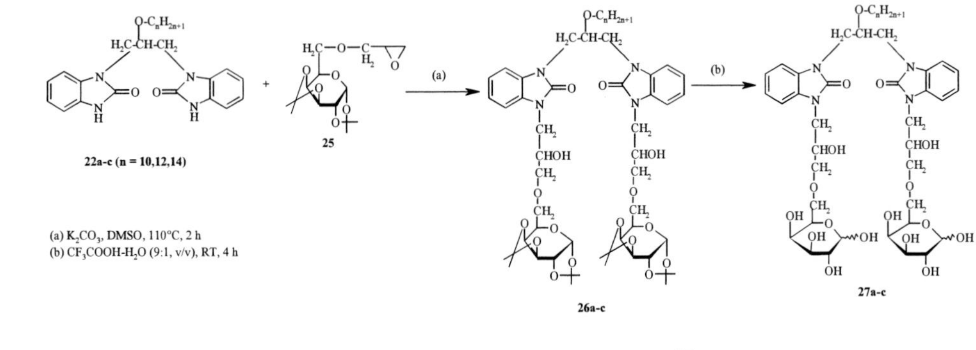

Scheme 5. Synthesis of *N,N'*-1,3-bis-[*N*-3-(6-(2'-hydroxypropyloxy)-D-galactopyranos-6-yl)-2-oxobenzimidazol-1-yl)]-2-alkyloxypropanes *27a–c*.

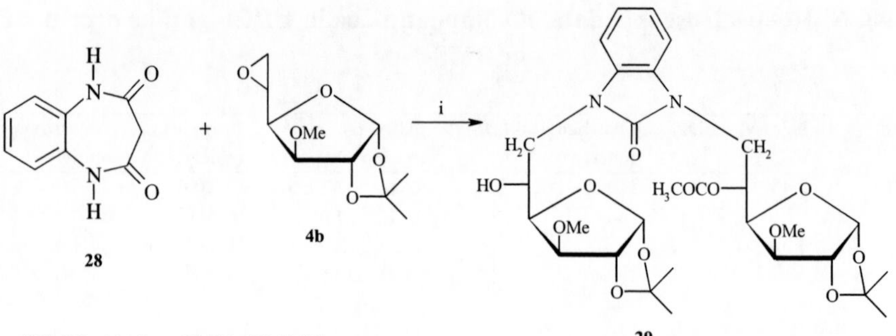

(i) K$_2$CO$_3$, 4:1 toluene-DMSO, 100-110 °C

Scheme 6. Synthesis of 1-*N*-(6-deoxy-5-*O*acetyl-1,2-*O*-isopropylidene-3-*O*-methyl-α-D-glucofuranos-6-yl)-3-*N*-6-deoxy-1,2-*O*-isopropylidene-3-*O*-methyl-α-D-glucofuranos-6-yl]-benzimidazol-2-one *29*.

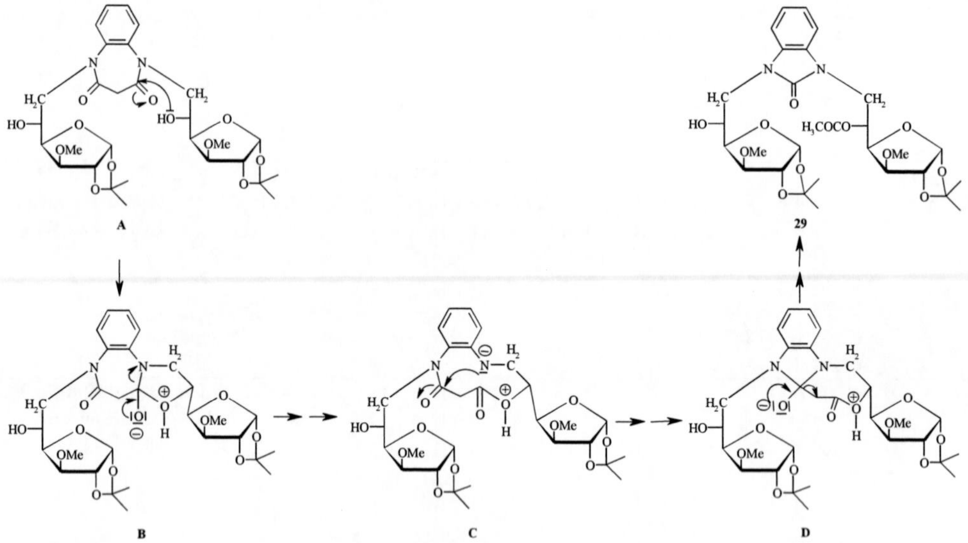

Scheme 7. Presentation of plausible mechanism.

It would seem reasonable that the first step in the reaction would involve formation of product *A*. The next step in the proposed mechanism is the intramolecular attack of the OH group at C5 of the sugar on the carbonyl of the diazepin-2,4-dione to give intermediate *B*. In the later steps,the cleavage of the N1-C2 bond give the intermediate *C*,which possesses a NH group easily deprotonated by basic catalyst (potassium carbonate) and attacking on the remaining carbonyl to give the tricyclic intermediate *D*. Lastly, cleavage of the C3-C4 bond of the putative oxazepine ring, would give the product *29*.

## 2.2. Surfactant Properties

Preliminary study on surfactant properties was performed to determine water solubility and surface tension of this new range of glycobenzimidazolones. All the compounds were evaluated for their amphiphilic characteristics and some one for their complexation properties.

**Table 9. NMR spectroscopic data of compound 29 in CDCl₃**

| Compo-und | Glucose moiety | Benzimidazolone moiety |
|---|---|---|
| 29 | $H^1$:5.93(d, 2H, $J_{1,2}$ = 3.6 Hz)<br>$H^2$:4.51-4.50 (2 d, 2H, $J_{2,3}$ = 0.0 Hz)<br>$H^5$:5.25-4.20 (2 m, 2H)<br>$H^{6b}$:4.42 (m, 2H)<br>$H^{6a}$: 4.40–4.25 (2·dd, 2H, $J_{5,6a}$= 5.2 Hz, $J_{6a,6b}$= 12.0 Hz)<br>$H^4$: 4.16–3.91 (2·dd, 2H, J3,4 = 3.0 Hz, J4,5 = 8.6 Hz)<br>$H^3$: 3.81–3.65 (2·d, 2H, $J_{3,4}$ = 3.0 Hz)<br>$OCH_3$: 3.45–3.24 (s, 6H)<br>$COCH_3$: 1.95 (s, 3H)<br>$CH_{3iso}$ : 1.45–1.15 (4s, 12H) | $H_{arom}$:7.25-7.00 (m, 4H) |
| 29 | $C^1$:105.6, 105.4<br>$C^2$: 82.1, 81.7<br>$C^3$: 82.8<br>$C^4$:80.4, 78.7<br>$C^5$:69.2, 68.9<br>$C^6$:45.9, 42.0<br>$OCH_3$:58.5, 58.3<br>$CH_{3iso}$:26.9, 26.8, 26.7, 26.4<br>$C_{iso}$:111.9<br>$COCH_3$: 170.1<br>$COCH_3$: 21.0 | C=O : 156.9<br>C-8,C-9:129.8, 129.6<br>C-5,C-6:130.1, 130.0<br>C-4,C-7:108.8 |

### 2.2.1.   1,3-N,N'-bis-(6-deoxy-D-glucopyranos-6-yl)benzimidazol-2-one derivatives 8-10(a-g) (type I) and 3-N-alkyl-1-N-(6-deoxy-3-O-methyl-D-glucopyranos-6-yl)benzimidazol-2-one derivatives 15a-e (Type II)

The purpose was also to evaluate the influence of alkyl substituents on these properties. The results are summarized in Tables *10* and *11*.

**Table 10. Water solubility (*Sw*, 10⁻³ mol L⁻¹) and surface tension (*γ*, mNm⁻¹) of benzimidazolone derivatives 8-10(a-g) (Type I) at 25 °C**

| Compound | | | | | | | | | | |
|---|---|---|---|---|---|---|---|---|---|---|
| | 1 | 2 | 3 | 8a | 8b | 8c | 8d | 8e | 8f | 8g |
| $R = C_nH_{2n+1}$ | - | - | - | H | $CH_3$ | n = 4 | n = 6 | n = 8 | n = 10 | n = 12 |
| *Sw* | <0.075 | <0.067 | <0.099 | >200 | >200 | 3.5 | 0.48 | <0.015 | < 0.014 | < 0.013 |
| *γ* | - | - | - | 52.2[a] | 46.6[a] | 41.5[b] | 44.9[b] | - | - | - |
| | 9a | 9b | 9e | 9f | 9g | 10a | 10b | 10e | 10f | 10g |
| $R = C_nH_{2n+1}$ | n = 4 | n = 6 | n = 8 | n = 10 | n = 12 | n = 4 | n = 6 | n = 8 | n = 10 | n = 12 |
| *Sw* | >200 | >200 | <0.014 | <0.013 | <0.012 | >200 | >200 | <0.014 | <0.013 | <0.012 |
| *γ* | 54.0[a] | 55.1[a] | - | - | - | 55.8[a] | 56.0[a] | - | - | - |

[a] 1 g.L⁻¹ solution.

[b] At water solubility value.

Data provided in Table *9* indicate that benzimidazolones *1-3* have water solubility (*Sw*) lower than $10^{-4}$ mol.L⁻¹ at 25 °C. On one hand, benzimidazolone derivatives *8-10(a,b)* (*Type I*) have a water solubility higher than 200 $10^{-3}$ mol.L⁻¹, while on the other hand, the water solubility of analogues *8-10(c,d)* bearing an alkyl chain (R = $C_4H_9$ to $C_6H_{13}$) decreases abruptly for analogues *8-10(c,d)* ($R_2$ = $C_8H_{17}$ to $C_{16}H_{33}$) until becoming close to the values of benzimidazolones *1-3*. Moreover no critical micelle concentration (*CMC*) was observed.

**Table 11. Water solubility ($10^{-3}$ mol $L^{-1}$) and surface tension ($\gamma$, mNm$^{-1}$) of benzimidazolone derivatives 13a-e and 15a-e (Type II) at 25 °C**

| Compound | | | | | | | | | | |
|---|---|---|---|---|---|---|---|---|---|---|
| | 13a | 13b | 13c | 13d | 13e | 15a | 15b | 15c | 15d | 15e |
| R =$C_nH_{2n+1}$ | n = 4 | n = 6 | n = 8 | n = 10 | n = 12 | n = 4 | n = 6 | n = 8 | n = 10 | n = 12 |
| Sw | <0.053 | <0.046 | <0.041 | < 0.036 | < 0.033 | 13.1 | 2.69 | 0.47 | 0.02 | 0.006 |
| $\gamma$ | - | - | - | - | - | 39.6[a] | 35.2[a] | 43.8[a] | 43.0[a] | - |

[a] 1 g.L$^{-1}$ solution.

As shown in Table *10*, *N*-alkylbenzimidazolones *13a-e* has water solubility lower than $10^{-4}$ mol.L$^{-1}$, whereas the graft of 6-deoxy-3-*O*-methyl-D-glucopyranos-6-yl *15a-e* (*Type II*) allows a partial water solubility that decreases with the alkyl chain length. As previously observed with the first series of benzimidazolone derivatives *8-10(a-e)*, we observed a strong reduction of water solubility when n > 6 (*15b*, $C_nH_{2n+1}$). Moreover, compounds *15a-d* have shown a lower surface tension than water ($\gamma$= 35-44 mNm$^{-1}$ vs 72 mNm$^{-1}$ for pure water), but these compounds have not shown any critical micelle concentration (*CMC*).

### 2.2.2. N,N'-1,3-bis-[N-3-(6-deoxy-3-O-methyl-D-glucopyranose-6-yl)-2-oxo-benzimidaz -ol-1-yl)]-2-alkyloxypropanes 24a-d (Type III)

### Critical Micellar Concentrations

The variation of surface tension with the logarithm of concentration at 25 °C for compounds *24a-d* is shown in Figure 3. At this temperature, all the compounds *24a-d* were completely soluble in water in the studied range of concentrations. It should be pointed out that other D-glucose derivatives show a more evident decrease of solubility with alkyl chain length (Bikanga et al., 1995).

The presence of two glucose moieties in compounds *24a-d* contributes to their high solubility in water. A typical break can be observed for every set of data in Figure 3, which is an indication of the onset of aggregation at the critical micellar concentration (*CMC*). The surface tension values at the *CMC* are around 33–37 mN/m and the *CMC* value derived from Figure 3 first decreases with the increase in alkyl chain length up to n = 14 and then increases back for n = 16. This is opposite to the typical decreasing trend in homologues with increasing chain length, e.g. in other sugar alkyl derivatives (Garofalakis et al., 2000; Wilk et al., 2000). An explanation for this anomalous phenomenon could be a change in the conformation for long hydrocarbon chains. This possibility has been considered previously (Ferrer et al., 2002). For some bulky surfactants (Folmer et al., 1999) there seems to be a competition between the hydrophobic effect and steric restrictions governed by the packing parameter, defined as $p$ = $v/(a\ l)$, where $v$, $a$ and $l$ are the volume, surface area and lipophilic chain length of the amphiphilic molecule, respectively (Israelachvili, 1992).

Pyrene has been widely used for the determination of the *CMC*. Figures 4a et 4b shows the results on fluorescence spectroscopy. There is an inflection point in *I1/I3* for all the compounds studied, suggesting a sudden decrease in the polarity of the environment surrounding the probe, as usually found when aggregates solubilizing pyrene are formed.

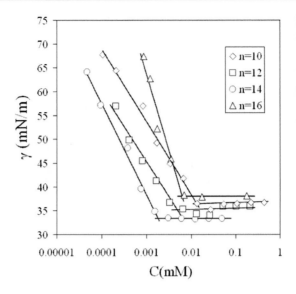

Figure 3. Surface tension at 25 °C as a function of concentration for compounds *24a-d* with different alkyl chain lengths (n).

Note that the decrease of *I1/I3* is much less steep for the compounds with longer alkyl chain length. Particularly for n = 16, the decrease stretches over nearly two decades of concentration. This kind of a behavior has been reported for amphiphiles with very low *CMC*, in which pyrene is partitioned between micelles and the aqueous phase (Zana and Levy, 1997; Regev and Zana, 1999); in such case, the *CMC* can be estimated from the first inflection point of the *I1/I3* versus concentration curve. Contrary to the surface tension, fluorescence measurements indicate a monotonical decrease in the *CMC* with alkyl chain length, which is the usual tendency.

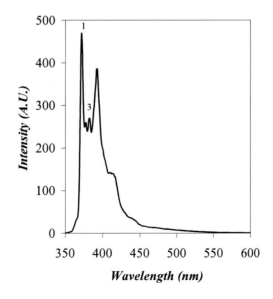

Figure 4a. Representative fluorescence spectra of pyrene at 25 °C for compounds *24b*, n = 12, $4 \times 10^{-4}$ mM in water.

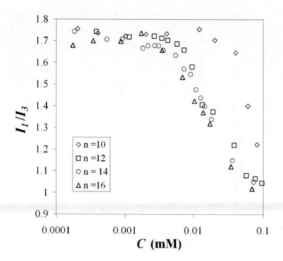

Figure 4b. Fluorescence $I_1/I_3$ ratio at 25 °C as a function of concentration for compounds *24a-d* with different alkyl chain lengths (*n*).

**Table 12. *CMC* values derived from surface tension and fluorescence Against the number of carbon atoms in the surfactant alkyl chain**

| compound | *CMC* (mM) | |
|---|---|---|
| | Surface tension | Fluorescence |
| **24a (n = 10)** | 0.0130 | 0.0104 |
| **24b (n = 12)** | 0.0040 | 0.0034 |
| **24c (n = 14)** | 0.0018 | 0.0029 |
| **24d (n = 16)** | 0.0069 | 0.0018 |

The results on *CMC* are summarized in Table 12 and Figure 5. Note the remarkably low *CMC* values, more than one order of magnitude lower than those of alkylglucosides (Shinoda et al., 1961). The experimental points for *CMCs* derived from fluorescence measurements can be approximately fitted to an equation of the form log *CMC* = *a - bn*, as in the case of other amphiphiles (Rosen, 1989). For the present series of compounds, *b* = 0.12, which is small when compared to other surfactants (Rosen, 1989), indicating that the effect of increasing the hydrophobic chain length on the aggregation tendency is less marked.

The significant difference between the results from surface tension and fluorescence spectroscopy concerning the *CMC* for n = 16 appears to be in agreement with the hypothesis about the formation of submicellar aggregates that in the present case can be detected by spectroscopy but not by surface tension measurements.

The decrease of *I1/I3* ratio over a wide range of concentration for n = 16 also points to the presence of premicellar aggregates that provides pyrene with a hydrophobic environment. Menger et al., 2009) have recently pointed out from considerations on the adsorption isotherm that "bulk" methods such as conductivity and spectroscopy are in some cases more reliable than surface tension to determine the *CMC*, since the break in the surface tension and interface saturation are not always directly correlated to micelle formation.

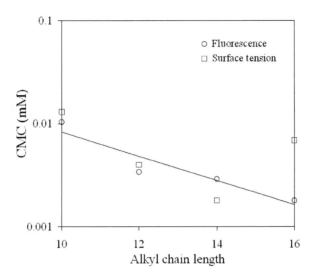

Figure 5. Plot of *CMC* values of compounds *24a-d* against the alkyl chain length derived from surface tension and fluorescence probe spectrometry. The line is a fitting to an equation of the form log *CMC* = *a-b*n, where *n* is the alkyl chain length, and *a* and *b* are constants.

## Surface Properties

The calculated values for surface excess concentration ($\Gamma_{max}$) and the surface area per molecule at the liquid/air interfaces ($A_{min}$) are summarized in Table 13.

The results follow the general behaviour described for conventional surfactants, namely, a decrease of the surface area when the alkyl chain increases because of a more closely-packed arrangement caused by the hydrophobic interactions between the alkyl chains, although some other saccharide-derived surfactants seem not to follow that trend (Wilk et al., 2000; Savelli et al., 1998). Due to the presence of two glucose moieties in the bulky hydrophilic head group, the surface areas in the present case are wider than that of alkyl glucosides with the same alkyl chain (Aveyard et al., 1998). However, Menger et al. (2009) have recently argued that the Gibbs analysis might overestimate the true areas-per-molecule at saturation.

**Table 13. Surface parameters derived from surface tension against the number of carbon atoms in the surfactant alkyl chain**

| Compound | $\Gamma_{max}$ x $10^{10}$ (mol/cm$^2$) | $A_{min}$ (Å$^2$) |
|---|---|---|
| **24a (n = 10)** | 2.8 | 60 |
| **24b (n = 12)** | 2.9 | 58 |
| **24c (n = 14)** | 3.4 | 49 |
| **24d (n = 16)** | 5.4 | 31 |

## Characterization of Liquid Crystals

The formation of lyotropic liquid crystals in water was also studied. Samples at different amphiphile concentrations were prepared and examined using a polarized light microscope (Figure 6). Optical textures typical for hexagonal liquid crystals were observed at 25 °C in all samples above a surfactant concentration of 60 wt%, except for n = 10, which need a higher concentration for liquid crystal formation (about 70 wt% as a minimum), indicating a weaker aggregation tendency due to its high hydrophilicity.

The lyotropic phases for n = 10, 12, 14 and 16 were characterized by the Bragg reflections derived from SAXS spectra. A representative spectrum is shown in Figure 7. The lyotropic phases are identified as an hexagonal liquid crystal (space group = p6 mm) showing up to five reflections at positions with ratios $1:\sqrt{3}:\sqrt{4}:\sqrt{7}:3$. SAXS results are then in agreement with observations made by the polarized light microscope. The number of well resolved SAXS peaks indicates a highly defined crystalline order. The presence of the hexagonal phase is not surprising as other disaccharide surfactants, such as β-D-alkyl maltosides, display such phase in water (Auvray et al., 1995; Boyd et al., 2000). However, in the present case, the hexagonal phase extends over a wider concentration range as compared to the phase domains of β-D-alkyl maltosides with similar alkyl chain length (Auvray et al., 1995; Boyd et al., 2000). This experimental fact can be attributed to the high specific surface area per molecule induced by the two glucose moieties in the head group, which would favour structures with high curvature.

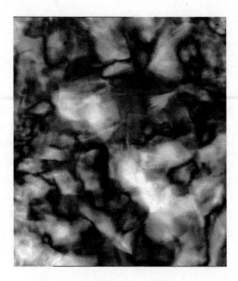

Figure 6. Polarized light microscopic images of liquid crystals for compound *24a* (n = 10) at 25 °C at 70 wt% surfactant in water : Texture of hexagonal liquid crystal.

The unit cell parameter in the hexagonal phase can be estimated from the equation $a = 2d/\sqrt{3}$, where d is the Bragg distance. The values of $a$ as a function of water concentration are plotted in Figure 8; a linear trend is observed for each alkyl chain length. The increasing tendency is expected because the distance between aggregates (and hence $a$) should grow as the sample is diluted and the liquid crystal swells with the solvent. For a fixed water concentration, $a$ increases with alkyl chain length as the diameter of the cylindrical aggregates forming the hexagonal phase also increases. $a$ values show no discontinuities as a function of concentration, confirming the presence of a single liquid crystal phase in the concentration range studied. The constants derived from the linear relationships of $a$ versus concentration are listed in Table 14. The constant $A$ reflects the swelling behavior of the hexagonal liquid crystal; there seems not to be a definite trend concerning swelling with water as a function alkyl chain length. On the other hand, the constant $B$ will give the cell parameter as extrapolated to the dry state. As can be seen in Figure 9, the constant $B$ does not follow a linear trend with $n$, suggesting that the change in the unit cell parameter is not only due to the contribution of methyl groups to the alkyl chain length, but also might come from changes in molecular arrangement within the hexagonal phase.

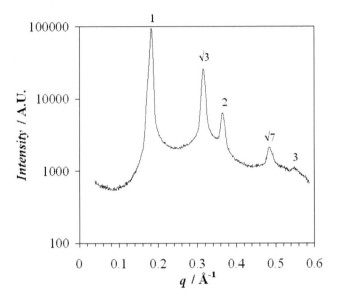

Figure 7. Representative X-ray spectrum of a sample at 70 wt% surfactant (30 wt% water) and alkyl chain length n = 10 (compound *24a*). The peak position ratios with respect to the first, most intense peak are also shown.

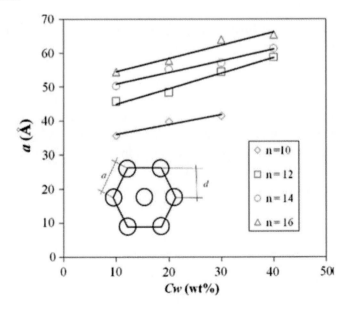

Figure 8. Unit cell parameter (*a*) as a function of water concentration (*Cw*) in hexagonal liquid crystals formed by compounds *24a–d*. The lines are best fits to the experimental points. The micellar array in the hexagonal phase is shown in the inset.

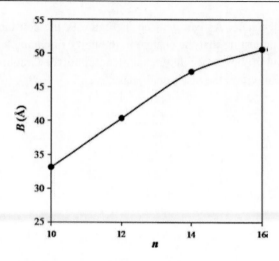

Figure 9. Constant B (Table 13) as a function of alkyl chain length n. The line is only a visual guide.

**Table 14. Empirical constants in the linear relationship of unit cell parameter (*a*) versus water concentration (*a* = *ACw* + *B*) for different alkyl chain lengths *n***

| Compound | A | B |
|---|---|---|
| **24a (n = 10)** | 0.29 | 33.2 |
| **24b (n = 12)** | 0.46 | 40.4 |
| **24c (n = 14)** | 0.34 | 47.3 |
| **24d (n = 16)** | 0.39 | 50.6 |

### 2.2.3. N,N'-1,3-bis-[N-3-(6-(2'-hydroxypropyloxy)-D-galactopyranos-6-yl)-2 -oxobenzimi-dazol-1-yl)]-2-alkyloxypropanes 27a-c (Type IV)

### Surface and Self-Aggregation Properties

The plot of surface tension versus logarithm of surfactant concentration of compound *27b* (alkyl chain length n = 12) is presented in Figure 10. The Critical Micellar Concentrations (*CMC*) values derived from the breaks are very low and the surface tension values at the *CMC*, namely, the effectiveness of surface tension reduction, are around, 40 mN/m (Table 15). The $\Gamma_{max}$ and $A_{min}$ values obtained (Table 14) are of the same order as those of alcohol ethoxylates with an average number of ethylene oxide units of 6–8 (Rosen, 1989; Lu et al., 2000), and very close to (*24b (n = 12) (Type III)*) homologue series (Figure 1) with alkyl chain lengths in the range n = 10-14 (Lakhrissi et al., 2010). The values of effective surface area per molecule at the interface ($A_{min}$) follow the typical decreasing trend with increasing hydrophobic tail length. Pyrene has been widely used for the determination of the *CMC*. Figure 10 shows the results on fluorescence probe spectroscopy for compound *27b* as example (alkyl chain length n = 12). As can be seen in Table *14*, the values of *CMC* derived from the breaks in *I1/I3* data are in agreement with those derived from surface tension measurements. Amphiphilic compounds usually form lyotropic liquid crystals in water. The small amount of surfactant available from the synthesis reported here made it difficult to prepare well mixed, concentrated samples in water with a precise surfactant concentration.

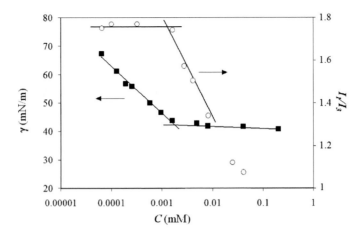

Figure 10. Surface tension (squares) and ratio of intensities of first and third peaks in pyrene fluorescence spectrum (*I1/I3*, circles) as a function of surfactant concentration (25 °C) for compound *27b* (n = 12). The lines serve to indicate the break for each set of data.

In such a case it is common to use the water penetration method to detect qualitatively the liquid crystal formation. Samples of the compounds *27a-c* were examined by means of polarized optical microscopy. Values of $\Gamma_{max}$ and $A_{min}$ for alcohol ethoxylates with an average number of ethylene oxide units of 6 and 8 and the same alkyl chain length of compounds *27a-c* are shown between brackets and in italics (data taken from References (Rosen, 1989; Lu et al., 2000)).

**Table 15. Surface properties of compounds 27a-c**

| Compound | CMC (mM) | | $\gamma_{CMC}$ (mN/m) | $\Gamma_{max} \, 10^{-10}$ (mol/cm$^2$) | $A_{min}$ (Å$^2$) |
|---|---|---|---|---|---|
| | from surface tension | from fluorescence | | | |
| 27a (n = 10) | 0.0025 | 0.0024 | 38 | 2.7 (*3* and *2.3*) | 60 (*55* and *70*) |
| 27b (n = 12) | 0.0016 | 0.0016 | 44 | 2.9(*3.2*and *2.5*) | 57 (*52* and *66*) |
| 27c (n = 14) | 0.0014 | 0.0013 | 41 | 3.4(*3.7*and *3.4*) | 48 (*45* and *48*) |

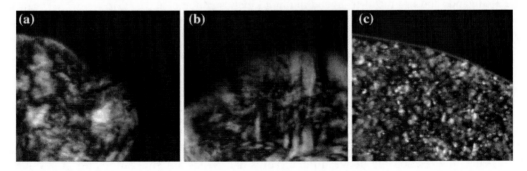

Figure 11. Images of optical polarized microscopy (25 °C) for compounds *27a-c* (*a*) n = 10 (*b*) n = 12 (*c*) n = 14. The compounds were put in contact with water (black region in the image) for the observation.

As it can be seen in Figure 11, when putting the synthesized compounds in contact with water, they form liquid crystals with hexagonal grainy optical texture for alkyl chain lengthsbof 10 and 12 carbons. For 14 carbons, clear liquid crystal optical textures could not be observed; birefringence seems to be produced by crystals of insoluble solid. The compound *(24b (n = 12) (Type III))*, with a similar structure, also forms hexagonal liquid crystals in water.

## Ion Complexation

We tried first to characterize the ion complexation properties of the synthesized compounds by UV–Vis spectrometry. In the absence of $Cu^{2+}$, the spectra of *27b* and *(24b (n = 12) (Type III))* compounds show a single absorption band with a maximum at 282 nm; compounds *4a* and *4c* show the same spectral features. The position of the characteristic band is almost the same as that of benzimidazolone in organic polar solvents such as ethanol and acetonitrile (Lazar et al., 2003). Upon addition of $Cu^{2+}$, $Mg^{2+}$ or $Na^+$, a slight bathochromic (red) shift was observed for the 282 nm band, and a new (overlapped) band seems to develop; from deconvolution of the spectra, the maximum of this band is estimated to be around 300–302 nm, almost in the same position of that found for neat cation (nitrate) solutions. The band remained even after subtraction of cation background, but results are not conclusive concerning the effect of ion complexation on UV-Vis spectra, particularly because the 302 nm band could not be detected at cation concentrations within the same order of magnitude of that of the synthesized compounds in the experiments.

Fluorescence spectroscopy is known to be an analysis technique much more sensitive than UV-Vis spectrometry. Fluorescence emission spectra of compounds *27b* upon titration with $Cu^{2+}$ are shown in Figure 12. Neat *27a-c* aqueous solutions (0.005 mM) show a single emission band at 312 nm, similar to benzimidazolone in organic polar solvents such as ethanol and acetonitrile (Lazar et al., 2003); this spectral feature is not changed by $Cu^{2+}$ addition, but the fluorescence intensity at the maximum decreases, i.e. there is a cation-induced quenching. Cation affinity of the imidazole group is determined by its complexing properties. The quenching process is induced by coordination of cations either directly to donor atoms of the fluorophore or to chelating groups covalently attached to the latter (Fabbrizzi et al. 1996). Particularly, $Cu^{2+}$ has a high thermodynamic affinity for typical *N, O*-chelate ligands and fast metal-to-ligand binding kinetics (Zhou et al., 2005).

As can be observed in Figure 13, fluorescence intensity quenching follows the Stern-Volmer relationship (Stern and Volrner, 1919), $Io/I = 1 + K_{SV} [Q]$, where $Io$ and $I$ are the fluorescence intensities in the absence and in the presence of quencher, respectively, $[Q]$ is the quencher concentration and $K_{SV}$ is the Stern-Volmer quenching constant; $K$ is a measure of the quenching efficiency.

Results points to a diffusion-controlled quenching process. $K_{SV}$ values for *27b* and *(24b (n = 12) (Type III))* (both with the same alkyl chain length) decrease in the order $Mg^{2+} > Cu^{2+} > Na^+$ (Table *16*). Ionic radii of $Mg^{2+}$ and $Cu^{2+}$ are very similar and both are lower than that of $Na^+$, hence, the relationship between ionic radius and $K_{SV}$ is not straightforward. $K_{SV}$ values for $Cu^{2+}$ as quencher are higher for *(24b, n = 12 (Type III))* when compared to *27b*, the latter having a bulkier group surrounding the benzimidazolone moiety. Therefore, steric effects might be playing a role. It should be mentioned here that other cations, such as $Ca^{2+}$ and $Pb^{2+}$ were also found to induce fluorescence quenching of the compound *27b*.

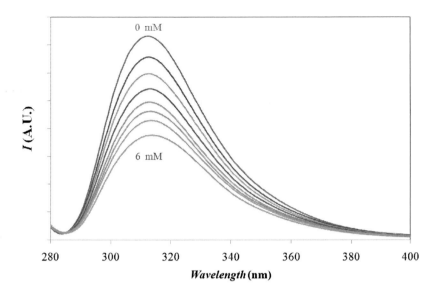

Figure 12. Fluorescence spectra (25 °C) for different $Cu^{2+}$ concentrations aqueous solutions of compound *27b*. The surfactant concentration is kept at 0.005 mM. $Cu^{2+}$ concentrations are varied from 0 to 6 mM in 1 mM steps.

**Table 16. Values for of Stern–Volmer constants ($K_{SV}$) in mM$^{-1}$ for different cations as quenchers (25 °C)**

| Surfactant | $Mg^{2+}$ | $Cu^{2+}$ | $Na^+$ |
|---|---|---|---|
| **27b** | 0.1922 | 0.1532 | 0.1098 |
| **24b** | 0.3106 | 0.2762 | 0.2510 |

The surfactant concentration is fixed at 0.005 mM.

Concerning the effect of amphiphile concentration, $K_{SV}$ for $Cu^{2+}$ increases from 0.1532 to 1.0141 mM when *27b* concentration is decreased from 0.005 mM (micellar state) to 0.0005 mM (monomer state); hence, the quenching efficiency and also ion sensitivity is improved at low amphiphile concentration. This tendency has been reported before for associating polymers and was attributed not only to stoichiometry but also to aggregation-related effects (Tan et al., 2002). On the other hand, the alkyl chain length has practically no effect on $K_{SV}$ for $Cu^{2+}$ as quencher. Nevertheless, there are differences in the fluorescence intensity as a function of *27a-c* concentration in neat solutions (no cation added): the shorter the alkyl chain, the stronger the emission intensity.

This effect was found for certain alkyl substituted fluorophores (Pu et al., 2009), and was attributed to changes in chain conformation that affect fluorescent properties. The fluorescence intensity in the absence of metal cations increased linearly with concentration of compounds *27a-c* with no apparent discontinuity or step-like fluorescence enhancement in the vicinity of the *CMC*, contrary to that observed for another fluorescent amphiphile (Iwunze et al., 1997). The position of the fluorescence intensity maximum also remained invariable below and above the *CMC*. This fact might be attributed to the location of the fluorescent moiety near the hydrophilic group, which remains highly solvated below and above the *CMC*, namely, the slight change in microenvironment, if any, cannot be detected by fluorimetry.

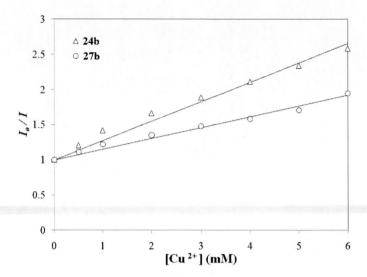

Figure 13. Stern-Volmer plot for surfactants *24b* and *27b* (both with the same alkyl chain length) with $Cu^{2+}$ as quencher (25 °C). *Io* and *I* are the fluorescence intensities in the absence and in the presence of quencher, respectively. The surfactant concentration is fixed at 0.005 mM. The position of fluorescence maxima remains constant at 312 nm.

## CONCLUSION

This study aimed to achieve the synthesis and physico-chemical properties of new heterocyclic compounds type benzimidazolone derivatives of sugar. A new rearrangement of 1,5-benzodiazepin-2,4-dione to a benzimidazol-2-one derivative during *N,N'*-Diglucosylation was developed. Grafting sugar unit on such compound increases strongly its water solubility. The bis-glycobenzimidazolone obtained form aggregates at very low concentrations and exhibit a high surface activity. Their surface properties are similar to some ethoxylated nonionic surfactants. It was found that the critical micellar concentration (CMC) derived from the break of surface tension *vs* concentration curve first decreases with alkyl chain length and then increases, which can be attributed to the formation of submicellar aggregates, as evidenced from fluorescence spectroscopy data. They are also able to form lyotropic liquid crystals within a certain range of alkyl chain lengths, whose characteristic nanoscopic lengths increase with water swelling and alkyl chain length. Moreover, they show UV–Vis absorption and fluorescence emission properties; the latter can be used for ion sensing as the fluorescence is quenched by cations that form complexes with the benzimidazolone moiety. Hence, the reported new amphiphiles are promising as self-assembling chemosensors. The quenching efficiency is higher in the monomer state as compared to the micellar state. It was also found that the emission intensity increased with decreasing alkyl chain length.

## REFERENCES

Ahsan F, Arnold JJ, Meezan E, Pillion DJ (2003) *Int J Pharm* 251:195-203.
Anderson NJ, Watson WP, Slough S (2006) *Eur J Pharm* 546:48-53. armaco 56:841-849.

Auvray X, Petipas C, Anthore R, Rico-Lattes I, Lattes A (1995) *Langmuir* 1:433-439.

Aveyard R, Binks BP, Chen J, Esquena J, Fletcher PDI, Buscall R, Davies S (1998) *Langmuir* 14:4699-4709.

Bais D, Trevisan A, Lapasin R, Partal P, Gallegos C (2005) *J Colloid Interf Sci* 290:546-556.

Baragatti B, Biagi G, Calderone V, Giorgi I, Livi O, Martinotti E, Scartoni V (2000) *Eur J Med Chem* 35:949-955.

Benali B, Lazar Z, Elblidi K, Lakhrissi B, Massoui M, Elassyry A, Cazeau-Dubroca C (2006) *J Mol Liq* 128:42-45.

Benksim A, Beaupère D, Wadouachi A (1994) *Org Lett* 6:3913-3915.

Bikanga R, Godé P, Ronco G, Gave G, Seiller M, Villa P (1995) S.T.P. *Pharma Sci* 5:316-323.

Boyd BJ, Drummond CJ, Krodkiewska I, Grieser F (2000) *Langmuir* 16:7359-7367.

Castro MJL, Kovensky J, Fernandez-Cirelli A (2002) *Langmuir* 18:2477-2482.

Christensen JE; Goodman L (1968) *Carbohydr Res* 7:507-509.

Cignitti M, Ramusino MC, Rufini L (1995) *J Mol Str* 350: 43–47.

Devor DC, Singh AK, Frizzell RA, Bridges R (1996) *J Am J Physiol* 271:775-784.

El Majzoub A, Cadiou C, Déchamps-Olivier I, Chuburu F, Aplincourt M, Tinant B (2009) *Inorg Chim Acta* 362:1169-1178.

El Meslouti A, Beaupère D, Demailly G, Uzan R (1994) *Tetrahedron Lett* 35:3913-3916.

Essassi EM, Lamkaddem A, Zniber R (1991) *Bull. Soc. Chim. Belg.,* 100:277-286.

Fabbrizzi L, Licchelli M, Pallavicini P, Perotti A, Taglietti A, Sacchi D (1996) *Chem Eur J* 2:75-82.

Ferrer M, Comelles F, Plou FJ, Cruces MA, Fuentes G, Parra JL, Ballesteros A (2002) *Langmuir* 18:667-673.

Folmer BM, Svensson M, Holmberg K, Brown W (1999) *J Colloid Interface Sci* 213:112-120.

Garofalakis G, Murray BS, Sarney DB (2000*) J Colloid Interface Sci* 229:391-398.

Goueth PY, Ronco G, Villa P (1994*) J Carbohydr Chem* 13:679-696.

Htay MM, Meth-Cohn O (1976) *Tet Lett* 1:79-82.

Htay MM, Meth-Cohn O (1976) *Tet Lett* 6:469-472.

Israelachvili JN (1992) *Intermolecular and Surface Forces.* Academic Press, London.

Iwunze MO, Lambert M, Silversmith EF (1997) *Monatsh Chem* 128: 585–592.

Jiao J (2008) *Adv Drug Deliver Rev* 60:1663-1673.

Köll P, Saak W, Pohl S, Steiner B, Miroslav Koos M (1994) *Carbohyd Res* 265:237-248.

Lakhrissi B, Benksim A, Massoui M, Essassi EM, Lequart V, Joly N, Beaupère D, Wadouachi A, Martin P (2008) *Carbohydrate Research* 343:421-433.

Lakhrissi B, El Azzaoui B, Nabil A, Essassi EM, Massoui M, Goethals G, Villa P, Solans C, Azemar N, Comelles F, Garcia-Celma MJ, Sadurni N, Godé P (2000) *Jorn Com Esp Deterg* 30:233-243.

Lakhrissi B, Essassi EM, Massoui M, Goethals G, Lequart V, Monflier E, Cecchelli R, Martin P (2004) *J Carbohydr Chem* 23:389-401.

Lakhrissi B, Lakhrissi L, Massoui M, Essassi EM, Comelles F, Esquena J, Solans C, Rodriguez-Abreu C (2010), *J Surfact Deterg,* 13 (3):329-338.

Lakhrissi B, Massoui M, Essassi EM, Lequart V, Joly N, Goethals G, Martin P (2004) *J. Heterocyclic Chem.,* 41:1011-1014.

Lakhrissi B, Massoui M, Ramli Y, Essassi EM, Weng Ng S (2012*) Acta* CrystE68, o351.

Lakhrissi L, Hassan N, Lakhrissi B, Massoui M., Essassi EM, Ruso JM, Solans C, Rodriguez-Abreu C (2011) *J Surfact Deterg* 14:487-495.

Lakowicz JR, Weber G (1973) *Biochemistry* 12:4161-4170.

Lazar Z, Benali B, Elblidi K, Zenkouar M, Lakhrissi B, Massoui M, Kabouchi B, Cazeau-Dubroca C (2003) *J Mol Liq* 106 (1):89-95.

Li Q, Li T, Woods KW, Gu WZ, Cohen J, Stoll V, Galicia T, Hutchins C, Frost D, Rosenberg SH, Sham HL (2005) *Bioorg Med Chem Lett* 15:2918-2922.

Lu JR, Thomas RK, Penfold J (2000) *Adv Colloid Interf Sci* 143-304.

Mancin F, Rampazzo E, Tecilla P, Tonellato U (2006) *Chem Eur J* 12:1844-1854.

Menger FM, Shi L, Rizvi SAA (2009) *J Am Chem Soc* 131:10380-10381.

Meth-Cohn O, Smith DI (1982) *J Chem Soc Perkin I* 261-270.

Nakamura N, Yamaguchi Y, Hakansson B, Olsson U, Tagawa T, Kunieda H (1999) *J Disper Sci Technol* 20:535-557.

Pina F, Bernardo MA, Garcia-Espana E (2000) *Eur J Inorg Chem* 2143-2157.

Pu S, Li M, Fan C, Liu G, Shen L (2009) *J Mol Struct* 919:100-111.

Rauter AP, Lucas S, Almeida T, Sacoto D, Ribeiro V, Justino J, Neves A, Silva FV, Oliveira MC, Ferreira MJ, Santos M-S, Barbosa E (2005) *Carbohydr Res* 340:191-201.

Regev O, Zana R (1999) *J Colloid Interface Sci* 210:8-17.

Ren X, Mao X, Cao L, Xue K, Si L, Qiu J, Schimmer AD, Li G (2009) *Eur J Pharm Sci* 36: 401-411.

Rodrıguez-Abreu C, Aramaki K, Tanaka Y, Lopez-Quintela MA, Ishitobi M, Kunieda H (2005) *J Colloid Interf Sci* 291:560-569.

Rosen MJ (1989) *Surfactant and interfacial phenomena,* 2nd edn. Wiley, New York.

Rozycka-Roszak B, Jurczak B, Wilk KA (2007) *Thermochim Acta* 453:27-30.

Sarri V, Kenfack S, Guillod O, Pulgarin C (2003) *J Photochem Photobiol* 159:89-99.

Savelli MP, Bault P, Douillet O, Godé P, Goethals G, Martin P, Ronco G, Villa P (1998) *Jorn Com Esp Deterg* 28:293-303.

Shinoda K, Yamaguchi T, Hori R (1961) *Bull Chem Soc Jpn* 34:237-241.

Singh A, Van Hamme JD, Ward OP (2007) *Biotechnol Adv* 25:99-121.

Stern O, Volrner M (1919) The fading time of fluorescence. *Z Phys* 20:183-188.

Stradner A, Mayer B, Sottmann T, Hermetter A, Glatter O (1999) *J Phys Chem B* 103:6680-6689.

Tan C, Pinto MR, Schanze KS (2002) *Chem Commun* 446-447.

Torres RA, Sarria V, Torres W, Peringer P, Pulgarin C (2003) *Water Res.* 37:3118-3124.

Townsend, LB; Devivar, RV; Turk, SR; Nassiri, RM; Drach, JC (1995) *J Med Chem* 38:4098-4105.

Tracy DJ, Ruoxin L, Yang JY (1999) US Patent 5863886.

Uchegbu IF, Vyas SP (1998) *Int J Pharm* 172:33-70.

Van Hamme JD, Singh A, Ward OP (2006) *Biotechnol Adv* 24:604-620

Wilk KA, Syper L, Burczyk B, Sokolowski A, Domagalska B (2000) *J Surf Deterg* 3:185-192.

Wu D-Q, Lu B, Chang C, Chen C-S, Wang T, Zhang Y-Y, Cheng S-X, Jiang X-J, Zhang X-Z, Zhuo R-X (2009) *Biomaterials* 30:1363-1371.

Yu KH, Wang XA, Civiello RL, Trehan AK, Pearce BC, Yin Z, Combrick K, Gulgeze HB, Zhang Y, Kadow K, Cianci C, Clarke J, Genovesi E, Medina I, Lamb L, Wyde P, Krystal M, Meanwell N (2006) *Bioorg. Med. Chem. Lett.* 16:1115-1122.

Zana R, Levy H (1997) *Colloids Surf* A127:229-232.

Zhang P, Terefenko EA, Wrobel J, Zhang Z, Zhu Y, Cohen J, Marschke KB, Mais D (2001) *Bioorg Med Chem Lett* 11:2747-2750.

Zhou LL, Sun H, Zhang XH, Wu SK (2005) *Spectrochim Acta* A 61:61-65.

Zhuo R-X (2009) *Biomaterials* 30:1363-1371.

In: Recent Advances in Ginseng and Glycosides Research
Editor: Claude J. Hopkins

ISBN: 978-1-62417-765-1
© 2013 Nova Science Publishers, Inc.

*Chapter 4*

# ISOFLAVONE *C*-GLYCOSIDES ISOLATED FROM THE ROOT OF KUDZU (*PUERARIA LOBATA*) AND THEIR ESTROGENIC AND ANTIMUTAGENIC ACTIVITIES

*Shin-ichi Kayano*[*1], Yoko Matsumura[1], Yoko Kitagawa[2],
Mayumi Kobayashi[1], Asuka Nagayama[1], Nami Kawabata[1],
Mayuka Tuchida[1], Minami Usuki[1], Hiroe Kikuzaki[3]
and Yoshimi Kitada[1]*

[1]Kio University, Japan
[2]Osaka Prefectural Institute of Public Health, Japan
[3]Nara Women's University, Japan

## ABSTRACT

The kudzu root (*Pueraria lobata*) is used as an ingredient in kudzu-starch which is an important material for cooking as well as processed foods in Japan. On the other hand, this root is a kind of oriental crude drug and has been used for various medicinal purposes. In this chapter, chemical structures, and estrogenic and antimutagenic activities of isoflavone *C*-glycosides isolated from the root of kudzu are investigated. Kudzu root, which was obtained from the Gose city area, Nara, Japan, was cut, crushed, and extracted with water, and the extract was purified with various chromatographic techniques to afford four compounds. The chemical structures of these isolated compounds were elucidated on the basis of the NMR and MS analyses to be 6″-*O*-α-D-glucopyranosylpuerarin, puerarin, 3′-methoxypuerarin, and 6″-*O*-α-D-apiofranosyl-puerarin, respectively. 6″-*O*-α-D-Glucopyranosylpuerarin was obtained from the natural origin for the first time, and 6″-*O*-α-D-apiofranosylpuerarin was a novel compound. Estrogenic activity of isolated compounds was evaluated using yeast two-hybrid assay. Four isoflavone *C*-glycosides, which are 8-*C*-β-D-glucosyl derivatives of daidzein,

---

* Corresponding author. E-mail address: s.kayano@kio.ac.jp (Shin-ichi Kayano)

showed no activities, on the other hand, daidzin, which is 7-$O$-β-D-glucoside of daidzein, exhibited the activity. These differences of the activity might be depended on the binding position (C-7 or C-8) or combination style ($O$- or $C$-) of glucose moiety to daidzein. Antimutagenic activity of daidzein, daidzin, puerarin, and 3'-methoxypuerarin was further assayed on the basis of Ames method using *Salmonella typhimurium* TA98 and TA100. Daidzein showed the activity, on the other hand, three glucosides of daidzein showed no activity to suggest that regardless of the position or the style, binding of glucose moiety inhibit the antimutagenic potency of daidzein.

# INTRODUCTION

The kudzu root (*Pueraria lobata*) is used as an ingredient in kudzu-starch which is an important material for cooking as well as processed foods in Japan. On the other hand, this root is a kind of oriental crude drug, and has been used as fever reducer, headache relief, as well as other medicinal purposes (McGregor, M. R., 2007; Saitoh, H., 1983). It is reported that the administration of kudzu root extract decreases LDL cholesterol in coronary patients with the combination of *Salvia miltiorrhiza* (Tam, W. Y., Chook, P., Qiao, M., Chan, L. T., Chan, T. Y. K., Poon, Y. K., Fung, K. P., Leung, P. C., and Woo, K. S., 2009). The water extract of the kudzu root alleviated adverse effects of ethanol ingestion in rats by enhancing the lipid metabolism as well as the hepatic antioxidant defense system (Lee, J. S., 2004), in addition to inhibiting cytopathy induced by Enterovirus 71 (Su, F., Chang, J., Wang, K., Tsai, J., and Chiang, L., 2008). The EtOH root extract reduces oxidative stress in streptozotocin induced diabetic rat (Bebrevska, L., Foubert, K., Hermans, N., Chatterjee, S., March, E. V., Meyer, G. D., Vlietinck, A., Pieters, L., and Apers, S., 2010), and also showed antimutagenic activity in Ames test (Cherdshewasart, W., Sutjit, W., Pulcharoen, K., and Chulasiri, M., 2009; Miyazawa, M., Sakano, K., Nakamura, S., and Kosaka, H., 2001).

It is also reported that *Pueraria lobata* crude extract has shown potent antioxidant activity and effects on rat livers CYP-catalysed drug metabolism (Guerra, M. C., Speroni, E., Broccoli, M., Cangini, M., Pasini, P., Minghetti, A., Crespi-Perellino, N., Mirasoli, M., Cantelli-Forti, G., and Paolini, M., 2000).

Previous studies show that *Pueraria lobata* contains large quantities of polyphenols such as isoflavones which are major phytochemicals in this plant. Puerarin, which is an isoflavone *C*-glycoside, was detected as main polyphenol in *Pueraria radix* by TLC and HPLC techniques (Zhao, S., and Zhang, Y., 1985; Rong, H.. Keukeleire, D. D.. Cooman, L. D.. Baeyens, W. R. G.. and Weken, G. V. D., 1998).

Rong et al. also detected fifteen isoflavones as principal polyphenols in the root of *Pueraria lobata* by HPCL coupled with mass spectroscopy (MS) using atomospheric pressure chemical ionization (APCI) in combination with collision-activated decomposition (CAD) (Rong, H., Stevens, J. F., Deinzer, M. L., Cooman, L. D., and Keukeleire, D. D., 1998). Recently, two new hexosyl isoflavone *C*-glycosides (Sun, Y., Wang, S., Feng, J., Xue, X., and Liang, X., 2008), as well as two new *C*-glucofranosides, neopuerarin A and neopuerarin B (Zhang, H., Yang, X., and Wang, K., 2010) were isolated from the root of *Pueraria lobata*.

It was also discovered that the constituents of *Pueraria lobata* show various pharmacological reactions. Oral administration of daidzin, daidzein, and puerarin isolated from *Pueraria lobata* was effective in suppressing alcohol preference in a pharmacogenetic rat model of alcoholism (Lin, R. C., Guthrie, S., Xie, C.-Y., Mai, K., Lee, D. Y., Lumeng, L., and Li, T.-K., 1996). Puerarin and daidzein exhibited the same level of antioxidant activity as α-tocopherol (Cherdshewasart, W., and Sutjit, W., 2008), and tectoridin, an isoflavone glycoside isolated from the flower of *Pueraria lobata*, protected against ethanol-induced liver steatosis of mice (Xiong, Y., Yang, Y., Yang, J., Chai, H., Li, Y., Yang, J., Jia, Z., and Wang, Z., 2010). Furthermore, saponins from *Pueraria radix* showed to inhibit the formation of advanced glycation end products (AGEs) (Kim, J. S., Lee, Y. M., Lee, G. Y., Jang, D. S., Bae, K. H., and Kim, J. S., 2006; Jang, D. S., Kim J. M., Lee, Y. M., Kim, Y. S., Kim. J., and Kim, J. S., 2006), and prevent *in vitro* immunological liver injury in rat primary hepatocyte cultures (Arano, T., Udayama, M., Kinjo, J., and Nohara, J., 1998; Arano, T., Udayama, M., Kinjo, J., Nohara, T., Funakoshi, F., and Kojima, S., 1997). It is expected that *Pueraria lobata* contains further unknown isoflavones on the basis of an HPLC analysis. In this chapter, chemical structures of isoflavones *C*-glycosides isolated from the root of *Pueraria lobata* are elucidated, and their estrogenic activity evaluated on the basis of yeast two-hybrid assay, as well as antimutagenic activity assayed using Ames method, are also discussed.

## MATERIALS AND METHODS

### Plant Material

Kudzu root (*Pueraria lobata*, 2.58 kg) was obtained from the Gose city area, Nara, Japan, in February 2006. The root was identified as *Pueraria lobata* by Dr. Hyoe Tsugawa, professor emeritus of Kobe University (Japan).

### Chemicals and Microbes

All solvents and chemicals were of the highest analytical grade commercially available. *o*-Nitrophenyl-β-galactoside (ONPG) was obtained from Sigma-Aldrich Japan Co. (Tokyo, Japan), 17 β-estradiol (E2), 1-methyl-3'-nitro-1-nitorsoguanidine (MNNG), and 3-amino- 1-methyl-5*H*-pyrido[4, 3-*b*]indole acetate (Trp-P-2) were purchased from Wako Pure Chemical Industries, Ltd. (Osaka, Japan), and zymolyase 20T was obtained from Seikagaku Co. (Tokyo, Japan). S9 mix was purchased from Oriental Yeast Co., Ltd. (Tokyo, Japan). Z buffer (pH 7) was prepared as follows; 16.1 g of $Na_2HPO_4 \cdot 7H_2O$, 5.5 g of $NaH_2PO_4 \cdot H_2O$, 0.75 g of KCl, and 0.236 g of $MgSO_4 \cdot 7H_2O$ were dissolved in water and then made up to 1L. Microbes for antimutagenic assay, *Salmonella typhimurium* TA 98 (NRBC14193), and TA100 (NRBC14194) were supplied from National Institute of Technology and Evaluation (Tokyo, Japan).

### General Procedures

$^{1}$H-, $^{13}$C-, and 2D NMR spectra (H–H COSY, $^{1}$H-$^{1}$H correlation spectroscopy; HMQC, $^{1}$H-detected multiple quantum coherence spectrum; HMBC, $^{1}$H-detected multiple-bond heteronuclear multiple quantum coherrence spectrum; NOESY, nuclear overhauser and exchange spectroscopy) were obtained on a Varian Unity Plus 500 spectrometer (Varian Inc., Palo Alto, CA) at 500 MHz ($^1$H) and 125 MHz ($^{13}$C) in CD$_3$OD and referenced to the residual solvent resonance (CD$_3$OD at 3.30 ppm for $^1$H and 49.0 ppm for $^{13}$C NMR). An Electrospray Ionization (ESI) / Time of Flight (TOF) MS was performed on Nano Frontier LD mass spectrometer (Hitachi High-Technologies Co., Tokyo, Japan).

Optical rotations were measured using Atago AP-300 automatic polarimeter (Atago Co., Tokyo, Japan), and UV spectra were run on a Shimadzu UV mini-1240 spectrophotometer (Shimadzu Co., Kyoto, Japan) Preparative HPLC was carried out on a Shimadzu LC-6A System equipped with LC-6AD pumps, SPD-20A UV Detector, and CTO-20A column oven (Shimadzu Co., Kyoto, Japan).

The PerkinElmer 2030 Multilabel Reader ARVO$^{TM}$ X4 (PerkinElmer Japan Co., Kanagawa, Japan), which is a type of micro plate reader, was used for the evaluation of estrogenic activity by yeast two-hybrid assay. Diaion HP-20 (Mitsubishi Chemical Co., Tokyo, Japan), Sephadex LH-20 (Pharmacia Biotech AB, Uppsala, Sweden), and silica gel 60 (70 – 230 mesh, Merck, Darmstadt, Germany) were used for column chromatography. Thin-layer chromatography (TLC) was performed on silica gel F-254 plates (Merck), and spots were detected by ultraviolet (UV) illumination.


## Preparative HPLC

The condition of preparative HPLC using Develosil ODS-HG-5 column ($\phi$20 × 250 mm; Nomura Chemical Co., Aichi, Japan) were as follows; guard column: Develosil ODS-HG-5 ($\phi$20 × 50 mm; Nomura Chemical Co.), mobile phase A: acetonitrile/water (10:90, v/v) with 1% formic acid, mobile phase B: acetonitrile/water (30:70, v/v) with 1% formic acid, gradient: 0min B0%, 35min 30%, 40min 30%, 50min 80%, 60min 80%, 65min 0%, 70min 0%, flow rate: 10mL/min, column temp.: 40°C, injection volume: 0.5mL, detection: 256nm. Another condition using Develosil RPAQUOUS-AR-5 column ($\phi$20 × 250 mm; Nomura Chemical Co.) were as follows; gradient: 0min B0%, 35min 30%, 40min 30%, 50min 100%, 60min 100%, 65min 0%, 70min 0%, and other conditions followed described above.


## Identification of Isolated Compounds

6″-$O$-α-D-glucopyranosylpuerarin (daidzein 8-$C$-[α-D-glucopyranosyl-(1→6)]-β-D-glucopyranoside) (1). Pale yellow powder; $[\alpha]^{25}_D$ +165.9 ($c$0.45, MeOH); UV (MeOH) $\lambda_{max}$ (log ε), 248.0 (4.42); $^1$H and $^{13}$C NMR: see Table 1; ESI/TOF MS ($m/z$): [M+H]$^+$ calcd for C$_{27}$H$_{31}$O$_{14}$, 579.1713: found, 579.1697.

Puerarin (2). White amorphous powder, ESI/TOF MS ($m/z$): [M + H]$^+$ calcd for C$_{21}$H$_{21}$O$_9$, 417.1179: found, 417.1176.

3′-methoxypuerarin (daidzein 8-$C$-β-D-glucopiranosyl-3′-methoxide) (3). White amorphous powder, ESI/TOF MS ($m/z$): [M+H]$^+$ calcd for C$_{22}$H$_{23}$O$_{10}$, 447.1291: found, 447.1293.

## Table 1. $^1$H$^a$- and $^{13}$C$^b$-NMR data of **1** and **4**

| | 1 | | 4 | |
|---|---|---|---|---|
| | $^{13}$C | $^1$H | $^{13}$C | $^1$H |
| 2 | 154.5 | 8.20 (*s*) | 154.5 | 8.18 (*s*) |
| 3 | 125.6 | | 125.6 | |
| 4 | 178.3 | | 178.3 | |
| 5 | 128.1 | 8.05 (*d*, 9.0) | 128.1 | 8.05 (*d*, 9.0) |
| 6 | 116.2 | 6.98 (*d*, 8.8) | 116.5 | 6.98 (*d*, 8.8) |
| 7 | 163.0 | | 163.0 | |
| 8 | 113.1 | | 113.0 | |
| 9 | 158.7 | | 158.0 | |
| 10 | 118.5 | | 118.5 | |
| 1′ | 124.2 | | 124.2 | |
| 2′ | 131.4 | 7.37 (*ddd*, 2.6, 2.6, 9.5) | 131.4 | 7.37 (*ddd*, 2.6, 2.6, 9.5) |
| 3′ | 116.2 | 6.86 (*ddd*, 2.6, 2.6, 9.4) | 116.2 | 6.86 (*ddd*, 2.6, 2.6, 9.4) |
| 4′ | 158.7 | | 158.7 | |
| 5′ | 116.2 | 6.86 (*ddd*, 2.6, 2.6, 9.4) | 116.2 | 6.86 (*ddd*, 2.6, 2.6, 9.4) |
| 6′ | 131.4 | 7.37 (*ddd*, 2.6, 2.6, 9.5) | 131.4 | 7.37 (*ddd*, 2.6, 2.6, 9.5) |
| 1″ | 75.6 | 5.06 (*d*, 10.0) | 75.8 | 5.09 (*d*, 9.8) |
| 2″ | 72.8 | 4.15 (*br*) | 73.1 | 3.57 (*br*) |
| 3″ | 80.0 | 3.51 (*dd*, 8.9,8.9) | 79.8 | 3.51 (*dd*, 8.8, 8.8) |
| 4″ | 71.5 | 3.65 (*dd*, 7.1, 9.0) | 71.5 | 3.57 (*br*) |
| 5″ | 81.4 | 3.61 (*m*) | 81.4 | 3.57 (*br*) |
| 6″α | 67.6 | 3.84 (*d*, 11.2) | 68.9 | 3.73 (*br*) |
| β | | 3.98 (*dd*, 3.7, 11.5) | | 4.00 (*d*, 11.0) |
| 1‴ | 100.1 | 5.93 (*d*, 2.4) | 111.0 | 4.96 (*d*, 2.4) |
| 2‴ | 73.8 | 3.36 (*dd*, 3.7, 9.6) | 78.0 | 3.89 (*d*, 2.4) |
| 3‴ | 75.2 | 3.63 (*m*) | 80.5 | |
| 4‴α | 71.5 | 3.27 (*dd*, 9.5, 9.5) | 75.0 | 3.75 (*d*, 9.5) |
| β | | | | 3.96 (d, 9.5) |
| 5‴α | 73.6 | 3.62 (*m*) | 65.5 | 3.55 (*s*) |
| β | | | | 3.55 (*s*) |
| 6‴α | 62.4 | 3.58 (*m*) | | |
| β | | 3.70 (*m*) | | |

$^a$ $^1$H-NMR data were obtained at 500 MHz with methanol *d*-4 (25 °C). Chemical shifts are shown in δ values relative to solvent peak. Multiplicity and coupling constant(s) in Hz are in parentheses.

$^b$ $^1$C-NMR data were obtained at 125 MHz with methanol *d*-4 (25 °C). Chemical shifts are shown in δ values relative to solvent peak.

6″-*O*-α-D-apiofranosylpuerarin (daidzein 8-*C*-[α-D-apiofranosyl-(1→6)]-β-D-gluco-pyranoside) (4). White amorphous powder; $[\alpha]^{25}_D$ −82.1 (*c*0.19, MeOH); UV (MeOH) $\lambda_{max}$ (log ε), 248.0 (4.39), 303.0 (3.96); $^1H$ and $^{13}C$ NMR: see Table 1; ESI/TOF MS (*m/z*): [M+H]$^+$ calcd for $C_{26}H_{29}O_{16}$, 549.1608: found, 549.1607.

# ISOLATION AND STRUCTURAL ELUCIDATION OF ISOFLAVONE *C*-GLYCOSIDES

The root of kudzu (2.58kg) was cut and crushed with a handsaw and scissors, and then 4L of water was added and homogenized with a mixer. After filtration of the homogenate, the extract was separated into water-soluble and insoluble fractions by decantation, and the supernatant was separated by DIAION HP-20 column chromatography using $H_2O$ as an eluting solution followed by eluting with 2%, 5%, 10%, 20%, 50%, and 100% MeOH and aceton (Ac). Each solution was evaporated *in vacuo* to give $H_2O$ eluate (81.7 g), 2% MeOH eluate (1.25 g), 5% MeOH eluate (1.97 g), 10% MeOH eluate (1.33 g), 20% MeOH eluate (4.22 g), 50% MeOH eluate (8.22 g), 100% MeOH eluate (2.85 g), and Ac eluate (0.08 g), respectively. An aliquot (5 g) of $H_2O$ eluate was dissolved in 10mL of acetnitrile/water (10:90, v/v), centrifuged at 3000rpm for 10 min, and the supernatant was further separated by preparative HPLC using Develosil ODS-HG-5 column into peak 1, peak 2, and peak 3 (Figure 1). Peak 1 (72 mg) was further subjected to a Sephadex LH-20 column chromatography eluted with 70% aqueous Ac to give compound 1 (43 mg), and peak 2 (487 mg) was dissolved in MeOH and recrystallized to afford compound 2 (290 mg). Peak 3 showed 2 spots on silica gel TLC analysis with UV detection, hence further purification was performed.

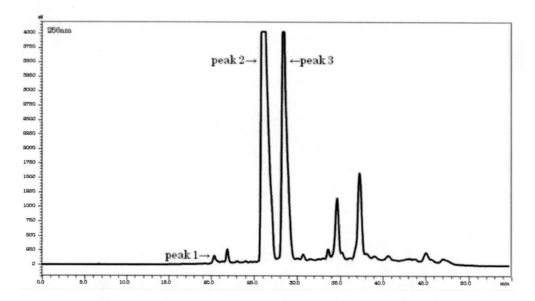

Figure 1. HPLC chromatogram of $H_2O$ eluate.

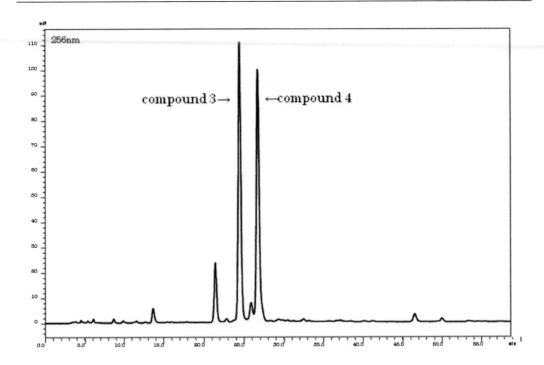

Figure 2. HPLC chromatogram of Peak 3.

Peak 3 (49 mg) was dissolved in acetnitrile/water (10:90, v/v) and applied to preparative HPLC using Develosil RPAQUOUS-AR-5 column (C30) to give compound 3 (5 mg) and compound 4 (14 mg) (Figure 2). The chemical structures of 1 – 4 were elucidated on the basis of the NMR and MS analyses.

Compound 1 was obtained as white amorphous powder, and exhibited an $[M+H]^+$ peak at $m/z$ 579.1697 in good agreement with the molecular formula $C_{27}H_{30}O_{14}$ by measurement of the positive mode ESI/TOF MS.

The $^1H$ NMR spectrum of 1 showed a typical signal at $\delta_H$ 5.83 (1H, *s*) ascribable to H-2 of the isoflavone, and signals due to aromatic $A_2X_2$ system and AX coupling pattern were observed. Moreover, peaks of two pentose moieties were also detected, suggesting that this compound is 4′, 7-disubustituted isoflavone di-glycoside, and the spectrum of $^{13}C$ NMR also supported this estimated structure. In addition, upfield shift signal of anomeric carbon at C-1″ ($\delta_C$ 75.6) revealed that 1 is a *C*-glycoside. Concerning a pentose moiety, the oxymethine signals due to H-1″ (*d*, 10.0), H-3″ (*dd*, 8.9, 8.9) and H-4″ (*dd*, 7.1, 9.0) showed di-axial coupling constants in the $^1H$ NMR analysis (Table 1). Therefore, oxymethines at H-2″ and H-5″ positions are also axial in orientation, indicating that this pentose is β-D-glucopiranose. Another pentose moiety was also predicted to be α- D-glucopiranose on the basis of its coupling constants (Table 1).

In the HMBC analysis, long-range correlation between anomeric proton of β-glucose (H-1″) and C-7 and C-8 of isoflavone skeleton, and H-6″ of β-glucose and oxymethine carbon of α-glucose (C-1‴) were observed (Figure 3). According to the above evidence, 1 was concluded to be 6″-*O*-α-D-glucopyranosylpuerarin (daidzein 8-*C*-[α-D-glucopyranosyl-(1→6)]-β-D-gluco- pyranoside) (Figure 4).

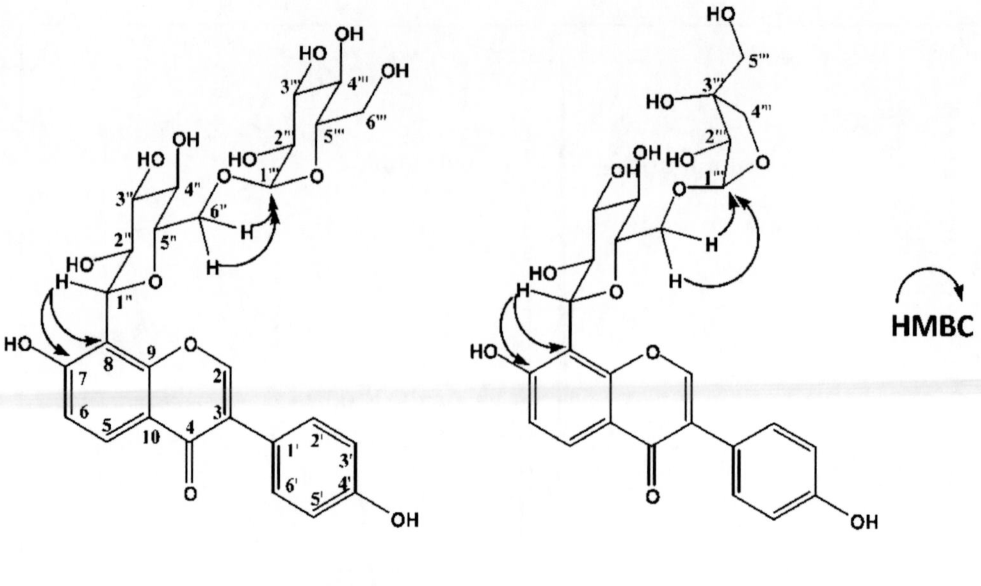

Figure 3. Significant long range correlations in the HMBC spectrum of compound 1 and 4.

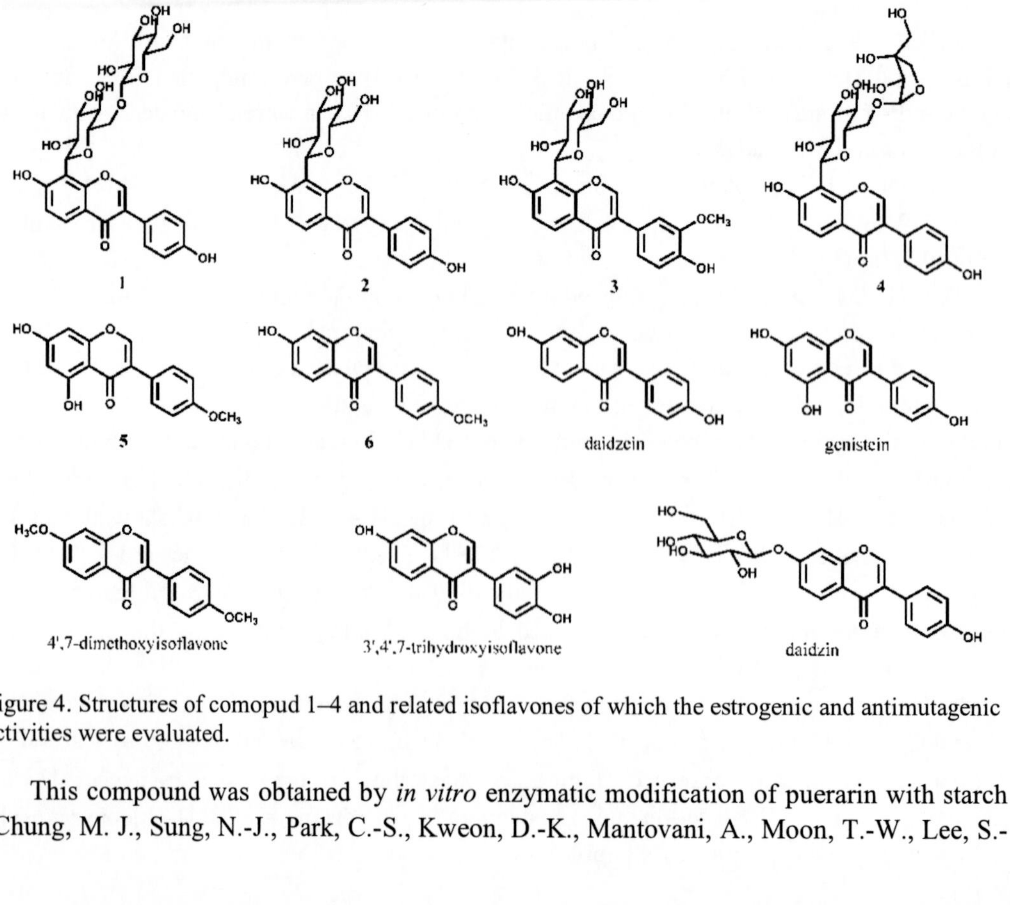

Figure 4. Structures of comopud 1–4 and related isoflavones of which the estrogenic and antimutagenic activities were evaluated.

This compound was obtained by *in vitro* enzymatic modification of puerarin with starch (Chung, M. J., Sung, N.-J., Park, C.-S., Kweon, D.-K., Mantovani, A., Moon, T.-W., Lee, S.-

J., and Park, K.-H., 2008; Li, D., Park, S.-H., Shim J.-H., Lee, H.-S., Tang, S.-Y., Park, C.-S., and Park, K.-H., 2004), however, it was the first time to be obtained from natural origin.

Compound 2 was isolated as white amorphous powder, and the ESI/TOF MS of 2 gave an $[M+H]^+$ peak at $m/z$ 417.1176 consistent with a molecular formula of $C_{21}H_{20}O_9$. The $^1H$ and $^{13}C$ NMR data of 2 showed a good agreement with those of authentic sample, thus 2 was identified as puerarin (Figure 4), which is a major isoflavone of *Pueraria radix*.

The $^1H$ and $^{13}C$ NMR of 3, which was afforded as white amorphous powder, showed very similar spectrum data to those of 2 except the additional signal of a methoxyl group. In the HMBC experiment, long-range correlation was observed between the methyl protons and aromatic carbon at the 3'-position, and the molecular formula of $C_{22}H_{22}O_{10}$ was confirmed on the basis of the $[M+H]^+$ ion at $m/z$ 447.1293 in the ESI/TOF MS spectrum. In these results, 3 was characterized as 3'-methoxypuerarin (daidzein 8-*C*-β-D-glucopiranosyl-3'-methoxide) (Figure 4).

Compound 4 was obtained as pale yellow powder, and the ESI/TOF MS spectrum of 4 showed an $[M+H]^+$ ion at $m/z$ 549.1607 which is attributable to molecular formula of $C_{26}H_{28}O_{16}$. The $^1H$ and $^{13}C$ NMR spectra of 4 indicated the presence of daidzein, hexsose, and pentose moieties, and upfield shift signal of anomeric carbon at C-1″ ($δ_C$ 75.6) of hexsose moiety suggested that compound 4 is also an isoflavone *C*-glycoside. In the HMBC analysis, long-range correlations were observed between anomeric proton of hexsose moiety (H-1″) and C-7 and C-8 of isoflavone skeleton, and H-6″ of hexsose moiety and oxymethine carbon of pentose moiety (C-1‴) (Figure 3), therefore, it is predicted that this compound is daidzein 8-[*C*-pentosyl (1→6)] hexsoside. Concerning the structure of pentose moiety, oxymethine signal at 2-position of $^1H$ NMR spectrum showed doublet peak ($δ_H$ 3.84, d, J = 2.4Hz) coupling with anomeric proton ($δ_H$ 4.96, d, J = 2.4Hz), suggesting the existence of quaternary carbon at 3-position. Furthermore, anomeric proton and C-3, oxymethine protone (H-2) and C-5, oxymehilene proton (H-4) and C-1, and oxymethilene proton (H-5) and both C-2 and C-4, were correlated in the HMBC analysis (Figure 5), and downfield sift of C-3 ($δ_C$ 80.5) was observed in the $^{13}C$ NMR spectrum.

In addition, NOESY correlations were observed between H-1 and H-2, H-2 and H-5, H-5 and H-4, H-4 and H-1 (Figure 5), indicating that this pentose is α-apiofranose. The signals due to hexsose moiety were overlapped each other in the $^1H$ NMR spectrum, hence, 4 was hydrolyzed with 1% trifluoroacetic acid at 90°C for 1 hr and extracted with ethyl acetate. The signals of $^1H$ and $^{13}C$ NMR spectra of hydrolyzed 4 were in complete agreement with those of purerarin (2), presenting hexsose moiety of 4 to be β-glucose. In these results, this compound was determined to be 6″-*O*-α-D-apiofranosylpuerarin (daidzein 8-*C*-[α-D-apiofranosyl-(1→6)]-β-D-glucopyranoside) (Figure 4). In an earlier paper, daidzein 8-*C*-[apyosyl-(1→6)]-glucoside was isolated from the root of *Pueraria lobata*, however, anomeric configuration of apiose moiety was not determined (Kinjo, J., Furusawa, J., Baba, J., Takeshita, T., Yamasaki, M., and Nohara, T., 1987). It was also reported that the apiosyl group from *Pueraria lobata* (Sun, Y., Wang, S., Feng, J., Xue, X., and Liang, X., 2008) or other natural origin (Fang, H., Tong, W., Shi, L. M., Blair, R., Perkins, R., and Branham, W., 2001; Wanjala, C. C. W., and Majinda, R. R. T., 1999; Higuchi, H., Fukui, K., Kinjo, J., and Nohara, T., 1992; Kinjo, J., Fukui, K., Higuchi, H., and Nohara, T., 1991; Kinjo, J., Higuchi, H., Fukui, K., and Nohara,

T., 1991) has β-configuration in other papers. In this chapter, the anomeric configuration of apiose moiety was concluded to be α-form on the basis of the NOESY analysis.

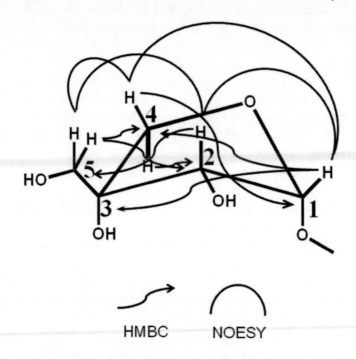

Figure 5. Significant long range correlations in the HMBC spectrum and significant NOEs in the NOESY spectrum of apiofranose moiety of compound 4.

## ESTROGENIC ACTIVITY OF ISOFLAVONE *C*-GLYCOSIDES AND RELATED COMPOUNDS

Estrogenic activity of each isoflavone was evaluated on the basis of the β-galactosidase activity reported by yeast two-hybrid assay, according to the method described previously (Nishihara, T., Nishikawa, J., Kanayama, T., Dakeyama, F., Saito, K., Imagawa, M., Takatori, S., Kitagawa, Y., Hori, S., and Utsumi, H., 2002; Nishikawa, J., Saito, K., Goto, J., Dakeyama, F., Matsuo, M., and Nishihara, T., 1999). The yeast cells (*Saccharomyces cerebisiae* Y190), to which the estrogen receptor (ERβ), coactivator, β-galactocidase reporter gene, and tryptophan and leucine genes were introduced, were preincubated for 36hr at 30°C in SD medium (lacking tryptophan and leucine), then diluted three times with additional SD medium. An aliquot (5 µL) of test chemicals (in DMSO, E2: $10^{-7}$, $10^{-6}$. $10^{-5}$. $10^{-4}$ mol/L; isoflavones: $10^{-4}$, $10^{-3}$, $10^{-2}$, $10^{-1}$ mol/L) was mixed with 495 µL of prepared culture in microcentrifuge tube, incubated for 4 hr at 30°C with rotation, centrifuged at 15,000rpm, and the collected cells were washed with Z buffer. After suspension of the washed cells in 250 µL of Z buffer, 150 µL of cell solution was transferred to each well of a 96-well microplate, and OD 595nm was measured. The yeast cells in residual suspensions (100µL) were digested enzymatically with 100mL of Zymolyase 20T solution (2mg/mL in Z buffer) for 15min at 37°C. After incubation, 40 µL of ONPG (4mg/mL in Z buffer) was added to digested cell solution and reacted for about 30min at 30°C until development of a yellow *o*-nitrophenol. The β-galactosidase reaction was stopped by addition of 100 μL of 1M $Na_2CO_3$, and 150 μL of react solutions were added to each well of a 96-well microplate. Abosorbance at 415nm and 570nm was measured, and β-galactosidase activity was calculated as follows;

$$U = 1000 \times ([OD_{415}] - [1.75 \times OD_{570}]) / ([t] \times [v] \times [OD_{595}])$$

where $t$ = time of reaction (min), $v$ = volume of culture used in assay (mL), $OD_{595}$ = cell density at the start of assay, $OD_{415}$ = absorbance of *o*-nitrophenol at the end of assay, and $OD_{570}$ = light scattering at the end of assay. Estrogenic activity of isoflavones was evaluated as relative activity in reported β-galactosidase, which is the concentration of the isoflavone showing 10% of the activity of $10^{-7}$M E2 solution [REC10 (M), The concentrations showing 10% activity of $10^{-7}$M 17β-estradiol].

On the basis of the above method, estrogenic activity of isolated isoflavone *C*-glycosides together with related compounds such as daidzein, an aglycon of isolated *C*-glycosides, daidzin, a *O*-glucoside of daidzein, baiochanin A, 4′,7-dimethoxyisoflavone, formononetin, genistein, and 3′,4′,7- trihydroxyisoflavone (Figure 4), were evaluated. Genistein exhibited the highest estrogenic activity among evaluated compounds at $10^{-6}$M followed by baiochanin A ($10^{-5}$M), daidzein ($10^{-5}$M), daidzin ($10^{-5}$M), 3′,4′,7-trihydroxyisoflavone ($10^{-3}$M), and formononetin ($10^{-2}$M), on the other hand, isolated isoflavone *C*-glycosides (1–4) and 4′,7-dimethoxyisoflavone showed no activities (Table 2). In regard to glycosides, daidzin showed similar activity to daidzein at $10^{-5}$M, on the other hand, compound 1–4, which are 8-*C*-β-D-glucosyl derivatives of daidzein, exhibited no activity. In a comparision of daidzin and puerain (2), each of these compounds is daidzein mono-glucoside, however, the binding position (C-7 or C-8) or combination style (*O*- or *C*-) of glucose were different, and these difference might be attributable to their estrogenic activity.

Concerning the aglycons, genistein showed estrogenic activity at $10^{-6}$M, and the activity higher than that of daidzein ($10^{-5}$M). These results agree with the previous studies in which an addition of hydroxyl group at 5-position enhances the estrogenic acitivity (Fang, H., Tong, W., Shi, L. M., Blair, R., Perkins, R., and Branham, W., 2001; Miksicek R. J., 1994). On the other hand, the substitution of hydroxyl group at 4′-position to methoxyl function seems to decrease the estrogenic activities as $10^{-6}$M of genistein to $10^{-5}$M of biochanin A, and $10^{-5}$M of daidzein to $10^{-2}$M of formononetin. The activity of 3′,4′,7-trihydroxyisoflavone ($10^{-3}$M) was also lower than that of daidzein ($10^{-5}$M). This decrement might be due to the additional hydroxyl group at 3′-position. Furthermore, di-substitution of hydroxyl groups at 3- and 4′-position to methoxyl functions seems to disappear the activity of 4′,7-dimethoxyisoflavone.

In the earlier papers, the activities of genistein, daidzein and daidzin are similar to the values in previous literature using the same method (Kinjo, J., Furusawa, J., Baba, J., Takeshita, T., Yamasaki, M., and Nohara, T., 1987). On the other hand, the activity of genistein (++++) was highest followed by biochanin A (+++), formononetin (+++), daidzein (++), 3′,4′,7-trihydroxyisoflavone (nd), and 4′,7-dimethoxyisoflavone (nd) in yeast transactivation assay (Choi, S. Y., Ha, T. Y., Ahn, J. Y., Kim, S. R., Kang, K. S., Hwang, I. K., and Kim, S., 2008).

**Table 2. Estrogenic activity of isolated isoflavone C-glycosides and related compounds**

|  | REC10 (M)[a] |
|---|---|
| 6″-O-α-D-glucopyranosylpuerarin (1) | nd[b] |
| puerarin (2), | nd[b] |
| 3′-methoxypuerarin (3) | nd[b] |
| 6″-O-α-D-apiofranosylpuerarin (4) | nd[b] |
| baiochanin A | $10^{-5}$ |
| daidzein | $10^{-5}$ |
| daidzin | $10^{-5}$ |
| 4′,7-dimethoxyisoflavone | nd[b] |
| formononetin | $10^{-2}$ |
| genistein | $10^{-6}$ |
| 3′,4′,7-trihydroxyisoflavone | $10^{-3}$ |

[a]REC10 (M), The concentrations showing 10% activity of $10^{-7}$M 17β-estradiol (relative activities) [b]nd, not detected.

**Table 3. Antimutagenic activity of daidzein, daidzin, and isolated isoflavone C-glycosides**

|  | IC50 (nmol/plate)[a] | |
|---|---|---|
|  | TA98 | TA100 |
| daidzein | 107.7 | 307.9 |
| daidzin | nd[b] | nd[b] |
| puerarin (2) | nd[b] | nd[b] |
| 3′-methoxypuerarin (3) | nd[b] | nd[b] |

[a]IC50 (nmol/plate), the amount required for 50% inhibition of the mutagenicity. [b]nd, not detected.

In their study, estrogenic activities of test compounds and E2 were evaluated at $10^{-4}$ % and relative activities to E2 were acquired, and the activity of formononetin was higher, and those of daidzein and 3′,4′,7-trihydroxyisoflavone were lower than our present results. These differences of the activity might depend on the preparative conditions of test compounds for each estrogenic assay.

## ANTIMUTAGENIC ACTIVITY OF DAIDZEIN, DAIDZIN, AND ISOFLAVONE C-GLYCOSIDES

Antimutagenic activities against a couple of mutagens, Trp-P-2 and MNNG, were evaluated according to the previous study (Yahagi, T., Nagao, T., and Seino, T. 1977), which is a modification of Ames method (Ames, B. N., McCann, J., and Yamasaki, E. 1975).

Against Trp-P-2, 100 μL of sample solution (250, 500, and 1000 nmol/mL in DMSO), 100 μL of Trp-P-2 in 100 mM phosphate buffer (pH 6.8, 0.4 μg/mL), 100 μL of S9 mix, 100 mL of bacterial suspension of *S. typhimurium* TA98, and 600 μL of phosphate buffer were mixed in each test tube and preincubated at 37°C for 30 min. The incubated mixture was added to 2 mL of molten top agar, poured on an agar medium of minimal glucose, and incubated at 37°C for 2 days. Against MNNG, 100 µL of sample solution (250, 500, and 1000 nmol/mL in DMSO), 100 µL of 0.003% MNNG solution (150 µL of MNNG in DMSO (1 mg/mL) + 4850 µL of phosphate buffer), 300 µL of bacterial suspension of *S. typhimurium* TA100, and 500 µL of phosphate buffer were mixed and the following procedures are similar to described above. After 2 days incubation, the number of His$^+$ revertant colonies was counted, and the antimutagenic activity was evaluated by determining IC50 values, the amount (nmol/plate) required for 50% inhibition of the mutagenicity, from an approximate curve of the scattergram.

Antimutagenic activity of daidzein, daidzin, puerarin (2), and 3'-methoxypuerarin (3) against Trp-P-2 and MNNG were evaluated using above method. Daidzein showed the activity against both mutagens, on the other hand, daidzin, puerarin (2), and 3'-methoxypuerarin (3) showed antimutagenic activity against neither Trp-P-2 nor MNNG. In previous studies, isoflavone aglycons such as daidzein, genistein, biochanin A and their derivatives showed antimutagenic activity, however, isoflavone glycoside such as daidzin, puerarin showed no activity (Chen, Y., Inaba, M., Abe, N., and Hirota, A., 2003; Miyazawa, M., Sakano, K., Nakamura, S., and Kosaka, H., 2001; Kanazawa, K., Yamashita, T., Ashida, H., and Danno, G., 1998; Edenharder, R., Petersdorff, I., and Rauscher, R., 1993). These results in this chapter and previous papers suggested that regardless of the binding position or the style, addition of glucose moiety to isoflavone aglycons inhibit their antimutagenic potency.

# CONCLUSION

Isoflavone *C*-glycosides isolated *Pueraria lobata* were identified on the basis of NMR and MS analyses to be 6"-*O*-α-D-glucopyranosylpuerarin (1), puerarin (2), 3'-methoxypuerarin (3), and 6"-*O*-α-D-apiofranosylpuerarin (4), respectively. 6"-*O*-α-D-Glucopyranosylpuerarin is isolated from natural origin for the first time, and 6"-*O*-α-D-apiofranosylpuerarin is a novel compound.

These isolated compounds are daidzein 8-*C*-glucoside and it's derivatives, and showed no estrogenic activity, on the other hand, daidzein and daidzin, which is 7-*O*-glucoside of daidzein, showed the activity. These results suggest that binding position (C-7 or C-8) or combination style (*O*- or *C*-) of glucose moiety to daidzein might be attributable to their estrogenic activity. Daidzein also exhibited antimutagenic activities against Trp-P-2 and MNNG, however, daidzin, puerarin (2), and 3'-methoxypuerarin (3) showed no activity. The addition of glucose moiety seems to inhibit antimutagenic activity of daidzein, regardless of the binding position or the style. In earlier papers, puerarin is converted to daidzein as a metabolite of human intestinal bacteria (Choo, M.-K., Park, E.-K., Yoon, H.-K., and Kim, D.-H., 2002; Kim, D.-H., Yu, K.-U., Bae, E.-A., and Han, M. J., 1998). Daidzein is one of phytoestrogens which reduce the risk of breast and endometrial cancer, alleviate osteoporosis, show protective effects against cardiovascular disease, and so on (Omoni, A. O. and Aluko, R. E., 2005), therefore, puerain is expected to be a major *in vivo* estrogenic and antimutagenic isoflavone in *Pueraria lobata*.

# REFERENCES

Ames, B. N., McCann, J., and Yamasaki, E., (1975). Methods for detecting carcinogens and mutagens with the Salmonella/mammalian-microsome mutagenicity. *Mutation Research*, 31, 347 – 363.

Arano, T., Udayama, M., Kinjo, J., and Nohara, J. (1998). Preventive effects of saponins from the *Pueraria lobata* root on *in vitro* immunological liver injury of rat primary hepatocyte cultures. *Planta Medica*, 64, 413 – 416.

Arano, T., Udayama, M., Kinjo, J., Nohara, T., Funakoshi, F., and Kojima, S. (1997). Preventive effects of saponins from Pueraria Radix (the root of *Pueraria lobata* OHWI) on *in vitro* immunological injury of rat primary hepatocyte cultures. *Biological and pharmaceutical bulletin*, 20, 988 – 991.

Bebrevska, L., Foubert, K., Hermans, N., Chatterjee, S., March, E. V., Meyer, G. D., Vlietinck, A., Pieters, L., and Apers, S. (2010). *In vivo* antioxidative activity of a quantified *Pueraria lobata* root extract. *Journal of Ethnopharmacology*, 127, 112 – 117.

Cheng, J., Zhao, Y., Wang, B., Qiao, L., and Liang, H. (2005). Flavonoids from *Millettia nitida* var. *hirsutissima*. *Chemical and pharmaceutical bulletin*, 53, 419 – 421.

Chen, Y., Inaba, M., Abe, N., and Hirota, A. (2003). Antimutagenic activity of 8-hydroxyisoflavones and 6-hydroxydaidzein from soybean miso. *Bioscience, Biotechnology, and Biochemistry*, 67, 903 – 906.

Cherdshewasart, W., Sutjit, W., Pulcharoen, K., and Chulasiri, M. (2009). The mutagenic and antimutagenic effects of the traditional phytoestrogen-rich herbs, *Pueraria mirifica* and *Pueraria lobata*. *Brazilian journal of medical and biological research*, 42, 816 – 823.

Cherdshewasart, W., and Sutjit, W. (2008). Correlation of antioxidant activity and major isoflavonoid contents of the phytoestrogen-rich *Pueraria mirifica* and *Pueraria lobata* tubers. *Phytomedicine*, 15, 38 – 43.

Choi, S. Y., Ha, T. Y., Ahn, J. Y., Kim, S. R., Kang, K. S., Hwang, I. K., and Kim, S. (2008). Estrogenic activities of isoflavones and flavones and their structure-activity relationships. *Planta Medica*, 74, 25 – 32.

Choo, M.-K., Park, E.-K., Yoon, H.-K., Kim, D.-H. (2002). Antithrombotic and antiallergic activities of daidzein, a metabolite of puerarin and daidzin produced by human intestinal microflora. Biol. Pharm. *Biological and pharmaceutical bulletin*, 25, 1328 – 1332.

Chung, M. J., Sung, N.-J., Park, C.-S., Kweon, D.-K., Mantovani, A., Moon, T.-W., Lee, S.-J., and Park, K.-H. (2008). Antioxidant and hypocholesterolemic activities of water soluble puerarin ih HepG2 cells and in C57 BL/6J mice. *European journal of pharmacology*, 578, 159 – 170.

Edenharder, R., Petersdorff, I., and Rauscher, R. (1993). Antimutagenic effects of flavonoids, chalcones and structurally related compounds on the activity of 2-amino-3-methylimidazo[4,5-*f*]quinoline (IQ) and other heterocyclic amine mutagenes from cooked food. *Mutation Research*, 287, 261 – 274.

Fang, H., Tong, W., Shi, L. M., Blair, R., Perkins, R., and Branham, W. (2001). Structure-activity relationships for a large diverse set of natural, synthetic, and environmental estrogens. *Chemical research in toxicology*, 14, 280 – 294.

Guerra, M. C., Speroni, E., Broccoli, M., Cangini, M., Pasini, P., Minghetti, A., Crespi-Perellino, N., Mirasoli, M., Cantelli-Forti, G., and Paolini, M. (2000). Comparison between Chinese medical herb *Pueraria lobata* crude extract and its main isoflavone puerarin antioxidant properties and effects on rat liver CYP-catalaysed drug metabolism. *Life Science*, 67, 2997 – 3006.

Higuchi, H., Fukui, K., Kinjo, J., and Nohara, T. (1992). Four new glycosides from Albizziae cortex. III. *Chemical and pharmaceutical bulletin*, 40, 534 – 535.

Jang, D. S., Kim J. M., Lee, Y. M., Kim, Y. S., Kim. J., and Kim, J. S. (2006) Puerariafuran, a new inhibitor of advanced glycagtion end products (AGEs) isolated from the roots of *Pueraria lobata*. *Chemical and pharmaceutical bulletin*, 54, 1315 – 1317.

Kanazawa, K., Yamashita, T., Ashida, H., and Danno, G. (1998). Antimutagenicity of flavones and flavonols to heterocyclic amines by specific and strong inhibition of the cytochrome P450 1A family. *Bioscience, Biotechnology, and Biochemistry*, 62, 970 – 977.

Kim, D.-H., Yu, K.-U., Bae, E.-A., and Han, M. J. (1998). Metabolism of puerarin and daidzin by human intestinal bacteria and their relation to in vitro cytotoxicity. *Biological and pharmaceutical bulletin*, 21, 628 – 630.

Kim, J. S., Lee, Y. M., Lee, G. Y., Jang, D. S., Bae, K. H., and Kim, J. S. (2006). Constituents of the roots of *Pueraria lobata* inhibit formation of advanced glycation end products (AGEs). *Archives of pharmacal research*, 29, 821 – 825.

Kinjo, J., Higuchi, H., Fukui, K., and Nohara, T. (1991). Lignoids from Albizziae cortex. II. A biodegradation pathway of syringaresinol. *Chemical and pharmaceutical bulletin*, 39, 2952 – 2955.

Kinjo, J., Fukui, K., Higuchi, H., and Nohara, T. (1991). The first isolation of lignin tri- and tetra-glycosides. *Chemical and pharmaceutical bulletin*, 39, 1623 – 1625.

Kinjo, J., Furusawa, J., Baba, J., Takeshita, T., Yamasaki, M., and Nohara, T. (1987). Studies on the constituents of *Pueraria lobata*. III. Isoflavonoids and related compounds in the roots and the voluble stems. *Chemical and pharmaceutical bulletin*, 35, 4846 – 4850.

Lee, J. S. (2004). Supplementation of *Pueraria* radix water extract on changes of antioxidant enzymes and lipid profile in ethanol-treated rats. *Clinica Chimica Acta*, 347, 121 – 128.

Li, D., Park, S.-H., Shim J.-H., Lee, H.-S., Tang, S.-Y., Park, C.-S., and Park, K.-H. (2004). In vitro enzymatic modification of puerarin to puerarin glycosides by maltogenic amylase. *Carbohydrate Research*, 339, 2789 – 2797.

Lin, R. C., Guthrie, S., Xie, C.-Y., Mai, K., Lee, D. Y., Lumeng, L., and Li, T.-K. (1996). Isoflavonoid compounds extracted from *Pueraria lobata* suppress alcohol preference in a pharmacogenetic rat model of alcoholism. *Alcoholism, clinical and experimental research*, 20, 659 – 663.

McGregor, M. R. (2007). *Pueraria lobata* (Kudzu root) hangover remedies and acetaldehyde-associated neoplasm risk. *Alcohol*, 41, 469 – 478.

Miksicek R. J. (1994). Interaction of naturally occurring nonsteroidal estrogens with expressed recombinant human estrogenic receptor. *The Journal of steroid biochemistry and molecular biology*, 49, 153 – 160.

Miyazawa, M., Sakano, K., Nakamura, S., and Kosaka, H. (2001). Antimuragenic activity of isoflavone from *Pueraria lobata*. *Journal of Agricultural and Food Chemistry*, 49, 336 – 341.

Nishihara, T., Nishikawa, J., Kanayama, T., Dakeyama, F., Saito, K., Imagawa, M., Takatori, S., Kitagawa, Y., Hori, S., and Utsumi, H. (2002). Estrogenic activities of 517 chemicals by yeast two-hybrid assay. *Journal of Health Science*, 46, 282 – 298.

Nishikawa, J., Saito, K., Goto, J., Dakeyama, F., Matsuo, M., and Nishihara, T. (1999). New screening methods for chemicals with hormonal activities using interaction of nuclear hormone receptor with coactivator. *Toxicology and applied pharmacology*, 154, 76 – 83.

Omoni, A. O. and Aluko, R. E. (2005). Soybean foods and their benefits: potential mechanisms of action. *Nutrition Reviews*, 63, 272 – 283.

Rong, H.. Keukeleire, D. D.. Cooman, L. D.. Baeyens, W. R. G.. and Weken, G. V. D. (1998). Narrow-bore HPLC analysis of isoflavonoid aglycones and their *o*- and *c*-glycosides from Pueraria lobata. *Biomedical chromatography*, 12, 170 – 171.

Rong, H., Stevens, J. F., Deinzer, M. L., Cooman, L. D., and Keukeleire, D. D. (1998). Identification of isoflavones in the roots of *Pueraria lobata*. *Planta Medica*, 64, 620 – 627.

Saitoh, H. (1983). Pharmacologically of Kakkon. *Kanpo-Igaku*, 7, 1 – 2.

Su, F., Chang, J., Wang, K., Tsai, J., and Chiang, L. (2008). A water extract of *Pueraria lobata* inhibited cytotoxicity of Enterovirus 71 in a human foreskin fibroblast cell line. *The Kaohsiung Journal of Medical Science*, 24, 523 – 530.

Sun, Y., Wang, S., Feng, J., Xue, X., and Liang, X. (2008). Two new isoflavone glycosides from Pueraria lobata. *Journal of Asian natural products research*, 10, 729 – 733.

Tam, W. Y., Chook, P., Qiao, M., Chan, L. T., Chan, T. Y. K., Poon, Y. K., Fung, K. P., Leung, P. C., and Woo, K. S. (2009). The efficacy and tolerability of adjunctive alternative herbal medicen (*Salvia miltiorrhiza* and *Pueraria lobata*) on vascular function and structure in coronary patients. *Journal of alternative and complementary medicine*, 15, 415 – 421.

Wanjala, C. C. W., and Majinda, R. R. T. (1999). Flavonoid glycosides from *Crotalaria podocarpa*. *Phytochemistry*, 51, 705 – 707.

Xiong, Y., Yang, Y., Yang, J., Chai, H., Li, Y., Yang, J., Jia, Z., and Wang, Z. (2010). Tectoridin, an isoflavone glycoside from the flower of *Pueraria lobata*, prevents acute ethanol-induced liver steatosis in mice. *Toxicology*, 276, 64 – 72.

Yahagi, T., Nagao, M., and Seino, T., (1977), Mutagenicity of N-nitorosamins on Salmonella. *Mutation. Research*. 48, 121 – 130.

Zhang, H., Yang, X., and Wang, K. (2010). Isolation of two new *C*-glucofuranosyl isoflavones from *Pueraria lobata* (Wild.) Ohwi with HPLC-MS guiding analysis. *Journal of Asian natural products research*, 12, 293 – 299.

Zhao, S., and Zhang, Y. (1985). Quantitative TLC-densitometry of isoflavones in *Pueraria lobata* (Willd.) Ohwi. *Acta pharmaceutica Sinica*, 20, 203 – 208.

In: Recent Advances in Ginseng and Glycosides Research        ISBN: 978-1-62417-765-1
Editor: Claude J. Hopkins                                      © 2013 Nova Science Publishers, Inc.

*Chapter 5*

# MOTIF-BASED EXPLORATION OF THE GLYCOSIDE HYDROLASES FAMILY 1

## *Hirokazu Suzuki**

Department of Bioscience and Biotechnology,
Faculty of Agriculture,
Graduate School, Kyushu University, Fukuoka, Japan

## ABSTRACT

Glycoside hydrolases cleave a wide variety of glycosidic linkages, including several industrially important enzymes. These enzymes are currently classified into 130 families based on amino acid sequence similarities.

Members of glycoside hydrolase family 1 (GH1) are widely distributed in all three domains of life and hydrolyze various glycosides with physiological roles. In addition to hydrolytic activity, GH1 enzymes exhibit glycosylation activity to form glycosidic linkages.

These properties suggest their utility not only as saccharolytic catalysts, but also as inexpensive glycosylation catalysts for the synthesis of valuable glycoconjugates. Many GH1 enzymes have been characterized to reveal that these contain β-glucosidases, β-fucosidases, β-mannosidases, 6-phospho-β-galactosidases, and 6-phospho-β-glucosidases. However, GH1 enzymes that are functionally characterized are extremely low compared to the entries described in the Carbohydrate-Active enZymes database, which accumulates over 4,000 entries for GH1 sequences. This fact suggests that the entries may harbor novel GH1 enzymes useful for glycoside research and applications.

This chapter, aiming at the discovery of useful GH1 enzymes, reviews their general features and our approaches to generate or identify novel GH1 enzymes. The approaches are based on a motif sequence conserved in GH1 members, termed as the DG motif. Distribution and variation of DG motifs are also discussed to facilitate novel GH1 discovery.

---

* Correspondence to: Hirokazu Suzuki (hirokap@xpost.plala.or.jp)

# INTRODUCTION

Glycoside hydrolases (GH) catalyze the hydrolytic cleavage of glycosidic linkages in a wide variety of glycosides. Numerous GH are identified and characterized across diverse organisms to reveal a variety of catalytic properties and physiological roles. Because many GH can catalyze the formation of glycosidic linkages, GH are historically attractive as not only saccharolytic catalysts, but also as robust, simple, and inexpensive glycosylation catalysts for the synthesis of valuable glycoconjugates including therapeutic oligosaccharides [5, 12, 28, 29, 35, 44, 54, 55]. In addition, due to concerns about the environment and energy issues on the earth, the plant-mass biorefinery involving GH catalysts has attracted a lot of attention in recent years [52]. Thus, GH remain challenging in broad research and industrial areas.

GH members are currently classified into 130 families (including deleted families 21, 40, 41, 60, and 69) based on amino acid sequence similarities [8]. Recent developments in DNA sequencing technologies have revealed numerous GH genes in various organisms. The Carbohydrate-Active enZymes (CAZy) database (http://www.cazy.org) has accumulated a staggering volume of information about GH, including gene sequences, deduced amino acid sequences, and source organisms. The sequence entries are now over 120,000 and have been increased logarithmically. However, most of them are uncharacterized and their catalytic properties remain to be established. This implies that GH entries in the CAZy database may harbor GH with novel substrate specificities useful for glycoside research and applications. This fact has led us to explore these uncharacterized members to identify novel GH catalysts.

This chapter focuses on GH family 1 (GH1) and reviews its general features. Aiming at providing important tips for novel GH1 discovery, our approaches to generate or identify novel GH1 enzymes are subsequently described along with two illustrations. The approaches are based on a motif sequence conserved in GH1 members, termed as the DG motif. Distribution and variation of DG motifs are further analyzed to reveal possible candidates of more novel GH1 enzymes.

# GENERAL FEATURES

GH1 consist of β-glycosidases with 17 different EC numbers, which hydrolyze disaccharides, phosphorylated disaccharides, oligosaccharides, and sugar–aromatic conjugates (Figure 1). The CAZy database describes more than 4,000 entries and 5,500 sequences with GenBank accessions for GH1 members. A comparison of GH entries in the database shows that GH1 is one of the largest families (Table 1). However, among the GH1 entries, those assigned with EC numbers are limited only to 7%. Moreover, no little EC numbers seems to be assigned on the basis of sequence homologies. Thus, GH1 members whose activities are enzymatically established are extremely low.

Generally, amino acid sequences of GH1 enzymes consist of 400–600 residues. The molecular weight per monomer is approximately 50 kDa. For subunit structures, a monomer [20, 56], dimer [57], tetramer [1, 10, 24–26, 39], octamer [40], and other oligomers [18] are observed by gel filtration, native polyacrylamido gel electrophoresis, and/or X-ray three dimensional analyses.

**Table 1. GH families containing over 2,000 entries in the CAZy database as of October 2012**

| Family | Total | Entry number from each source organism | | | | | EC number[a] |
| --- | --- | --- | --- | --- | --- | --- | --- |
| | | Archaea | Bacteria | Eukaryota | Virus | Unknown | |
| 1 | 4,007 | 80 | 3,246 | 672 | 0 | 9 | 19 |
| 2 | 3,759 | 33 | 3,515 | 204 | 0 | 7 | 5 |
| 3 | 4,165 | 54 | 3,507 | 566 | 0 | 38 | 7 |
| 5 | 3,334 | 37 | 2,144 | 1,053 | 5 | 98 | 18 |
| 7 | 4,938 | 0 | 0 | 4,933 | 0 | 5 | 4 |
| 13 | 12,515 | 187 | 10,411 | 1,796 | 2 | 119 | 22 |
| 16 | 2,385 | 9 | 949 | 1,413 | 7 | 7 | 10 |
| 18 | 4,983 | 36 | 2,771 | 2,052 | 79 | 45 | 2 |
| 23 | 7,965 | 0 | 7,712 | 122 | 122 | 9 | 2 |
| 28 | 2,002 | 6 | 620 | 1,373 | 0 | 3 | 6 |
| 34 | 32,526 | 0 | 0 | 0 | 32,526 | 0 | 1 |
| 43 | 2,567 | 9 | 1,991 | 558 | 0 | 9 | 6 |
| 73 | 2,162 | 1 | 2,095 | 0 | 65 | 1 | 1 |

[a] The values indicate EC number variations that are found in the family members.

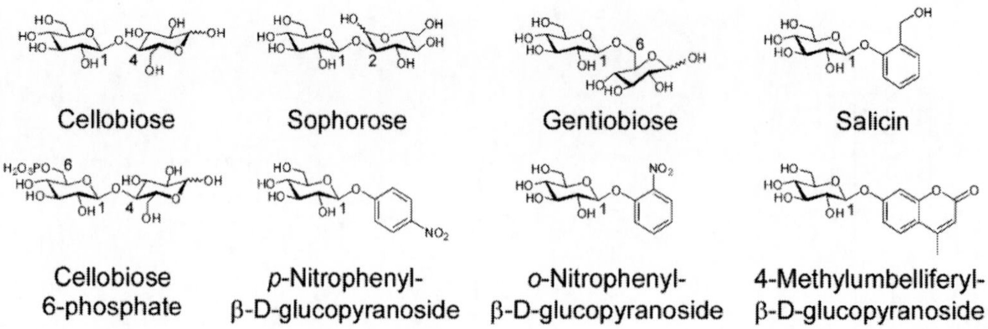

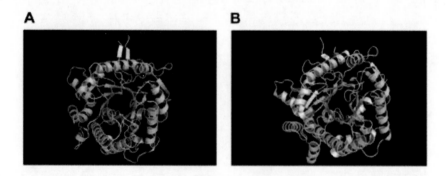

Cellobiose          Sophorose          Gentiobiose          Salicin

Cellobiose          p-Nitrophenyl-      o-Nitrophenyl-       4-Methylumbelliferyl-
6-phosphate    β-D-glucopyranoside   β-D-glucopyranoside    β-D-glucopyranoside

Figure 1. Conventional substrates of GH1 enzymes.

The activities are exhibited without adding cofactors, such as metal ions and vitamins, and are not enhanced by adding the cofactors. Metal-chelating agents have negligible effects in most cases, although a few β-glucosidase activities are inhibited by ethylenediaminetetraacetic acid [13, 24]. These observations suggest that GH1 activities require no cofactors in general. The GH1 activity and stability tend to prefer neutral pH for the optimum. The members from thermophiles exhibit thermostability [4, 6, 17, 23, 26, 39, 61]. Many crystal structures have been reported [1, 2, 10, 15, 18, 24, 37, 40, 43, 56, 57, 61], revealing shared $(\beta/\alpha)_8$ barrel (also called TIM barrel) structures (Figure 2) and interactions between amino acid residues and ligand components within the active sites. Substitutions of the ligand-interacting residues decrease the activities, supporting their involvements in ligand interactions [11, 19, 25, 26, 42].

Figure 2. The $(\beta/\alpha)_8$ barrel structures of *Paenibacillus polymyxa* BglA (*A*, RCSB-PDB entry 1BGG) [40] and *Lactococcus lactis* LacG (*B*, RCSB-PDB entry 4PBG) [57].

The GH1 reaction is performed by a double-displacement mechanism through a covalent glycosyl–enzyme intermediate retaining the configuration at the anomeric carbon (Figure 3) [15, 27, 62]. In the reaction, two glutamic acids are involved as catalytically important residues [36]. One acts as a general acid/base and the other as a nucleophile. The first step to form the intermediate is to protonate the glycosidic oxgen by the acid/base residue, accompanied by an attack of the nucleophile on the anomeric carbon. In the second step, a water molecule is deprotonated by the acid/base, providing a nucleophilic species. It attacks the anomeric carbon along with cleaving the glycosyl–enzyme bond, producing cleaved glycosides. GH1 enzymes also catalyze the formation of glycosidic linkages by thermodynamically controlled reverse reactions and/or kinetically controlled transglycosylations [11, 17, 19, 46, 48, 58]. Reported examples include glycosylations producing methyl β-D-glucopyranoside 6-phosphate [58], methyl β-D-galactopyranoside [11, 19], methyl β-D-mannopyranoside [11, 19], and glucose oligomers [17]. Thus, GH1 attracts as saccharolytic and glycosylation catalysts as well as other GH enzymes.

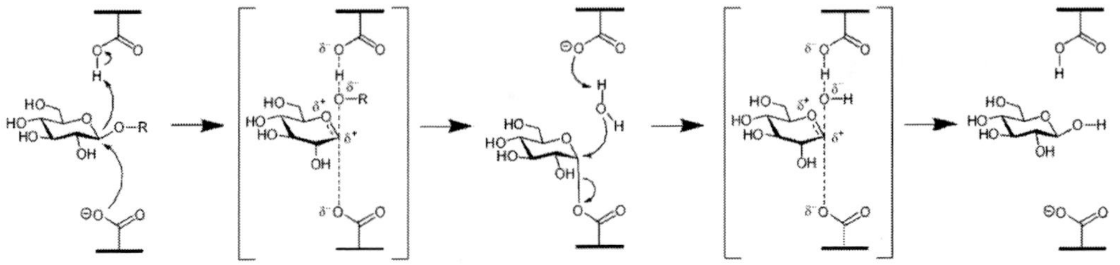

Figure 3. Hydrolysis mechanism of β-glycosidic linkages.

## SUBSTRATE SPECIFICITY

GH1 enzymes hydrolyze various glycosides (Figure 1). These include oligosaccharides (e.g., cello-oligosaccharides, laminartibiose, gentiobiose, sophorose, sucrose, lactose, laminarin, and manno-oligosaccharides) [6, 13, 16, 20, 21, 31, 33, 36, 39] and plant secondary metabolites containing phenolic structures (e.g., salicin, amygdalin, flavonoids, ipecosides, and gensenosides) [6, 7, 16, 21, 33, 38, 47, 53]. In addition, these hydrolyze synthesized substrates, such as p-nitrophenyl (pNP)- and o-nitrophenyl-glycosides (chromogenic substrates), and 4-methylumbelliferyl-glycosides (fluorescent substrates). These substrates have been used for analyzing GH1 substrate specificities for the glycoside moiety (glycon specificity), showing that GH1 enzymes have individual glycon specificities (Table 2). Based on glycon specificity, GH1 members can be classified into three main classes:

(i) β-glycosidases: members of this class preferentially hydrolyze β-D-glycosidic linkages. Although their glycon specificities are various, the majority are the β-glucosidase (EC 3.2.1.21)/β-fucosidase (EC 3.2.1.38) type that preferentially acts on β-D-glucosidic and/or β-D-fucosidic linkages (members 1–15). Minorities include β-mannosidases (EC 3.2.1.25) that act on β-D-mannosidic linkages (members 16 and 17).

(ii) 6-phospho-β-galactosidases (EC 3.2.1.85): members of this class hydrolyze definitely 6-phospho-β-D-galactosidic linkages, exemplified by members 18–20. The 6-phospho-β-D-glucosidic linkages are also cleaved in a measure. However, these show negligible activity toward pNP-glycosides that are not phosphorylated.

(iii) 6-phospho-β-glucosidase class (EC 3.2.1.86): two members from *Escherichia coli*, 21 and 22, have been reported for this class. These hydrolyze 6-phospho-β-D-glucosidic linkages specifically. Neither glycosidic nor 6-phospho-β-D-galactosidic linkages are hydrolyzed by the enzymes.

**Table 2. Glycon specificities of GH1 enzymes**

| GH1 enzyme[a] | Relative activity of pNP-glycoside hydrolysis (%)[b] | | | | | | | | | References |
|---|---|---|---|---|---|---|---|---|---|---|
| | GL | CB | GA | MN | FC | XY | AR | GP | LP | |
| β-glycosidases | | | | | | | | | | |
| **1** | 100 | 3.3 | 20 | | | 3 | | | | [16] |
| **2** | 100 | 7.6 | 4.1 | | | 0.3 | | | | [16] |
| **3** | 100 | | 7.6 | 0.7 | | | | | | [4, 25, 26] |
| **4** | 100 | 0 | 32 | | | 0 | | | | [13] |
| **5** | 100 | 7.5 | 15 | | | 4 | | | | [23] |
| **6** | 100 | | 31 | | | 8 | | | | [33] |
| **7** | 100 | 60 | 0 | | 55 | 0 | | | | [41] |
| **8** | 100 | | 6.4 | 0 | 95 | 1.1 | | | | [20] |
| **9** | 99 | | 60 | 0 | 100 | 0 | | | | [53] |
| **10** | 77 | | 92 | | 100 | 0 | 21 | | | [21] |
| **11** | 71 | 87 | 0 | | 100 | 1.8 | | | | [6] |
| **12** | 70 | | 30 | 0.3 | 100 | 1.8 | | | | [36] |
| **13** | 54 | | 5.3 | | 100 | | | | | [17] |
| **14** | 43 | | 3 | | 100 | 1 | | | | [31] |
| **15** | 19 | | | | 100 | | | | | [7] |
| **16** | 26 | | 20 | 100 | | | | | | [26] |
| **17** | 13 | | | 100 | | | | | | [4, 39] |
| 6-Phospho-β-galactosidases | | | | | | | | | | |
| **18** | 2.1 | | | | | | | 17 | 100 | [42, 59] |
| **19** | | | | | | | | 17 | 100 | [59] |
| **20** | | | | | | | | 8.8 | 100 | [59] |

**Table 2. (Continued)**

| GH1 enzyme[a] | Relative activity of pNP-glycoside hydrolysis (%)[b] | | | | | | | | | | References |
|---|---|---|---|---|---|---|---|---|---|---|---|
| | GL | CB | GA | MN | FC | XY | AR | GP | LP | | |
| 6-Phospho-β-glucosidases | | | | | | | | | | | |
| **21** | | | | | | | | | 100 | 0 | [58] |
| **22** | | | | | | | | | 100 | 0 | [58, 59] |

[a] These indicate: **1**, *Paenibacillus polymyxa* BglA (GenBank accession number, AAA22263); **2**, *Paenibacillus polymyxa* BglB (AAA22264); **3**, *Pyrococcus furiosus* CelB (AAL80566); **4**, *Micrococcus antarcticus* BglU (ACM66669); **5**, *Fervidobacterium islandicum* Bgl1A (CCA60742); **6**, *Sphingomonas paucimobilis* Bgl1 (AAG59862); **7**, *Reticulitermes flavipes* BGluc1 (ADK12988); **8**, *Paenibacillus* sp. HC1 BglA (BAE48718); **9**, *Sphingomonas* sp. 2F2 BglSp (ADY18331); **10**, *Bacillus* sp. GL1 BglA (BAA36160); **11**, *Thermoanaerobacter brockii* BglT (CAA91220); **12**, *Sulfolobus solfataricus* P2 LacS (AAA72843); **13**, *Thermus thermophilus* β-gly (ABW87307); **14**, *Spodoptera frugiperda* β-gly (AAC06038); **15**, *Dalbergia cochinchinensis* Bglu1 (AAF04007); **16**, *Pyrococcus horikoshii* BglB (BAA29589); **17**, *Pyrococcus furiosus* BmnA (AAL81332); **18**, *Lactococcus lactis* LacG (AAA25183); **19**, *Staphylococcus aureus* LacG (AAA26650); **20**, *Lactobacillus casei* LacG (AAD15134); **21**, *Escherichia coli* BglA (AAC75939); and **22**, *Escherichia coli* BglB (AAC76744).

[b] These indicate the relative values of pNP-glycoside hydrolyzing activities (specific activity or $k_{cat}/K_m$ value) using the maximum value in each enzyme as 100%. pNP-glycosides are: GL, pNP-β-D-glucopyranoside; CB, pNP-β-D-cellobioside; GA, pNP-β-D-galactopyranoside; MN, pNP-β-D-mannopyranoside; FC, pNP-β-D-fucopyranoside; XY, pNP-β-D-xylopyranoside; AR, pNP-α-L-arabinofuranoside; GP, pNP-6-phospho-β-D-glucopyranoside; and LP, pNP-6-phospho-β-D-galactopyranoside.

It has been suggested that 6-phospho-β-glycosidases are involved in the metabolism of extracellular glycosides.

In bacteria, extracellular glycosides are transported into cells by phosphoenolpyruvate-dependent phosphotransferase systems that catalyze phosphotransfer from phosphoenolpyruvate to incoming glycosides concomitant with their translocation across the cell membrane [3]. Glycosides that are incorporated and phosphorylated are hydrolyzed by 6-phospho-β-glycosidases to excise 6-phospho-glycoside moieties, which is further metabolized.

## THE DG MOTIF

The DG motif is a crucial region that governs glycon specificities of GH1 enzymes. We originally identified this motif by comparing analyses among deduced amino acid sequences, substrate specificities, and structural information associated with GH1 members that had been characterized [46]. The motif comprises a short amino acid sequence flanked by aspartic acid and glycine residues (Figure 4A).

These residues and arginine residues are well conserved in most DG motifs. Crystal structures of GH1 members reveal that DG motifs constitute GH1 active sites and form loop structures by the interaction between the carboxyl group of the aspartic acid residue and the guanidinium group of the arginine residue (Figure 4B, C). Crystal structures also reveal that the motifs contain ligand-interacting residues. Substitutions of these residues reduce the GH1 activities [11, 19, 25, 42].

Intriguingly, DG motif sequences can be categorized into the following three classes with the relation of the three classes regarding glycon specificities (see above):

(i)   DG motifs of β-glycosidases consist of 14 amino acids and contain glutamic acid as a ligand-interacting residue [40]. Examples are DG motifs of members 1–17. The member 6 is an exception whose DG motif sequence contains a histidine instead of the highly-conserved arginine residue. It is noteworthy that 6 has notable β-D-xylosidase activity (Table 2). BAD0156 is one other exception. The DG motif sequence lacks the glycine and arginine residues and the enzyme has unique substrate specificity (see below).

(ii)  DG motifs of 6-phospho-β-galactosidases consist of 14 amino acids as well as those of β-glycosidases. Examples are DG motifs of members 18–20 and GK3214 (see below). These contain a serine residue at the position corresponding to the glutamic acid residue conserved in β-glycosidase DG motifs. In addition, lysine and tyrosine residues are contained as ligand-interacting residues. These residues interact with the phosphate group of the ligand in a crystal structure of member 18 [57].

(iii) DG motifs of 6-phospho-β-glucosidases consist of 15 amino acids and contain serine, lysine, and tyrosine residues. Examples are DG motifs of members 21 and 22. Crystal structures of 6-phospho-β-glucosidases remain to be established.

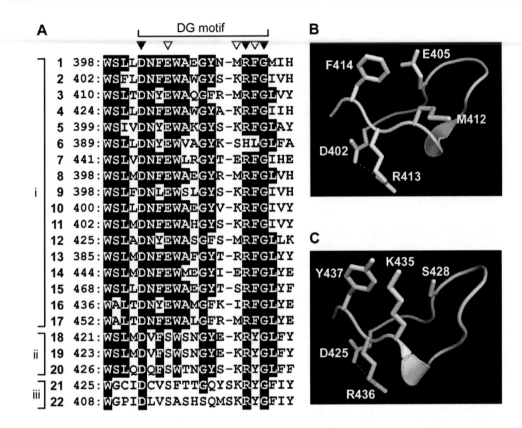

Figure 4. Amino acid sequences (**A**) and three-dimensional structures (**B**, **C**) of DG motifs. (**A**) DG motif sequences of GH1 members **1–22** (see the legend of Table 2 for enzymes). Three amino acids conserved in DG motifs, aspartic acid (D), arginine (R), and glycine (G) residues, are indicated by solid triangles. In addition, glutamic acid residues (open triangle) are shared in β-glycosidases (i) whereas serine residues are shared in 6-phospho-β-glalactosidases (ii) and 6-phospho-β-glucosides (iii) at the position. The 6-phospho-β-glycosidases (ii and iii) also share lysine and tyrosine residues (open triangle). (**B**, **C**) Loop structures of DG motifs of members **1** (**B**, RCSB-PDB entry 1BGG) [40] and **18** (**C**, RCSB-PDB entry 4PBG) [57]. Possible interactions between highly conserved aspartic acid and arginine residues are indicated by dashed lines.

## MOTIF ALTERATION

We previously characterized three GH1 enzymes encoded by the thermophile *Geobacillus kaustophilus* HTA426 genome and identified the 6-phospho-β-galactosidase GK3214 (Table 3). This is a thermostable protein that is stable at 60°C for 1 hour at the wide pH range of 4.5–10.5. At pH 6.0, the enzyme retains more than 80% of its activity even after 7 days of incubation at 60°C. Transglycosylation activity is also observed.

We further dissected information of GH1 members that had been reported and identified the DG motif as a possible region that governed glycon specificities of GH1 enzymes. The DG motif sequence of GK3214 was categorized to the 6-phospho-β-galactosidase class (Figure 5). We examined alterations of the DG motif and generated two mutants, M11 and M8. Mutant M11 was constructed by replacing the motif with that of member **22** (belonging to the 6-phospho-β-glucosidase class). Mutant M8 had the DG motif of member **1** (belonging to the β-glycosidase class). As expected, mutant M11 showed 6-phospho-β-glucosidase activity with high specificity (Table 3), although the motif alteration somewhat decreased protein thermostability and the catalytic efficiency in great measure. This suggests that the alteration of the DG motif sequence to the 6-phospho-β-glucosidase class is accompanied by the alteration of the glycon specificity to ghe 6-phospho-β-glucosidase class. Moreover, in mutant M8, β-glucosidase activity was 130-fold increased and the 6-phospho-glycosidase activity was $10^{-8}$-fold decreased without affects on protein thermostability. In addition to β-glucosidase activity, unexpected but substantial enhancements (more than 10-fold) were observed in β-fucosidase, β-xylosidase, β-glucuronidase, β-mannosidase, β-cellobiosidase, and α-arabinofuranosidase activities. Overall, the alteration caused activity alteration to the β-glycosidase class, generating a thermostable β-fucosidase with high specificity (Table 3). Activity enhancements observed are dramatic changes when compared to cases with point mutations of GH1 enzymes [11, 19, 25, 42].

**Table 3. Glycon specificities of GK3214, GK3214 mutants, and BAD0156**

| GH1 enzyme[a] | Relative activity of pNP-glycoside hydrolysis (%)[b] | | | | | | | | | References |
| | GL | CB | GA | MN | FC | XY | AR | GP | LP | |
|---|---|---|---|---|---|---|---|---|---|---|
| GK3214 | 0 | 0 | 0 | 0 | 0.1 | 0 | 0 | 90 | 100 | [46] |
| Mutant M8 | 2.1 | 0.1 | 1.0 | 0 | 100 | 0.2 | 0 | 0 | 0 | [46] |
| Mutant M11 | 0 | 0 | 1.4 | 0 | 0 | 0 | 0 | 100 | 1.4 | [46] |
| BAD0156 | 0 | 0 | 0 | 0 | 0 | 0 | 100 | 0 | 0 | [45] |

[a] GK3214, *Geobacillus kaustophilus* GH1 (GenBank accession number, BAD77499); mutant M8, GK3214 mutant having DG motif of member **1**; mutant M11, GK3214 mutant having DG motif of member **22**; BAD0156, *Bifidobacterium adolescentis* GH1 (BAF38937).

[b] These indicate relative $k_{cat}/K_m$ values of pNP-glycoside hydrolyzing activities using the maximum value in each enzyme as 100%. See the legend of Table 2 for pNP-glycosides.

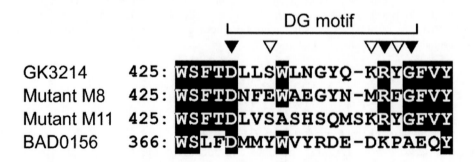

Figure 5. DG motif sequences of GK3214 and its mutants (M8 and M11) and the comparable sequence of BAD0156. Three amino acids that are highly conserved in DG motifs, aspartic acid (D), arginine (R), and glycine (G) residues, are indicated by solid triangles. The GK3214 sequence contains ligand-interacting residues of 6-phospho-β-galactosidase class (open triangles). BAD0156 has an unusual sequence in this region.

Note that an enzyme that specifically hydrolyzes the β-D-fucosyl linkage has not been previously reported, although β-fucosidase activities have been reported for GH1 [6, 7, 17,

20, 21, 31, 36, 41, 53], GH5 [60], and GH42 [5] members and the latex serum of *Lactuca sativa* [14]. These results suggest that DG motif alteration has the potential to dramatically modify glycon specificities of GH1 enzymes and thereby to generate novel GH1 catalysts.

## MOTIF MINING

The successful modification of GK3214 substrate specificity by the DG motif alteration led us the hypothesis that DG motif sequences might be used to predict substrate specificities of uncharacterized GH1 enzymes. Thus, we analyzed DG motif sequences of over 2,000 GH1 members described in the CAZy database as of October 2010 and identified *Bifidobacterium adolescentis* BAD0156 that had an unusual DG motif sequence [45], which lacked glycine and arginine residues (Figure 5). Because DG motifs constitute GH1 active sites, the observation implied that BAD0156 had an unusual active center, and thus, novel substrate specificity. In order to establish its catalytic activity, we characterized BAD0156 using recombinant proteins and revealed that this enzyme specifically hydrolyzes pNP-α-L-arabinofuranoside among pNP-glycosides examined (Table 3). Among natural glycosides, α-1,5-linked arabino-oligosaccharides served as substrates. These results suggest that BAD0156 is a 1,5-α-L-arabinofuranosidase (EC 3.2.1.99).

GH members that preferentially act on α-L-arabinosides are found in six GH families (GH3, GH43, GH51, GH54, GH62, and GH93). According to EC numbers, these are classified into two types: one type, arabinan endo-1,5-α-L-arabinanase (EC 3.2.1.99), catalyzes the endo-hydrolysis of (1→5)-α-arabinofuranosidic linkages in arabinans and arabino-oligosaccharides. Examples for this type are *Bacillus subtilis* Abn2 [22] and *Pseudomonas fluorescens* ArbA [34]. The other type, exo-α-L-arabinofuranosidase (EC 3.2.1.55), catalyzes the exo-hydrolysis of terminal, non-reducing α-L-arabinofuranoside residues in α-L-arabinosides such as arabinans, arabinoxylans, and arabinogalactans. This type includes *Bifidobacterium longum* AbfB [32] and *Fusarium graminearum* Arb93A [9]. It is noteworthy that among GH1 members, glycoside hydrolases preferentially acting on arabinosides, including endo-1,5-α-L-arabinanases and exo-α-L-arabinofuranosidases, had not been previously reported, although member 9 exhibits a pNP-α-L-arabinofuranoside hydrolyzing activity [53]. Thus, BAD0156 is the first example of a GH1 enzyme preferentially acting on arabinosides. These results provide new insight concerning GH1 members and suggest that a genome mining based on DG motif sequences is a practical approach to identify GH1 enzymes with novel substrate specificities.

## DISTRIBUTION AND VARIATION

To analyze the distribution and variation of DG motifs and identify possible candidates of more novel GH1 enzymes, we collected GH1 sequences from a total of 5,574 GenBank accessions described in the CAZy database as of October 2012 and extracted DG motif sequences. Partial sequences, deleted GenBank accessions, and sequences for other types of proteins, including dTDP-4-dehydrorhamnose reductases, were eliminated from this analysis, although duplicate sequences may be included. A total of 5,071 motif sequences were extracted from 115 sequences of archaeal GH1, 3,638 sequences of bacterial GH1, 1,312 sequences of eukaryotic GH1, and 6 sequences of unknown organisms (Table 4).

**Table 4. Distribution and variation of DG motif sequences**

| DG motif class | Source organism | | | |
| --- | --- | --- | --- | --- |
| | Archaea | Bacteria | Eukaryote | Unknown |
| Categorized to DG motif[a] | 115 | 3,606 | 1,306 | 6 |
| β-Glycosidase class | 96 | 597 | 1,064 | 3 |
| 6-Phospho-β-galactosidase class | 0 | 1,350 | 0 | 1 |
| 6-Phospho-β-glucosidse class | 0 | 1,463 | 1 | 1 |
| Arginine substitution | 19 | 121 | 241 | 1 |
| Others | 0 | 75 | 0 | 0 |
| Uncategorized to DG motif[b] | 0 | 32 | 6 | 0 |
| **Total sequences[c]** | **115** | **3,638** | **1,312** | **6** |

[a] Sequences that are flanked by aspartic acid and glycine residues are counted as "Categorized to DG motif". Among these sequences, those that are categorized to the three main classes (i.e., β-glycosidase, 6-phospho-β-galactosidase, and 6-phospho-β-glucosidase classes) are counted, whereas those that lack the arginine residue highly conserved in DG motifs are counted as "Arginine substitution". DG motif sequences that are uncategorized to the above four classes are counted as "Others".

[b] Sequences that lack either aspartic acid or glycine residue are counted as "Uncategorized to DG motif".

[c] These indicate total counts for "Categorized to DG motif" and "Uncategorized to DG motif".

Among motif sequences extracted, the number of sequences flanked by aspartic acid and glycine residues was 5,033 sequences (>99%). Moreover, 4,576 sequences (>90%) were categorized into the three main classes (i.e., DG motifs of β-glycosidases, 6-phospho-β-galactosidases, and 6-phospho-β-glucosidases; see above). The classes for 6-phospho-β-galactosidases and 6-phospho-β-glucosidases are identified exclusively in bacterial members. This may be associated with the fact that 6-phospho-β-glycosidases are involved in metabolisms of extracellular glycosides in cooperation with phosphotransferase systems in bacteria [3]. A part of the DG motifs (382 sequences) had amino acids substituted at the position corresponding to the arginine residue conserved in most DG motifs. Among these, 170 sequences contained lysine or histidine at the position. Because these can act as basic amino acids, such DG motifs may even form loop structures. Thus, almost all DG motifs were "usual". However, we identified 38 unusual sequences that were not flanked by aspartic acid and glycine residues (Table 5). The sequences imply that these GH1 enzymes may have unusual substrate specificities as well as BAD0156 (see above). Their enzymatic activities remain to be clarified. Characterization of these enzymes could represent a promising opportunity to identify novel GH1 enzymes.

## CONCLUSION

Numerous GH1 sequences are now available due to developments in DNA sequencing, computational, and electronic communication technologies. This has provided us great opportunities to identify novel GH1 enzymes by genome mining approaches. However, it is not easy to definitely predict GH1 functions only based on amino acid sequences. Recently, we have identified the DG motif as an important region that affects GH1 substrate specificities.

### Table 5. GH1 members containing unusual DG motifs

| GH1 member[a] | DG motif sequence | Source organism |
|---|---|---|
| AEU39992 | ALVSAGTGEMSKRYG | *Lactococcus lactis* |
| CCJ06467 | ALVTWAYRQGLRPLH | *Methylocystis* sp. SC2 |
| ACB76900 | ALVTWGYRQGDLPPQ | *Opitutus terrae* |
| BAB92992 | DCWSWLNAYKNRYAL | *Serratia marcescens* |
| CBG21229 | DCWSWLNAYKNRYAL | *Serratia marcescens* |
| AFK08221 | DLINWDYRYGSEPVE | *Mesotoga prima* |
| ACL70805 | DLVNWDYMEGHKPVE | *Halothermothrix orenii* |
| CBL32908 | DLVSAGTGEIEKTLR | *Enterococcus* sp. 7L76 |
| AEU39667 | DLVSAGTGEMKKRYV | *Lactococcus lactis* |
| ABI27480 | DLYSWKNGVEKRYRL | *Listeria monocytogenes* |
| ABI27483 | DLYSWKNGVEKRYRL | *Listeria monocytogenes* |
| BAF38937 | DMMYWVYRDEDKPAE | *Bifidobacteriu adolescentis* |
| ACZ20274 | DMYEWTYRHGTAPRE | *Sanguibacter keddieii* |
| BAJ74921 | DMYEWTYRHSDEPRS | *Microbacterium testaceum* |
| BAA75349 | DNWSWANAYKNRLWV | *Bacillus halodurans* |
| CBG21241 | DNWSWANAYKNRLWV | *Bacillus halodurans* |
| NP_924949 | DQIDWDIELAEQRGT | *Gloeobacter violaceus* |
| ADB41436 | DQIDWDLQLGELNNH | *Spirosoma linguale* |
| CCH00905 | DQIDWDTGLAEENNR | *Fibrella aestuarina* |
| ACG78487 | DQIDWDVGLREQNNR | *Phenylobacterium zucineum* |
| CCJ08930 | DQVDWDIALREKRGH | *Methylocystis* sp. SC2 |
| GH1 member[a] | DG motif sequence | Source organism |
| CCJ05931 | DQVDWDIALREPLGN | *Methylocystis* sp. SC2 |
| ACL37107 | DQVDWDIGLAEKKGK | Uncultured bacterium |
| ADV15326 | DQVDWDSALRENNGR | *Mesorhizobium ciceri* |
| ACG80041 | DQVDWDTALREKNGR | *Phenylobacterium zucineum* |
| ABY49715 | DYYEWAVAFSKRYAL | Uncultured bacterium |
| ADB40148 | GLYDWHCLLTRREDR | *Spirosoma linguale* |
| ADB41232 | GMYDWHCLLTRQEDR | *Spirosoma linguale* |
| AEV96418 | HQVDWDSALRNDAGN | *Niastella koreensis* |
| CAW94744 | NCWSWLNAYKNRYGL | *Streptococcus equi* |
| ABJ57924 | TAFLPELVKCPSGMA | *Lactobacillus delbrueckii* |
| ADY84422 | TAFLPELVKCPSGMA | *Lactobacillus delbrueckii* |
| AAG52622 | DNYEFGNGYTLRFDM | *Arabidopsis thaliana* |
| NP_175560 | DNYEFGNGYTLRFDM | *Arabidopsis thaliana* |
| AEE32673 | DNYEFGNGYTLRFDM | *Arabidopsis thaliana* |
| NP_175560 | DNYEFGNGYTLRFDM | *Arabidopsis thaliana* |
| AED95661 | DNYELWPSRSFHVSP | *Arabidopsis thaliana* |
| NP_680406 | DNYELWPSRSFHVSP | *Arabidopsis thaliana* |

[a] These indicate Genbank accession numbers.

Our studies demonstrate that the DG motif is a promising tool for novel GH1 discovery. The strategies based on the DG motif would facilitate an expansion of useful GH1 catalysts and contribute to glycoside research.

## ACKNOWLEDGMENT

This work was supported by the Special Coordination Funds for Promoting Science and Technology under the project of Creation of Innovation Centers for Advanced Interdisciplinary Research Areas (Innovative Bioproduction Kobe), MEXT, Japan. I thank Ken-ichi Yoshida, Kobe University, for his continued support of this work.

## REFERENCES

[1]    Aguilar, C. F., Sanderson, I., Moracci, M., Ciaramella, M., Nucci, R., Rossi, M. & Pearl, L. H. (1997). Crystal structure of the β-glycosidase from the hyperthermophilic archeon *Sulfolobus solfataricus*: resilience as a key factor in thermostability. *J. Mol. Biol.*, 271, 789–802.

[2]    Akiba, T., Nishio, M., Matsui, I. & Harata, K. (2004). X-ray structure of a membrane-bound β-glycosidase from the hyperthermophilic Archaeon *Pyrococcus horikoshii*. *Proteins*, 57, 422–431.

[3]    Barabote, R. D. & Saier, M. H. Jr. (2005). Comparative genomic analyses of the bacterial phosphotransferase system. *Microbiol. Mol. Biol. Rev.*, 69, 608–634.

[4]    Bauer, M. W., Bylina, E. J., Swanson, R. V. & Kelly, R. M. (1996). Comparison of a β-glucosidase and a β-mannosidase from the hyperthermophilic archaeon *Pyrococcus furiosus*. *J. Biol. Chem.*, 271, 23749–23755.

[5]    Benešová, E., Lipovová, P., Dvořáková, H. & Králová, B. (2010). β-D-Galactosidase from *Paenibacillus thiaminolyticus* catalyzing transfucosylation reactions. *Glycobiology*, 20, 442–451.

[6]    Breves, R., Bronnenmeier, K., Wild, N., Lottspeich, F., Staudenbauer, W. L. & Hoffmeister, J. (1997). Genes encoding two different β-glucosidases of *Thermoanaerobacter brockii* are clustered in a common operon. *Appl. Environ. Microbiol.*, 63, 3902–3910.

[7]    Cairns, J. R. K., Champattanachai, V., Srisomsap, C., Wittman-Liebold, B., Thiede, B. & Svasti, J. (2000). Sequence and expression of Thai rosewood β-glucosidase/β-fucosidase, a family 1 glycosyl hydrolase glycoprotein. *J. Biochem.*, 128, 999–1008.

[8]    Cantarel, B. L., Coutinho, P. M., Rancurel, C., Bernard, T., Lombard, V. & Henrissat, B. (2009). The Carbohydrate-Active EnZymes database (CAZy): an expert resource for glycogenomics. *Nucleic Acids Res.*, 37, D233–D238.

[9]    Carapito, R., Imberty, A., Jeltsch, J., Byrns, S. C., Tam, P., Lowary, T. L., Varrot, A. & Phalip, V. (2009). Molecular Basis of arabinobio-hydrolase activity in phytopathogenic Fungi. *J. Biol. Chem.*, 284, 12285–12296.

[10]    Chi, Y., Martinez-Cruz, L. A., Jancarik, J., Swanson, R. V., Robertson, D. E. & Kim, S. (1999). Crystal structure of the β-glycosidase from the hyperthermophile *Thermosphaera aggregans*: insights into its activity and thermostability. *FEBS Lett.*, 445, 375–383.

[11]    Corbett, K., Fordham-Skelton, A. P., Gatehouse, J. A. & Davis, B. G. (2001). Tailoring the substrate specificity of the β-glycosidase from the thermophilic archaeon *Sulfolobus solfataricus*. *FEBS Lett.*, 509, 355–360.

[12]    Faijes, M. & Planas, A. (2007). In vitro synthesis of artificial polysaccharides by glycosidases and glycosynthases. *Carbohydr. Res.*, 342, 1581–1594.

[13]    Fan, H., Miao, L., Liu, Y., Liu, H. & Liu, Z. (2011). Gene cloning and characterization of a cold-adapted β-glucosidase belonging to glycosyl hydrolase family 1 from a psychrotolerant bacterium *Micrococcus antarcticus*. *Enzyme Microb. Technol.*, 49, 94–99.

[14]    Giordani, R. & Noat, G. (1988). Isolation, molecular properties and kinetic studies of a strict β-fucosidase from *Lactuca sativa* latex. *Eur. J. Biochem.*, 175, 619-625.

[15]    Gloster, T. M., Macdonald, J. M., Tarling, C. A., Stick, R. V., Withers, S. G. & Davies, G. J. (2004). Structural, thermodynamic, and kinetic analyses of tetrahydrooxazine-derived inhibitors bound to β-glucosidases. *J. Biol. Chem.*, 279, 49236–49242.

[16]    González-Candelas, L., Aristoy, M. C., Polaina, J. & Flors, A. (1989). Cloning and characterization of two genes from *Bacillus polymyxa* expressing β-glucosidase activity in *Escherichia coli*. *Appl. Environ. Microbiol.*, 55, 3173–3177.

[17]    Gu, N., Kim, J., Kim, H., You, D., Kim, H. & Jeon, S. (2009). Gene cloning and enzymatic properties of hyperthermostable β-glycosidase from *Thermus thermophilus* HJ6. *J. Biosci. Bioeng.*, 107, 21–26.

[18]    Hakulinen, N., Paavilainen, S., Korpela, T. & Rouvinen, J. (2000). The crystal structure of β-glucosidase from *Bacillus circulans* sp. *alkalophilus*: ability to form long polymeric assemblies. *J. Struct. Biol.*, 129, 69–79.

[19]    Hancock, S. M., Corbett, K., Fordham-Skelton, A. P., Gatehouse, J. A. & Davis, B. G. (2005). Developing promiscuous glycosidases for glycoside synthesis: residues W433 and E432 in *Sulfolobus solfataricus* β-glycosidase are important glucoside- and galactoside-specificity determinants. *ChemBioChem*, 6, 866–875.

[20]    Harada, K. M., Tanaka, K., Fukuda, Y., Hashimoto, W. & Murata, K. (2005). Degradation of rice bran hemicellulose by *Paenibacillus* sp. strain HC1: gene cloning, characterization and function of β-D-glucosidase as an enzyme involved in degradation. *Arch. Microbiol.*, 184, 215–224.

[21]    Hashimoto, W., Miki, H., Nankai, H., Sato, N., Kawai, S. & Murata, K. (1998). Molecular cloning of two genes for β-D-glucosidase in *Bacillus* sp. GL1 and identification of one as a gellan-degrading enzyme. *Arch. Biochem. Biophys.*, 360, 1–9.

[22]    Inácio, J. M. & de Sá-Nogueira, I. (2008). Characterization of *abn2* (*yxiA*), encoding a *Bacillus subtilis* GH43 arabinanase, Abn2, an its role in arabino-polysaccharide degradation. *J. Bacteriol.*, 190, 4272–4280.

[23]    Jabbour, D., Klippel, B. & Antranikian, G. (2012). A novel thermostable and glucose-tolerant β-glucosidase from *Fervidobacterium islandicum*. *Appl. Microbiol. Biotechnol.*, 93, 1947–1956.

[24] Jeng, W., Wang, N., Lin, M., Lin, C., Liaw, Y., Chang, W., Liu, C., Liang, P. & Wang, A. H. (2011). Structural and functional analysis of three β-glucosidases from bacterium *Clostridium cellulovorans*, fungus *Trichoderma reesei* and termite *Neotermes koshunensis*. *J. Struct. Biol.*, 173, 46–56.

[25] Kaper, T., Lebbink, J. H. G., Pouwels, J., Kopp, J., Schulz, G. E., van der Oost, J. & de Vos, W. M. (2000). Comparative structural analysis and substrate specificity engineering of the hyperthermostable β-glucosidase CelB from *Pyrococcus furiosus*. *Biochemistry*, 39, 4963–4970.

[26] Kaper, T., van Heusden, H. H., van Loo, B., Vasella, A., van der Oost, J. & de Vos, W. M. (2002). Substrate specificity engineering of β-mannosidase and β-glucosidase from *Pyrococcus* by exchange of unique active site residues. *Biochemistry*, 41, 4147–4155.

[27] Kempton, J. B. & Withers, S. G. (1992). Mechanism of *Agrobacterium* β-glucosidase: kinetic studies. *Biochemistry*, 31, 9961–9969.

[28] Kim, S., Oh, D., Kang, H. A. & Kwon, O. (2011). Features and applications of bacterial sialidases. *Appl. Microbiol. Biotechnol.*, 91, 1-15.

[29] Kittl, R. & Withers, S. G. (2010). New approaches to enzymatic glycoside synthesis through directed evolution. *Carbohydr. Res.*, 345, 1272–1279.

[30] Lagaert, S., Pollet, A., Delcour, J. A., Lavigne, R., Courtin, C. M. & Volckaert, G. (2010). Substrate specificity of three recombinant α-L-arabinofuranosidases from *Bifidobacterium adolescentis* and their divergent action on arabinoxylan and arabinoxylan oligosaccharides. *Biochem. Biophys. Res. Commun.*, 402, 644–650.

[31] Marana, S. R., Jacobs-Lorena, M., Terra, W. R. & Ferreira, C. (2001). Amino acid residues involved in substrate binding and catalysis in an insect digestive β-glycosidase. *Biochim. Biophys. Acta.*, 1545, 41–52.

[32] Margolles, A. & de los Reyes-Gavilán, C. G. (2003). Purification and functional characterization of a novel α-L-arabinofuranosidase from *Bifidobacterium longum* B667. *Appl. Environ. Microbiol.*, 69, 5096–5103.

[33] Marques, A. R., Coutinho, P. M., Videira, P., Fialho, A. M. & Sá-Correia, I. (2003). *Sphingomonas paucimobilis* β-glucosidase Bgl1: a member of a new bacterial subfamily in glycoside hydrolase family 1. *Biochem. J.*, 370, 793–804.

[34] McKie, V. A., Black, G. W., Millward-Sadler, S. J., Hazlewood, G. P., Laurie, J. I. & Gilbert, H. J. (1997). Arabinanase A from *Pseudomonas fluorescens* subsp. *cellulosa* exhibits both an endo- and an exo- mode of action. *Biochem. J.*, 323, 547–555.

[35] Miyazaki, T., Sato, T., Furukawa, K. & Ajisaka, K. (2010). Enzymatic synthesis of lacto-*N*-difucohexaose I which binds to *Helicobacter pylori*. In M. Fukuda (Eds.), Methods in Enzymology: Glycobiology (vol. 480, pp. 511–524). New York, St F115: Academic Press.

[36] Moracci, M., Capalbo, L., Ciaramella, M. & Rossi, M. (1996). Identification of two glutamic acid residues essential for catalysis in the β-glycosidase from the thermoacidophilic archaeon *Sulfolobus solfataricus*. *Protein Eng.*, 9, 1191–1195.

[37] Nijikken, Y., Tsukada, T., Igarashi, K., Samejima, M., Wakagi, T., Shoun, H. & Fushinobu, S. (2007). Crystal structure of intracellular family 1 β-glucosidase BGL1A from the basidiomycete *Phanerochaete chrysosporium*. *FEBS Lett.*, 581, 1514–1520.

[38] Nomura, T., Quesada, A. L. & Kutchan, T. M. (2008). The New β-D-glucosidase in terpenoid-isoquinoline alkaloid biosynthesis in *Psychotria ipecacuanha*. *J. Biol. Chem.*, 283, 34650–34659.

[39]   Park, S. H., Park, K. H., Oh, B. C., Alli, I. & Lee, B. H. (2011). Expression and characterization of an extremely thermostable β-glycosidase (mannosidase) from the hyperthermophilic archaeon *Pyrococcus furiosus* DSM3638. *N. Biotechnol.*, 28, 639–648.

[40]   Sanz-Aparicio, J., Hermoso, J. A., Martínez-Ripoll, M., Lequerica, J. L. & Polaina, J. (1998). Crystal structure of β-glucosidase A from *Bacillus polymyxa*: insights into the catalytic activity in family 1 glycosyl hydrolases. *J. Mol. Biol.*, 275, 491–502.

[41]   Scharf, M. E., Kovaleva, E. S., Jadhao, S., Campbell, J. H., Buchman, G. W. & Boucias, D. G. (2010). Functional and translational analyses of a β-glucosidase gene (glycosyl hydrolase family 1) isolated from the gut of the lower termite *Reticulitermes flavipes*. *Insect Biochem. Mol. Biol.*, 40, 611–620.

[42]   Schulte, D. & Hengstenberg, W. (2000). Engineering the active center of the 6-phospho-β-galactosidase from *Lactococcus lactis*. *Protein Eng.*, 13, 515–518.

[43]   Seshadri, S., Akiyama, T., Opassiri, R., Kuaprasert, B. & Cairns, J. K. (2009). Structural and enzymatic characterization of Os3BGlu6, a rice β-glucosidase hydrolyzing hydrophobic glycosides and (1→3)- and (1→2)-linked disaccharides. *Plant Physiol.*, 151, 47–58.

[44]   Shaikh, F. A. & Withers, S. G. (2008). Teaching old enzymes new tricks: engineering and evolution of glycosidases and glycosyl transferases for improved glycoside synthesis. *Biochem. Cell Biol.*, 86, 169–177.

[45]   Suzuki, H., Murakami, A. & Yoshida, K. Motif-guided identification of endo-1,5-α-L-arabinanase of glycoside hydrolase family 1 in *Bifidobacterium adolescentis*. submitted.

[46]   Suzuki, H., Okazaki, F., Kondo, A. & Yoshida, K. Genome mining and motif modifications of glycoside hydrolase family 1 members encoded by *Geobacillus kaustophilus* HTA426 provide thermostable 6-phospho-β-glycosidase and β-fucosidase. *Appl. Microbiol. Biotechnol.* in press.

[47]   Suzuki, H., Takahashi, S., Watanabe, R., Fukushima, Y., Fujita, N., Noguchi, A., Yokoyama, R., Nishitani, K., Nishino, T. & Nakayama, T. (2006). An isoflavone conjugate-hydrolyzing β-glucosidase from the roots of soybean (*Glycine max*) seedlings: purification, gene cloning, phylogenetics, and cellular localization. *J. Biol. Chem.*, 281, 30251–30259.

[48]   Trincone, A., Nicolaus, B., Lama, L., Morzillo, P., De Rosa, M. & Gambacorta, A. (1991). Enzyme-catalyzed synthesis of alkyl β-D-glycosides with crude homogenate of *Sulfolobus solfataricus*. *Biotechnol. Lett.*, 13, 235–240.

[49]   van den Broek, L. A. M., Lloyd, R. M., Beldman, G., Verdoes, J. C., McCleary, B. V. & Voragen, A. G. J. (2005). Cloning and characterization of arabinoxylan arabinofuranohydrolase-D3 (AXHd3) from *Bifidobacterium adolescentis* DSM20083. *Appl. Microbiol. Biotechnol.*, 67, 641–647.

[50]   van Laere, K. M. J., Voragen, C. H. L., Kroef, T., van den Broek, L. A. M., Beldman, G. & Voragen, A. G. J. (1999). Purification and mode of action of two different arabinoxylan arabinofuranohydrolases from *Bifidobacterium adolescentis* DSM 20083. *Appl. Microbiol. Biotechnol.*, 51, 606–613.

[51] van Laere, K. M. J., Beldman, G. & Voragen, A. G. J. (1997). A new arabinofuranohydrolase from *Bifidobacterium adolescentis* able to remove arabinosyl residues from double-substituted xylose units in arabinoxylan. *Appl. Microbiol. Biotechnol.*, 47, 231–235.

[52] Vocadlo, D. J. & Davies, G. J. (2008). Mechanistic insights into glycosidase chemistry. *Curr. Opin. Chem. Biol.*, 12, 539–555.

[53] Wang, L., Liu, Q., Sung, B., An, D., Lee, H., Kim, S., Kim, S., Lee, S. & Im, W. (2011). Bioconversion of ginsenosides $Rb_1$, $Rb_2$, Rc and Rd by novel β-glucosidase hydrolyzing outer 3-O glycoside from *Sphingomonas* sp. 2F2: cloning, expression, and enzyme characterization. *J. Biotechnol.*, 156, 125–133.

[54] Wang, L. (2008). Chemoenzymatic synthesis of glycopeptides and glycoproteins through endoglycosidase-catalyzed transglycosylation. *Carbohydr. Res.*, 343, 1509–1522.

[55] Wang, L. & Huang, W. (2009). Enzymatic transglycosylation for glycoconjugate synthesis. *Curr. Opin. Chem. Biol.*, 13, 592–600.

[56] Wang, X., He, X., Yang, S., An, X., Chang, W. & Liang, D. (2003). Structural basis for thermostability of β-glycosidase from the thermophilic eubacterium *Thermus nonproteolyticus* HG102. *J. Bacteriol.*, 185, 4248–4255.

[57] Wiesmann, C., Hengstenberg, W. & Schulz, G. E. (1997). Crystal structures and mechanism of 6-phospho-β-galactosidase from *Lactococcus lactis*. *J. Mol. Biol.*, 269, 851–860.

[58] Wilson, G. & Fox, C. F. (1974). The β-glucoside system of *Escherichia coli. J. Biol. Chem.*, 249, 5586–5598.

[59] Witt, E., Frank, R. & Hengstenberg, W. (1993). 6-Phospho-β-galactosidases of Gram-positive and 6-phospho-β-glucosidase B of Gram-negative bacteria: comparison of structure and function by kinetic and immunological methods and mutagenesis of the *lac*G gene of *Staphylococcus aureus. Protein Eng.*, 6, 913–920.

[60] Yoshida, S., Park, D. S., Bae, B., Mackie, R., Cann, I. K. O. & Nair, S. K. (2011). Structural and functional analyses of a glycoside hydrolase family 5 enzyme with an unexpected β-fucosidase activity. *Biochemistry*, 50, 3369–3375.

[61] Zechel, D. L., Boraston, A. B., Gloster, T., Boraston, C. M., Macdonald, J. M., Tilbrook, D. M. G., Stick, R. V. & Davies, G. J. (2003). Iminosugar glycosidase inhibitors: structural and thermodynamic dissection of the binding of isofagomine and 1-deoxynojirimycin to β-glucosidases. *J. Am. Chem. Soc.*, 125, 14313–14323.

[62] Zechel, D. L. & Withers, S. G. (2000). Glycosidase mechanisms: anatomy of a finely tuned catalyst. *Acc. Chem. Res.*, 33, 11–18.

In: Recent Advances in Ginseng and Glycosides Research    ISBN: 978-1-62417-765-1
Editor: Claude J. Hopkins    © 2013 Nova Science Publishers, Inc.

*Chapter 6*

# CHANGE IN THE COMPOSITION OF SACCHARIDES IN RICE GRAINS THROUGH COOKING AND DIGESTION USING SYNTHETIC HUMAN SALIVA

*Yasutaka Uda[1], Yoshiyuki Watanabe[1,\*], Tomoki Matsugami[1],*
*Akiko Fujita[2], Hiroshi Kanagawa[2], Kunimoto Takatsu[2],*
*Koji Kawakami[2] and Masato Nomura[1]*
[1]Department of Biotechnology and Chemistry, Faculty of Engineering,
Kinki University, Takaya, Higashi-Hiroshima, Japan
[2]Taste Research Office, Products Development Engineering Division,
Satake Corporation, Higashi-Hiroshima, Japan

## ABSTRACT

Various factors, such as texture, smell, taste and external, influence the delicious quality of rice. Attention to taste in these factors, the amounts of mono-, di- and trisaccharides, such as glucose, fructose, sucrose, maltose and maltotriose, which largely contribute to the taste of rice, in raw, cooked and digested rice were measured. Three cultivars of Koshihikari, Akitakomachi and Hoshinoyume were selected. As rice samples, not only freshly harvested rice but also two types of rice preserved at the milled state of the fresh rice at 40°C for one and two months were used. The digested rice was prepared through *in vitro* enzymatic reaction for cooked rice using artificially synthetic human saliva containing a digestive enzyme. Moreover, amylose and reducing saccharides contents in rice starch were also measured to examine the relationship between the changes in the amount of the tastable saccharides and the state of starch through cooking and subsequent digestion.

For raw rice of three cultivars, glucose contents were the largest in the tastable saccharides. The decrease of sucrose and the increases of fructose and glucose in cooked rice grains during the preservation were concurrently observed. These phenomena would

---
\* E-mail address: wysyk@hiro.kindai.ac.jp

be due to the hydrolysis of sucrose, which consists of fructose and glucose. The large amounts of maltose and maltotriose were detected in the digested rice samples, suggesting that these oligosaccharides would be liberated through the hydrolysis of $\alpha$-1,4 glucoside bonds in amylose and amylopectin molecules by the catalysis of $\alpha$-amylase in the synthetic saliva as these were hardly detected in the raw and cooked rice samples. It was found that the heating preservation affected the sweetness of rice and the heating-dependency of the sweetness was different among rice cultivars by the estimation of the relative sweetness of rice samples from the amount of tastable saccharides. The structure of the rice grains of the Koshihikari cultivar has difficulty with the heating effect during the preservative period, in contrast with the other two cultivars. The amylose contents for all cooked rice cultivars increased during preservation. It was observed that the amylose content in digested rice of each cultivar was lower than those in raw and cooked rice. This is mainly due to the hydrolysis catalyzed by $\alpha$-amylase in synthetic saliva in the digestion process. The reducing saccharides in all rice samples increased 20 to 50 fold by the debranching treatment.

**Keywords:** Amylose and amylopectin; Cooked and digested rice; Relative sweetness; Synthetic human saliva; Tastable Saccharides

# 1. INTRODUCTION

Rice, wheat and corn are the three major grains in the world. The consumption of rice per person in Japan has decreased sharply from 118.3 kg/year in 1962 to 61.4kg/year in 2005. Therefore, the rice powder that can be a flour substitute has been used to increase the consumption of domestic rice. However, the color, smell, texture and taste of rice grains decrease during circulation, preservation and rice-polishing. From the viewpoint of improvement of the delicious quality of rice and the demand expansion, it is important to obtain a basic finding for preserved rice. For that, it is indispensable to clarify the factors that influence the delicious quality of the rice and the mechanism and extent of their contribution. There are many reports about the structure and composition of the saccharides in rice grains. For example, the relationship between the texture of cooked rice and starch structure using some rice cultivars as samples was reported [1]. The composition and structure of compounds leached from rice grains during cooking were also examined for their contribution to the adhesiveness of cooked grains [2]. These contain important findings in relation to behavior of the saccharide molecules, especially polysaccharides, affecting the delicious quality of rice during cooking. However, the structure of some saccharide components will change by catalysis of some digestive enzymes in saliva during occlusion in the mouth. Therefore, the change in the amount of tastable saccharides from polishing rice to its digestion is shown in this chapter. In this chapter, "taste" is defined as a chemical property in a mouth, not physical as the texture. Three rice cultivars of Koshihikari, Akitakomachi and Hoshinoyume were selected and the amount of the tastable saccharides at their raw, cooked and digested states were quantitatively analyzed and compared. The digested rice was prepared through *in vitro* enzymatic reaction for cooked rice using artificially synthetic human saliva containing in hydrolytic enzyme. The rice preserved under 40°C for one and two months was also used similar to the freshly harvested rice. Furthermore, the amylose content in rice grains were also measured, and the changes in the amounts of the tastable saccharides through the cooking and mastication processes and the effect of the preservation were examined.

## 2. MATERIALS AND METHODS

### 2.1. Materials

The rice cultivars of Koshihikari, Akitakomachi, and Hoshinoyume, which had been harvested in 2008 in Fukushima, Akita and Hokkaido prefecture in Japan, respectively, were selected as rice samples. Their white rice obtained by milling, yielding more than 90% was used as raw rice.

A part of the freshly harvested rice was preserved at 40°C for one and two months, and each sample was used similarly as a fresh one for some experiments. Phenolphthalein solution was prepared by solubilizing phenolphthalein in 95% (v/v) ethanol at a specific volume to confirm the achieved extent of the deproteinization for some samples. An acetate buffer was prepared by mixing 0.1 mol/L acetic acid with 0.1 mol/L sodium acetate at a specific ratio and adjusting the pH at 3.5.

For the preparation of phosphate buffer, sodium chloride, potassium chloride and sodium hydrogen phosphate were mixed in distilled water, and the pH was adjusted to 7.4 by adding hydrochloric acid solution. Somogi reagent was prepared as follows; a given amount of disodium hydrogen phosphate and potassium sodium tartrate were added to 1 mol/L sodium hydroxide, and copper sulfate solution was mixed with it during heating. Further, sodium sulfate was added.

The reagent was obtained after leaving it for 2 days and the filtration, and was used for the measurement of the amount of reducing saccharides in each rice sample. All the chemicals used were of analytical grade and were purchased from Wako Pure Chemical Industries, Osaka, Japan and Sigma-Aldrich Fine Chemicals, St. Louis, MO, USA.

### 2.2. Preparation of Raw Rice Sample

Raw rice grains were deproteinized before some experiments in order to prevent proteins in rice grains from inhibiting the measurement of the amylose content in each sample.

At first, ca. 2 g of raw rice grains were mechanically milled to the powder size less than 40 mesh. Tenfold weight of 0.2% (w/v) sodium hydroxide solution was added and the mixture was stirred at 5°C for 3 h. After centrifuging at 6,000 rpm for 5 min, the supernatant was removed.

Then, 30 mL of distilled water was added to the precipitate. The centrifugation, under the same conditions as above, was carried out after stirring for 5 min. The obtained supernatant was repeatedly washed by distilled water, until the color disappeared, mixed with phenolphthalein solution. The washed supernatant was dehydrated by the addition of methanol and was dried for 15 h at 30°C. The mixture was milled to the size less than 250 mesh again.

## 2.3. Cooking Rice Grains

Cooking rice was carried out as follows [3-5]: Eighty grams of raw rice grains were washed three times with cold distilled water. Then it was left for 1 h at 5°C with 120 mL of distilled water in a dark container. Rice grains were cooked with a small rice cooker. Then, 2 g of cooked rice grains were milled in a mortar, and it was stirred for 3 h at 5°C with 20 g of 0.2% (w/v) sodium hydroxide solution. After centrifugation at 6,000 rpm for 5 min, the supernatant was removed. Twenty milliliters of distilled water was added to the precipitate. The additional centrifugation at above-mentioned conditions was executed after stirring for 5 min. Similar to the methods in subsection 2.2, the supernatant was repeatedly washed for deproteinization and dehydrated using methanol. It was dried for 1 day at room temperature. The powder was further milled, and it was used as a cooked rice sample.

## 2.4. *In Vitro* Digestion using Synthetic Human Saliva

Synthetic saliva of Greenwood prescription was prepared as follows [6, 7]: First, 500 mL of aqueous solution containing 1.2 g of potassium chloride, 300 mg of tricalcium phosphate, 700 mg of dipotassium hydrogen phosphate, 450 mg of potassium sulfate, and 400 mg of trisodium phosphate were prepared. The precipitation was excluded by the centrifuge at 5,000 rpm for 5 min. After heating it at 37°C, 2.5 g of albumin was dissolved in it. Then, pH of the solution was adjusted to 6.8 by blowing the carbon dioxide gas. α-Amylase from human saliva was dissolved at 20 U/mL.

Six grams of the cooked rice, which corresponded to about 150 grains, were added to 7.5 mL of the artificial saliva, and the occlusion treatment for the mixture was executed 20 times, which took about 13 s, at 37°C using specially made glass stick and vessel [8, 9]. The enzyme in the mixture was deactivated by heating at 80°C for 10 min [10, 11]. The deproteinization and drying processes, described in subsections 2.2 and 2.3, were applied to the digested rice sample.

## 2.5. Measurement of Amylose Content in Rice Grains

The amylose content in rice grains was measured with a slight modification according to the previous reports [12]. Fifty milligrams of the powdery samples deproteinized as shown in above subsections were dissolved in the mixture of 0.5 mL of 99.5% (v/v) ethanol and 4.5 mL of 1 mol/L sodium hydroxide solution. After incubation for 10 min at 80°C, it was diluted with distilled water up to 50 mL of the volume for the solution. Then, 2.5 mL of this solution was mixed with 0.5 mL of 1 mol/L acetic acid and 1.0 mL of iodine-potassium iodide solution, which was constructed with 0.2% (w/v) iodine and 2.0% (w/v) potassium iodide, and repeatedly diluted with distilled water up to 50 mL. After incubation for 30 min at 27°C, the absorbance of the sample solution at 620 nm was measured using a UV-VIS spectrophotometer (V-630, JASCO Corporation, Tokyo, Japan). For calibration curves, several solutions with the different compositions between amylose type-III (Sigma-Aldrich Fine Chemicals) and glutinous rice as an amylopectin standard were used.

## 2.6. Extraction of Tastable Saccharides from Rice Samples and HPLC Analysis

The extraction of tastable saccharides from the rice sample was carried out using slightly modified methods [3-5, 13, 14]. Ten grams of raw rice grains were mechanically milled and were added to 50 mL of distilled water. The tastable saccharides were extracted for 2 h at 20°C in a water bath with gentle shaking. After the filtration, the additional extraction was executed in 50 mL of distilled water for 1 h. The filtration was repeated, and the filtrate was freeze-dried by a freeze-drier (DC400, Yamato Scientific Co., Ltd., Tokyo). The distilled water was added to the dried powder to obtain 5 mL of the sample solution. Then, the solution was filtered with two hydrophilic membranes, whose pore sizes were 0.80 and 0.45 μm. The filtrate was diluted two fold by 50% (v/v) acetonitrile solution, and was filtered to the membrane at the pore size of 0.20 μm. Twenty microliters of the filtrate was used for HPLC analysis. For the cooked rice sample, 100 mL of 50% (v/v) ethanol solution was first added to 10 g of the rice sample. It was milled in a mortar and the mixture was incubated at 20°C for 2 h.

After the filtration, 50 mL of 50% (v/v) ethanol solution was added to the residue, and the mixture was again incubated at 20°C for 1 h. These processes were repeated twice. The solvent in the filtrate was evaporated, and the condensate was freeze-dried. The distilled water was added to the dried powder up to 5 mL of the volume for the solution, and the mixture was filtered to the above membranes at each pore size of 0.80 and 0.45 μm. The filtrate (10 μL) was used as a sample for HPLC analysis.

After the digestion process, 25 mL of 50% (v/v) ethanol solution was added to the digested rice, and the mixture was incubated at 20°C for 2 h. After the filtration, 12.5 mL of 50% (v/v) ethanol solution was added to the residue. The mixture was incubated at 20°C for 1 h and these processes were repeated twice, similar to the case of the cooked rice sample.

After evaporation and freeze-drying, distilled water was added to the dried powder up to 5 mL, and the mixture was filtered to the membrane, whose pore size was 0.20 μm. Ten microliters of the filtrate was used for HPLC analysis. In HPLC equipment, two YMC-Pack NH$_2$ columns, each 150 × 4.6 mmI.D. (YMC, Kyoto, Japan) were connected in series, and the differential refractometer (RID-10A, Shimadzu, Kyoto) was used as a detector. The eluent used was acetonitrile/water (75/25 (v/v)), and the flow rate was 0.80 mL/min. The concentrations of glucose, fructose, sucrose, maltose and maltotriose as a tastable saccharide were measured by this HPLC system.

## 2.7. Amount of Reducing Saccharides in Starch

The debranching treatment was executed as follows [15]: The raw, cooked or digested rice sample (150 mg) dissolved in 2.5 mL of 1 mol/L sodium hydroxide solution was left at 5°C overnight for starch gelatinization. After adding 5 mL of the distilled water, the pH was adjusted to 7.0 by hydrochloric acid. Then, it was incubated for 24 h at 40°C with 5,900 U of isoamylase and 1.0 mL of 1.0 mol/L acetate buffer (pH 3.5). Further, 50 U of pullulanase was added, and the solution was incubated for 24 h at 40°C to achieve complete debranching. For inactivation of used enzymes after the reaction, the solution was heated at 80°C for 10 min.

After the concentration under the reduced pressure, 0.1 mol/L sodium hydroxide solution was added up to 5 mL of the volume. Two milliliters of this solution was mixed with 2 mL of Somogi reagent, and it was heated in boiling water for 15 min. The solution was left for 5 min at room temperature after cooling by cold water. Two milliliters of Nelson reagent was added and adequately mixed, and the mixture set for 15 min.

It was diluted by the distilled water up to 20 mL and then filtered. The absorbance of the solution was measured at 520 nm using the spectrophotometer. Instead of the debranched sample solutions, 2, 5, 10, 15 and 20 mg% (w/v) glucose solution was used for calibration curves.

# 3. RESULTS AND DISCUSSIONS

## 3.1. Amount of Tastable Saccharides in Rice Grains

The amounts of tastable saccharides, which were glucose, sucrose and maltose, in fresh and preserved rice grains of Koshihikari, Akitakomachi and Hoshinoyume at raw state are shown in Figures 1-3.

The total amounts of tastable saccharides in fresh Koshihikari cultivar, preserved for 1 and 2 months, were 359, 241 and 321 mg/100 g-rice powder, respectively. The tastable saccharides in fresh rice consisted of 46.7% glucose, 28.1% sucrose and 25.2% maltose. The saccharides in rice preserved for 1 and 2 months were constituted of 58.2% glucose, 24.3% sucrose and 17.5% maltose, and 63.0% glucose, 19.8% sucrose and 17.2% maltose, respectively. The composition of glucose was the largest and increased during preservation. It seems that oligo- and polysaccrarides in rice grains were hydrolyzed to glucose during the preservation. For the rice cultivar of Akitakomachi, the total amounts of tastable saccharides in fresh, preserved for 1 and 2 months samples, were 525, 567 and 316 mg/100 g-rice powder, respectively. The composition of tastable saccharides in fresh rice was 46.3% glucose, 23.3% sucrose and 30.4% maltose. The saccharides in rice samples preserved for 1 and 2 months consisted of 41.5% glucose, 13.7% sucrose and 44.8% maltose, and 53.7% glucose, 25.9% sucrose and 20.4% maltose, respectively. The amounts of glucose and sucrose decreased during the preservation.

The decrement of sucrose would be due to its hydrolysis. Glucose might react with the compounds having an amino group, because it is a reducing saccharide. The total tastable saccharides contents in fresh, preserved for 1 and 2 months rice cultivar of Hoshinoyume were 476, 517 and 482 mg/100 g-rice powder, respectively. The saccharides in fresh rice consisted of 39.6% glucose, 22.8% sucrose and 37.7% maltose. The saccharides compositions in rice preserved for 1 and 2 months were 41.3% glucose, 22.1% sucrose and 36.6% maltose, and 49.6% glucose, 20.2% sucrose and 30.2% maltose, respectively. Similar to the rice cultivar of Koshihikari, the amount of glucose increased with the decrements of disaccharides.

For all cultivars, glucose contents were the largest in the tastable saccharides and the compositions of sucrose were similar among the three cultivars. There is no tendency for the amount of maltose among these cultivars. This might indicate that the maltose contents depend on both the decrement due to its hydrolysis to glucose and the increment based on the hydrolysis of starch, such as amylose and amylopectin, in raw rice.

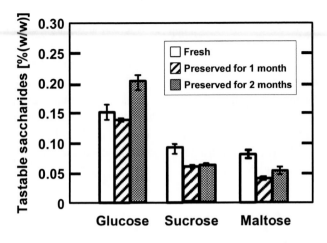

Figure 1. The amount of tastable saccharides in fresh and preserved rice grains of Koshihikari at raw state. The preservation was carried out at 40°C for one and two months. The error bars present the standard deviations ($n = 3$).

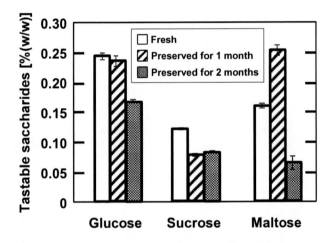

Figure 2. The amount of tastable saccharides in fresh and preserved rice grains of Akitakomachi at raw state. The preservation was carried out at 40°C for one and two months. The error bars present the standard deviations ($n = 3$).

Figures 4-6 shows the compositions for tastable saccharides in rice grains after cooking fresh and preserved rice of Koshihikari, Akitakomachi and Hoshinoyume. Maltose was not detected by HLPC analysis, while the concentration of fructose was measured for the rice samples preserved for 1 and 2 months.

The total amounts of three tastable saccharides in fresh Koshihikari rice cultivar, preserved for 1 and 2 months, were 161, 195 and 172 mg/100 g-rice powder, respectively. In fresh rice, the tastable saccharides consisted of 35.8% glucose and 64.2% sucrose. The saccharides in the rice preserved for 1 and 2 months were composed of 4.9% fructose, 56.2% glucose and 38.9% sucrose, and 7.2% fructose, 57.5% glucose and 35.3% sucrose, respectively. The decrease of sucrose and the increases of fructose and glucose during the preservation were concurrently observed. Such two phenomena would be due to the hydrolysis of sucrose, because sucrose consists of fructose and glucose. In comparison with raw rice, the total amounts of tastable saccharides in cooked rice were small. The tastable saccharides might be present in the outside of the rice grains, and therefore some of them would be removed when washed by the distilled water. For Akitakomachi cultivar, the total amounts of tastable saccharides in fresh, preserved for 1 and 2 months, samples were 212,199 and 199 mg/100 g-rice powder, respectively. The tastable saccharides in fresh rice were composed of 28.9% glucose and 71.1% sucrose. The saccharides in rice samples preserved for 1 and 2 months consisted of 5.9% fructose, 48.8% glucose and 45.3% sucrose, and 5.2% fructose, 52.4% glucose and 42.5% sucrose, respectively.

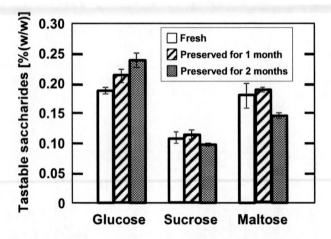

Figure 3. The amount of tastable saccharides in fresh and preserved rice grains of Hoshinoyume in raw state. The preservation was carried out at 40°C for one and two months. The error bars present the standard deviations ($n = 3$).

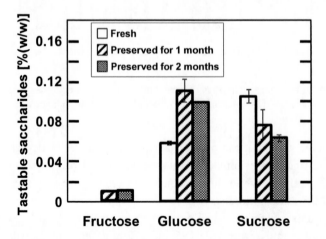

Figure 4. The amount of tastable saccharides in rice grains after cooking fresh and preserved rice of Koshihikari. The preservation was carried out at 40°C for one and two months. The error bars present the standard deviations ($n = 3$).

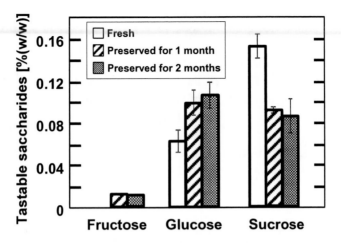

Figure 5. The amount of tastable saccharides in rice grains after cooking fresh and preserved rice of Akitakomachi. The preservation was carried out at 40°C for one and two months. The error bars present the standard deviations ($n = 3$).

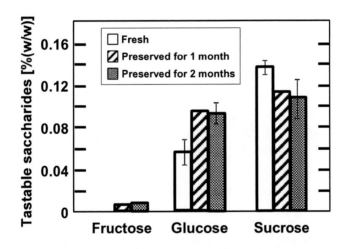

Figure 6. The amount of tastable saccharides in rice grains after cooking fresh and preserved rice of Hoshinoyume. The preservation was carried out at 40°C for one and two months. The error bars present the standard deviations ($n = 3$).

The total tastable saccharides contents in fresh, preserved for 1 and 2 months rice of Hoshinoyume cultivar were 190, 209 and 203 mg/100 g-rice powder, respectively. The saccharides in fresh rice were constituted of 29.2% glucose and 70.8% sucrose. The compositions of the saccharides in rice preserved for 1 and 2 months were 2.5% fructose, 44.0% glucose and 53.5% sucrose, and 3.3% fructose, 45.1% glucose and 51.6% sucrose, respectively. For the cultivars of Akitakomachi and Hoshinoyume, both the decrement of sucrose and the increment of fructose and glucose during the preservation were the same as the Koshihikari cultivar. For the determination of the occlusion treatment conditions for the digestion of cooked rice grains, the amount of cooked rice grains eaten at one bite and the occlusion speed were evaluated. Seven panelists, who were from 21 to 23 years old and consisted five males and two females, participated in these tests. The average and standard deviation values for the amount eaten at a bite were 12.2 ± 3.2 g of cooked rice grains, which corresponded to about 300 rice grains. It took 13 ± 1.5, 25 ± 2.4 and 38 ± 3.7 s to bite the amount of the grains eaten at one bite at 20, 40 and 60 times, respectively.

The scale of the glass vessel for the occlusion treatment was assumed to be half of the average volume of oral cavity. Therefore, the occlusion treatment procedures were adopted as described in subsection 2.4. The amounts of tastable saccharides in rice grains digested using artificially synthetic human saliva after cooking fresh and preserved rice of three cultivars are shown in Figures 7-9. The sums of tastable saccharides contents in fresh, preserved for 1 and 2 months, rice cultivar of Koshihikari were 2.48, 2.37 and 2.04 g/100 g-rice powder, respectively. The saccharides in fresh rice consisted of 3.4% glucose, 3.6% sucrose, 35.5% maltose and 57.5% maltotriose. For the rice preserved for 1 and 2 months, the saccharides were composed of 3.9% glucose, 3.1% sucrose, 41.3% maltose and 51.7% maltotriose, and 5.9% glucose, 4.6% sucrose, 32.5% maltose and 57.1% maltotriose, respectively.

Large amounts of maltose and maltotriose were detected in the digested rice sample. It was suggested that these oligosaccharides are formed through the hydrolysis of α-1,4 glucoside bonds in amylose and amylopectin molecules by the catalytic action of α-amylase in the synthetic saliva, because these were hardly detected in the raw and cooked rice samples.

The lower amounts of tastable saccharides were observed for the longer preservative period, indicating the structural alteration of starch in rice grains to the state that enzymes were hard to act to. For the cultivar of Akitakomachi, the total amounts of tastable saccharides in fresh, preserved for 1 and 2 months samples were 2.19, 1.97 and 1.87 g/100 g-rice powder, respectively. The saccharides composition in fresh rice was 3.5% glucose, 4.9% sucrose, 30.9% maltose and 60.6% maltotriose. The saccharides in rice samples preserved for 1 and 2 months consisted of 4.9% glucose, 4.1% sucrose, 37.2% maltose and 53.7% maltotriose, and 6.8% glucose, 5.7% sucrose, 34.4% maltose and 53.1% maltotriose, respectively.

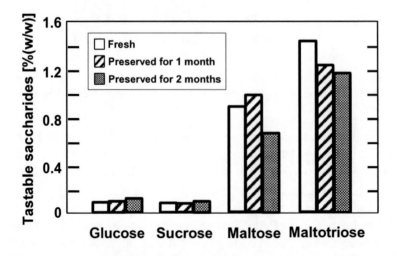

Figure 7. The amount of tastable saccharides in rice grains digested using artificially synthetic human saliva after cooking fresh and preserved rice of Koshihikari. The preservation was carried out at 40°C for one and two months.

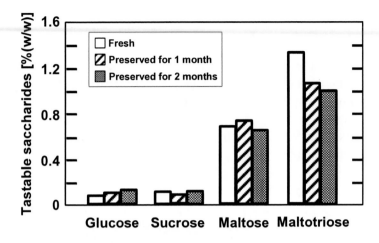

Figure 8. The amount of tastable saccharides in rice grains digested using artificially synthetic human saliva after cooking fresh and preserved rice of Akitakomachi. The preservation was carried out at 40°C for one and two months.

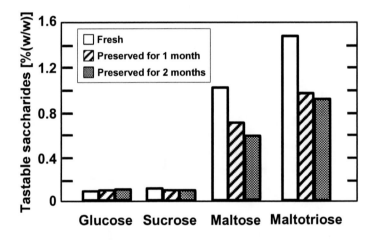

Figure 9. The amount of tastable saccharides in rice grains digested using artificially synthetic human saliva after cooking fresh and preserved rice of Hoshinoyume. The preservation was carried out at 40°C for one and two months.

The amounts of maltose and maltotriose were smaller than those of the cultivar of Koshihikari. The total tastable saccharides contents in fresh, preserved for 1 and 2 months rice of the Hoshinoyume cultivar were 2.68, 1.85 and 1.70 g/100 g-rice powder, respectively. The tastable saccharides in fresh rice consisted of 3.1% glucose, 4.2% sucrose, 37.9% maltose and 54.8% maltotriose. The compositions of four saccharides in rice preserved for 1 and 2 months were 5.1% glucose, 5.0% sucrose, 37.8% maltose and 52.2% maltotriose, and 6.1% glucose, 5.7% sucrose, 34.4% maltose and 53.8% maltotriose, respectively. Among the three cultivars, there was the same tendency for change in the amount of each tastable saccharide in the digested samples. That is; the amount of glucose slightly increased and that of sucrose was almost constant throughout the preservation. Furthermore, oligosaccharide contents tended to decrease in the preservative term.

## 3.2. Relative Sweetness of Rice

The relative sweetness of rice grains at raw, cooked and digested states was examined for three rice cultivars, Koshihikari, Akitakomachi and Hoshinoyume. The relative sweetness of each tastable saccharide was calculated based on unity for the sweetness of sucrose using the results shown in Figs. 1-9. That is, the relative values for fructose, glucose, maltose and maltotriose were used as 1.7, 0.7, 0.4 and 0.3, respectively [16]. The relative sweetness on raw, cooked and digested rice grains for fresh rice and preserved rice at 40°C for one and two months was shown in Figure 10.

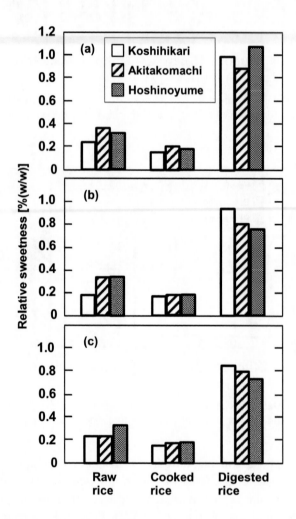

Figure 10. The relative sweetness on raw, cooked and digested rice grains for (a) fresh rice and preserved rice at 40°C for (b) 1 and (c) 2 months.

For fresh rice, the sweetness of Akitakomachi rice was the highest among the three cultivars of raw rice. Three cultivars of cooked rice have similar sweetness values. It was, however, shown that the cultivar of Hoshinoyume had the highest relative sweetness when digesting rice in the mouth. For the rice preserved for one month, the relative sweetness of Koshihikari was the lowest at raw state while it was the highest in digested rice. Moreover, the relative sweetness for raw rice of Akitakomachi and for digested rice of Hoshinoyume decreased during the preservation for 2 months. It was found that the heating preservation affected the sweetness of the rice and the heating-dependency of the sweetness was different among rice cultivars. The rice grain of Koshihikari cultivar has a hard structure  for the heating effect during the preservative period. On the other hand, the structure of starch in the rice grain of Hoshinoyume would change during the term so that digestive enzymes could function more facilely as a catalyst.

## 3.3. Amylose Content in Rice Grains

The amylose contents in fresh and preserved rice grains of Koshihikari, Akitakomachi and Hoshinoyume at raw state are shown in Figure 11. In the raw rice of Akitakomachi cultivar, the amylose amount increased during the preservation for two months.

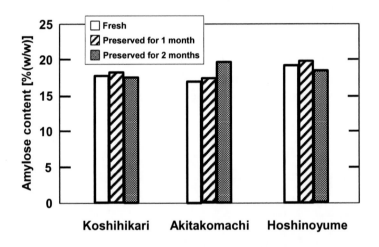

Figure 11. The amylose contents in fresh and preserved rice grains of Koshihikari, Akitakomachi and Hoshinoyume at raw state. The preservation was carried out at 40°C for one and two months.

The three-dimensional structure of amylopectin in rice grains would slacken under a heating condition so that amylose molecules could increase through the hydrolysis catalyzed by the native enzymes, such as α-glucosidase I, α- and β-amylases, in rice grains[3][Kasai, 2000]. The amylose contents in Koshihikari and Hoshinoyume rice grains changed little during the preservation. The amylose contents for the three cultivars were from 17.4 to 20.3% (w/w). These samples with such amylose contents generally have a good texture.

Figure 12 shows the amounts of the amylose in rice after cooking fresh and preserved rice grains in the above three cultivars. The amylose contents for all rice cultivars increased during the preservation. Clearer changes for the amylose contents in each cooked rice during the preservation than for raw rice were observed, as some chemical and enzymatic reactions in rice grains are accelerated by adding water and heating in cooking. The amylose contents in rice digested using artificially synthetic human saliva after cooking fresh and preserved rice grains are shown in Figure 13. It was observed that the amylose content in digested rice of each cultivar was lower at *ca.* 2% (w/w) than those in raw and cooked rice.

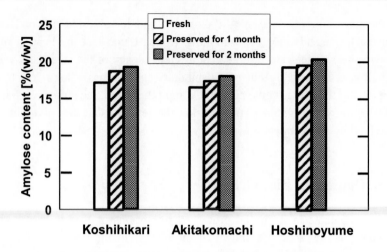

Figure 12. The amylose contents in rice after cooking fresh and preserved rice grains of Koshihikari, Akitakomachi and Hoshinoyume. The preservation was carried out at 40°C for one and two months.

This would be mainly due to the hydrolysis catalyzed by α-amylase in the synthetic saliva in the digestion process. In contrast, the amounts of maltose and maltotriose increased through the digestion as shown in Figures 1-9. These tastable saccharides, including glucose, would form through the hydrolysis of amylose in the digestion (Figure 14).

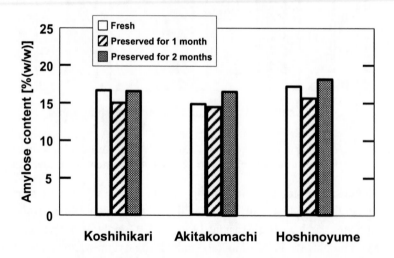

Figure 13. The amylose contents in rice digested using synthetic human saliva after cooking fresh and preserved rice grains of Koshihikari, Akitakomachi and Hoshinoyume. The preservation was carried out at 40°C for one and two months.

## 3.4. Branched Structure of Starch

In order to examine the change in the state of starch molecules in rice grains during cooking and digesting in a mouth, the amounts of reducing saccharides in raw, cooked and digested rice grains were measured. Further, the debranching treatment using isoamylase and pullulanase for each rice sample was carried out as described in subsection 2.7 to evaluate the branched structure of amylopectin molecules in rice starch. The debranching was achieved by this procedure as shown in Figure 15.

The hydrolysis of α-1,6 glucoside bonds in starch was catalyzed by these two enzymes. Thus, the branched structure of amylopectin in starch would be shown by measuring the change in the amount of reducing saccharides between, before, and after the debranching process. Figure 16 shows the reducing saccharide contents in fresh rice grains of Koshihikari at raw, cooked and digested state. The reducing saccharides in all the samples except amylose standard increased at 20 to 50 fold with the debranching treatment.

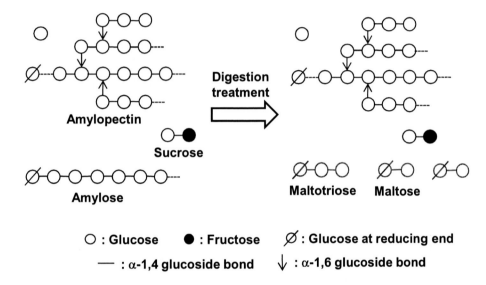

Figure 14. Scheme of digestion process for starch in rice grains.

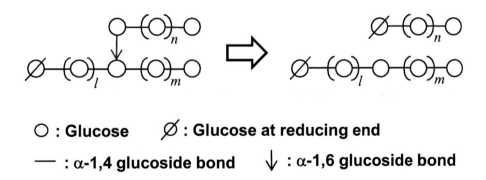

Figure 15. Scheme of debranching process for amylopectin in rice grains.

The amount of the reducing saccharides after the treatment was large in order of digested rice > cooked rice > raw rice, indicating both digestion and debranching effects on liberating oligosaccharides and branched glucoside-chains. The reducing saccharides in amylose standard also increased, because amylose is not completely linear and contains 5 to 20 branching points per molecule.

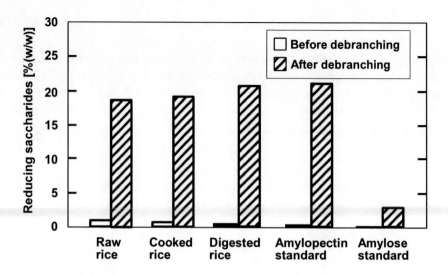

Figure 16. The amount of reducing saccharides in fresh rice grains of Koshihikari at raw, cooked and digested state.

## CONCLUSION

In this chapter, the changes in the composition of the tastable saccharides and the structure of starch molecules were shown. Glucose contents were the largest in the tastable saccharides for raw rice grains. The decrease of sucrose and the increases of fructose and glucose in cooked rice grains during the preservation were concurrently observed due to the hydrolysis of sucrose.

Maltose and maltotriose were detected in the digested rice, suggesting the liberation through the hydrolysis of $\alpha$-1,4 glucoside bonds in amylose and amylopectin molecules by the catalysis of $\alpha$-amylase in the synthetic saliva. It was found that the heating preservation influenced the sweetness of rice and the heating-dependency of the sweetness was different among rice cultivars. The amylose contents for all cooked rice cultivars was increased by preservation.

The amylose content decreased due to the hydrolysis catalyzed by $\alpha$-amylase in the synthetic saliva. The reducing saccharides in all rice samples increased at 20 to 50 fold by the debranching treatment. The increasing rate for digested rice sample was the highest. However, some points remain unclear. For example, the amounts and the activities of the native hydrolytic enzymes in rice grains would be different among the rice cultivars but they could not be evaluated. Further, the amount of the reducing saccharides, which contains monosaccharides except for glucose and oligosaccharides such as maltose and maltotriose, was estimated as the amount corresponding to glucose in this chapter.

The change in the molecular weight distributions of amylose, amylopectin and its branched chains in rice grains before/after cooking and subsequent digestion should be examined in the future.

# REFERENCES

[1] Takahashi, S.; Sugiura, T.; Naito, H.; Shibuya, N.; Kainuma, K. Correlation between Taste of Cooked Rice and Structural Characteristics of Rice Starch, *Journal of applied glycoscience* 1998, *45*, 99-106 (in Japanese).

[2] Hanashiro, I.; Ohta, K.; Takeda, C.; Mizukami, H.; Takeda, Y. Leaching of Amylose and Amylopectin during Cooking of Rice Grains and Their Effect on Adhesiveness of Cooked Rice, *Journal of applied glycoscience* 2004, *51*, 349-354 (in Japanese).

[3] Kasai, M.; Ishiguro, K.; Kyouda, H.; Hamazono, T.; Hatae, K.; Shimada, A. Change in the Amounts of Reducing Sugars and Free Amino Acids in Rice during the Cooking Processes, *Nihon Kasei Gakkaishi* 2000, *51*, 579-585 (in Japanese).

[4] Kasai, M.; Ohishi, K.; Shimada, A.; Hatae, K. Taste Property of Cooked Rice based on an Analysis of the Coole Rice Extracts, *Nippon Chouri Kagakkaisi* 2001, *34*, 27-33. (in Japanese).

[5] Baba, Y.; Ookura, T.; Kasai, M. Effects of Rate of Temperature Increase and Holding Temperature During Cooking on the Amounts of Chemical Components in Rice Grains, *Nippon Chouri Kagakkaisi* 2007, *40*, 323-328 (in Japanese).

[6] Imai, K.; Terashima, H.; Izutani, K.; Akagi, H.; Nakamura, M. Development of Cytotoxicity Test Medium Containing Saliva Factors for Dental Biomaterials, *Shikazairyo Kikai* 1998, *17*, 362-369 (in Japanese).

[7] Etienne, O.; Schneider, A.; Taddei, C.; Richert, L.; Schaaf, P.; Voegel, J. C.; Egles, C.; Picart, C. Degradability of Polysaccharides Multilayer Films in the Oral Environment: an in Vitro in Vivo Study, *Biomacromolecules* 2005, *6*, 726-733.

[8] Imai, T.; Kurashima, S.; Katsuna, T.; Fukui, T.; Hirashita, A.; Shiosawa, K. Analysis of adult open bite patient in masticating foods with different consistency, *Tsurumi Shigaku* 2003, *29*, 13-21 (in Japanese).

[9] Uchida, A.; Nakamura, M.; Ohashi, M.; Yurikusa, M.; Matsuda, H. Effect of Meals on Blood Glucose Level (Part 2 ): Difference between Free mastication and Forced mastication, *Journal of Nagoya Bunri University* 2009,

[10] Tanimoto, S.; Shimoda, M.; Matsumoto, H.; Fujii, K.; Ohdoi, R.; Sakamoto, K.; Izuwa, S.; Yamane, Y.; Osajima, Y. Thermal inactivation behavior of enzymes in fresh sake during pasteurization, Journal of the Brewing Society of Japan 2004, 99, 208-214 (in Japanese).

[11] Arai, E.; Ishikawa, Y.; Ito, K. Purification and Characteristics of ana-Amylase Contained in Miso, *Nihon Kasei Gakkaishi* 1991, *42*, 767-773 (in Japanese).

[12] McGrance, S. J.; Cornell, H. J.; Rix, C. J. A Simple and Rapid Colorimetric Method for the Determination of Amylose in Starch Products, *Starch* 1998, *50*, 158-163.

[13] Sugiyama, S.; Konishi, M.; Terasaki, D.; Hatae, K.; Shimada, A. Determination of the Chemical. Components and. Distribution in the Milled Rice Kernel, *Nippon Shokuhin Kagaku Kogaku Kaishi* 1995, *42*, 401-409 (in Japanese).

[14] Yamakura, M.; Okadome, H.; Suzuki, K.; Tran, U. T.; Homma, S.; Sasagawa, A.; Yamazaki, A.; Ohtsubo, K. Effects of High-Pressure Treatment and Soaking to the Cooked Rice, *Nippon Shokuhin Kagaku Kogaku Kaishi* 2005, *52*, 60-67 (in Japanese).

[15]  Tahara, M.; Kishida, E.; Misaki, A. Fractionation of Wild Rice (Zizania palustris) Polysaccharides and Characterization of the Starch Fraction, *Nippon Eiyo Syokuryo Gakkaishi*, 2000, *53*, 111-118. (in Japanese).

[16]  Kato, Y.; Nakamura, T. *In Shokuhingaku I*; Nankodo Co., Ltd.: Tokyo, 2007; p 27 (in Japanese).

In: Recent Advances in Ginseng and Glycosides Research     ISBN: 978-1-62417-765-1
Editor: Claude J. Hopkins     © 2013 Nova Science Publishers, Inc.

*Chapter 7*

# EFFECTS OF ULTRASOUND ASSISTED EXTRACTION OF WATER SOLUBLE CONSTITUENTS ON BRAZILIAN GINSENG ROOTS

## *D. T. Santos[1],\*, R. Vardanega[1], J. Q. Albarelli[2], R. B. Rabelo[2], M. M. Beppu[2] and M. A. A. Meireles[1]*

[1]LASEFI (LAboratory of Supercritical technology: Extraction, Fractionation, and Identification of vegetable extracts) / DEA (Department of Food Engineering) / FEA (School of Food Engineering) /UNICAMP (University of Campinas), Campinas, São Paulo, Brazil
[2]School of Chemical Engineering / UNICAMP (University of Campinas), Campinas, São Paulo, Brazil

## ABSTRACT

Ultrasound-assisted extraction (UAE) is an effective technique to recovery analytes from different matrices in shorter time than other extraction techniques. The recognition of the efficiency of dynamic UAE coupled with the additional advantages offered by the use of water as an environmentally friendly solvent has prompted researchers to investigate the potential of UAE for industrial-scale extraction of natural products. Species of the genus Pfaffia (Amaranthaceae) are commercialized in Brazil as substitutes for Panax spp. (ginseng, Araliaceae). Due to the similar morphology of its roots to those of ginseng, they are popularly known as "Brazilian ginseng". Recently, highly chemical constituents used in the pharmaceutical, cosmetic and food industries have been identified in Brazilian ginseng (Pffafia glomerata) roots. Thus, the effects of dynamic ultrasound assisted extraction of water soluble constituents on Brazilian Ginseng (Pffafia glomerata) roots were evaluated in order to understand how ultrasound interacts with cell walls and enhance mass transfer of the cell contents. The roots were analyzed before and after being subjected to the extraction process by scanning electron microscopy (SEM),

* E-mail address: diego_tresinari@yahoo.com.br.

X-ray diffraction (XRD), Fourier transform infrared spectroscopy (FTIR) and Differential Thermal (DT) analyses.

# INTRODUCTION

Extraction is the important step for the recovery of bioactive compounds from the plant raw materials. Extraction technologies must be versatile, relatively simple and safe for the operating personnel and the consumers and inexpensive to use. The traditional techniques of solvent extraction of plant raw materials are mostly based on the correct choice of solvents and the use of heat and-or agitation to increase the solubility of analytes and the rates of mass transfer. Usually, the traditional techniques require long extraction hours and may have low efficiency. Moreover, many natural products are thermally unstable and degradate during thermal extraction [1].

Many extraction techniques, such as soxhlet extraction (SE), reflux extraction (RE), microwave-assisted extraction (MAE), supercritical fluid extraction (SFE), superheated water extraction (SWE) and ultrasound assisted extraction (UAE) have been used to extract bioactive compounds from ginseng [2-4]. Ginseng is a common name for various *Panax* plants, particularly *Panax ginseng* (Asian ginseng) and *Panax quinquefolium* (American ginseng). They are among the most precious and famous plant herbs, their roots, are widely used for health foods and traditional medicine. Species of Pfaffia genus, as *Pfaffia glomerata*, belong to the Amaranthaceae family, and are the Brazilian substitutes for the Panax genus plants, receiving the popular name of *Brazilian Ginseng*. [5]. So far, much less work about obtaining bioactive compounds from Brazilian ginseng has been done.

Ultrasonic vibrations are the source of energy facilitating the release of analytes from the sample matrix. Compared with traditional solvent extraction methods, UAE improves extraction efficiency and rate, reduces extraction temperature, and increases the selection ranges of the solvents. In comparison with more advanced techniques such as SFE and MAE, the equipment is relatively simpler and inexpensive. Moreover, UAE is beneficial to the botanical materials which are sensitive to temperature. The other advantages of ultrasound in extraction from plants are mass transfer intensification, cell disruption, improved solvent penetration and capillary effect [3, 6].

Ultrasound assisted extraction in a dynamic system is rarely reported. The dynamic UAE approach has been shown to be a fast and cost-effective method that facilitated recover larger amounts of bioactive compounds from vegetable samples, as compared to the static method. Furthermore, a number of advantages that must be taken into account are the possibility of drives the extract after extraction to a continuous manifold for on-line performance of other steps in the analytical process, such as preconcentration, derivatization or detection, thus allowing the method to be fully automated [7].

The recognition of the efficiency of dynamic UAE coupled with the additional advantages offered by the use of water as an environmentally friendly solvent has prompted researchers to investigate the potential of UAE for industrial-scale extraction of natural products [8]. In this study, the effects of dynamic ultrasound assisted extraction of water soluble constituents on Brazilian Ginseng (*Pffafia glomerata*) roots were evaluated in order to understand how ultrasound interacts with cell walls and enhance mass transfer of the cell contents. The roots were analyzed before and after being subjected to the extraction process by scanning electron microscopy (SEM), X-ray diffraction (XRD), Fourier transform infrared spectroscopy (FTIR) and differential thermal (DT) analyses.

## MATERIALS AND METHODS

### Raw Material Preparation

Brazilian ginseng roots (*Pffafia glomerata*) were cultivated in the experimental field of CPQBA (Campinas, Brazil), where they were collected on March 25, 2004, being 3 years old. They were washed and dried in a forced air circulation dryer at 40 °C for 5 days. The dried roots (8.89 % moisture) were then comminuted in a pulse mill (Marconi, model MA 340, Piracicaba, Brazil) for few seconds. Next, the particles of higher size were milled again, this time using a knife mill (Tecnal, model TE 631, Piracicaba, Brazil) for 2 s at 18,000rpm and finally, they were separated according to their size using sieves (Series Tyler, W.S. Tyler, Wheeling, IL). The milled roots were stored in freezer (Metalfrio, model DA 420, São Paulo, Brazil) at - 10 °C. For the extraction assays, particles of 7.89 μm of diameter, according to ASAE methodology [1], were used. The humidity of the dried roots was determined by the AOAC method (Method 4.1.03) [2]. The roots were analyzed before and after being subjected to the extraction process.

### Raw Material Characterization

#### *By Fourier Transform Infrared Spectroscopy (FTIR)*
Fourier transform infrared (FTIR) spectra of the Brazilian ginseng roots were recorded in the frequency range of 650–4000 cm$^{-1}$ using an FTIR spectrophotometer (Nicolet, Protégé 460, Madison, WI, USA).

#### *By Differential Thermal (DT) Analyses*
DTA thermograms were measured using a thermogravimetric analyzer (TGA-50, Shimadzu, Tokyo, Japan), and the measurements were conducted over 25–900°C at a heating rate of 10°C/min in an oxidant atmosphere.

#### *By Scanning Electron Microscopy (SEM)*
The root samples were observed using scanning electron microscopy (SEM) (LEO-440i, Cambridge, England) under a vacuum of 1.33 × 10−4 Pa after coating with a thin layer of gold using a Sputter Coater (Polaron Model SC7620, Newhaven, England). A voltage of 15-20 kV was used to generate the flow of secondary electrons necessary for the formation of the surface.

#### *By X-Ray Diffraction (XRD)*
The X-ray pattern was also determined for all of the samples. The X-ray diffraction (XRD) studies were accomplished using a D5000 Siemens Difractor (D5000, Siemens, Amsterdam, Holland) with a Cu-K as a radiation source and a voltage of 40 kV and 30 mA;

the scan was performed with steps 0.01 in size, the time per step equal to 5 s and a range of reflection of 10 – 60.

## Ultrasound Assisted Extraction (UAE) Process

The ultrasound assisted extraction setup is shown in Figure 1. The dynamic UAE system was designed and assembled at LASEFI/DEA/FEA (School of Food Engineering)/UNICAMP (University of Campinas). The extractions were performed using an extractor which consisted of a glass cylindrical extraction cell. The extraction cell is closed with plugs at either end and permits the circulation of the fluid through the sample for a preset time under ultrasonic irradiation.

The extraction cell was prepared by adding a small plug of glass wool to ensure that the sample remained in the extractor, 4.5 g of dried and milled roots and suitable amount of glass beads. The extraction cell was completely immersed into an ultrasonic (40 kHz, 135 W) cleaner bath (Maxi clean 1400, Unique, Indaiatuba, Brazil), with inlet connected to a peristaltic pump (Masterflex, Cole-parmer, Chicago, USA) by a tube, and outlet to a flask. Dynamic UAE was carried out by continuously feeding extraction solvent (fresh distilled water) into the extractor by the pump and assisting by ultrasonic wave for 20 min, where a flow rate of 4 mL·min$^{-1}$ was employed, and temperature was set at 25°C by adjusting the regulation of the thermostatic bath (MA 127BO, Marconi, Piracicaba, Brazil) coupled to the ultrasonic cleaner bath. The extraction process was also done without ultrasound irradiation for comparison purposes.

Besides the used configuration (open system), this home made system also allows the configuration in which a pre-set volume of extracting solvent is continuously circulated through the solid sample (closed system) subjected to the action of the ultrasound waves. Go-and-backward circulation can be achieved programming the peristaltic pump for changing the rotation direction.

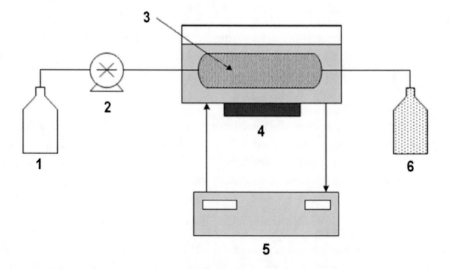

Figure 1. Dynamic ultrasound assisted extraction set-up. . Solvent reservoir; 2. Pump; 3. Extraction cell; 4. Ultrasound bath; 5. Thermostatic bath; 6. Extract reservoir.

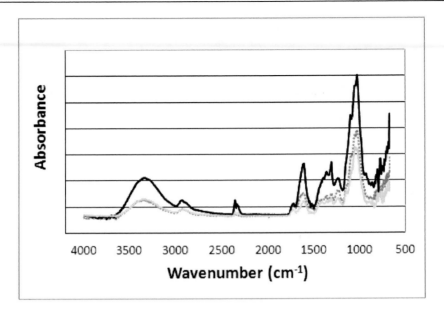

Figure 2. FTIR spectra of each sample. *Pffafia glomerata* roots before extraction process (Solid black line); *Pffafia glomerata* roots after extraction process with ultrasound irradiation (Dashed dark-gray line); *Pffafia glomerata* roots after extraction process without ultrasound irradiation (Solid light-gray line).

## RESULTS AND DISCUSSION

FTIR spectroscopy is a rapid and simple methodology and non-destructive for analytes. The whole chemical property of sample can be revealed and shown in FTIR spectrum. Some research works in literatures demonstrated that herbs could be rapidly identified by FTIR spectroscopy, including the differentiation of among the roots of Asian ginseng (*Panax ginseng*) and American ginseng (*Panax quinquefolius*) [9]. The FTIR spectra of the roots and the solid residues after extraction were shown in Figure 2.

In the entire FTIR spectra, twelve peaks were chosen as characteristic peaks based on the FTIR spectra of and summarized in Table 1. Among these peaks, peak 1 (3340 cm$^{-1}$) was assigned as the stretching vibration of O–H The peak at about 2900 cm$^{-1}$ (peak 2) is due to the C–H stretching caused by aliphatic saturated compounds.

These two stretching peaks correspond to the aliphatic moieties in cellulose and hemicellulose. Peaks 10 (1100 cm$^{-1}$), 11 (1050 cm$^{-1}$) and 12 (1030 cm$^{-1}$) were assigned as the bending vibration of C–C–O or C–C–OH in starch [9, 10]. The peaks 3 (2350 cm$^{-1}$) and 4 (2330 cm$^{-1}$) are attributed to P–H stretching and P–OH stretching. Peak at 1736 cm$^{-1}$ (peak 5) is assigned to the C=O stretching of the acetyl and uronic ester groups of hemicellulose or to the ester linkage of carboxylic group of the ferulic and p-coumaric acids of lignin. The sharp peak at 1620 cm$^{-1}$ (peak 6) was reflected for N–H stretching in protein chain.

The bands in the range of peaks 7 and 8 were attributed to the C–H symmetric and asymmetric deformations in methyl and phenolic alcohol or C–H rocking in alkanes. The band region of 1270–1250 cm$^{-1}$ (peak 9) represents Si–CH$_2$ stretching in alkane or C–C plus C–O plus C–O stretching and deformation bands in cellulose and lignin. [11, 12].

**Table 1. Characteristic peaks in the FTIR profile of Brazilian ginseng**
**(*Pffafia glomerata*)**

| Peak | cm$^{-1}$ |
|------|-----------|
| 1 | 3340 |
| 2 | 2940 |
| 3 | 2350[*] |
| 4 | 2330[*] |
| 5 | 1730 |
| 6 | 1620 |
| 7 | 1380 |
| 8 | 1320 |
| 9 | 1260 |
| 10 | 1110 |
| 11 | 1050 |
| 12 | 1030 |

From the analysis of the peaks above, it can be concluded that *Pffafia glomerata* roots as well the roots of *Panax* plants contain considerably quantity of polysaccharides (starch probably is the main type) which was revealed from the high intensity of a peak at 1180-930 cm$^{-1}$. Besides starch, cellulose, hemicellulose, lignin and protein might be in the constitution of this plant material. The chemical constituents presents in the *Pffafia glomerata* roots are not well known. *Pffafia glomerata* roots contain very complicated chemical constituents, such as polysaccharides, saponins, inorganic elements, among others [5].

The entire profiles of the tree samples were found to be generally similar to each other stating that their chemical properties were not distinctively different. On the other hand, the weak absorption of several peaks in the solid residues demonstrated that during the extraction occurs partial leaching of some constituents [13]. It can be seen that the variation in peak intensity in the solid residues was different in the tested extraction processes resulting in different product (extract) and different solid residue.

In literature, many publications described about the differentiation between Asian ginseng and American ginseng by different analytical procedures [14]. To the best of our knowledge, the FTIR spectrum of *Pffafia glomerata* roots was presented in this study for the first time. The presence of two peaks (peaks 3 and 4) in our FTIR spectra is not reported in the Asian and American ginsengs roots [9], which can be a 'marker' feature to distinguish itself from these samples.

X-ray diffraction patterns of Brazilian ginseng roots before and after being subjected to the extraction processes are shown in Figure 3. There was no change in the type of X-ray diffraction pattern when the extraction process was done without ultrasound irradiation, but the intensity of the peaks decreases as a result of loss of crystallinity during the extraction of the water soluble constituents. The single peak around 22 2 θ that is a characteristic of the A-type X-ray diffraction pattern remained unchanged [15]. Nevertheless, the action of ultrasound waves on the roots changed the single peak from 22° to around 28°, reflecting that the use of ultrasound irradiation during extraction altered the physical structure of the roots.

The X-ray diffraction patterns can reflect the packing of amylopectin side chains in starchy plant materials. The A type has a closely packaged double helices, and formed from short chain amylopectin. The differences in packaging of amylopectin side chains have caused different degrees of crystallinity. In general, the A-type have higher degree of crystallinity compared to the B-type. This difference could bring some implications in functionality of starches. The higher degree of crystallinity imparts the higher structural stability that subsequently may cause a higher gelatinization temperature since the water molecules need longer time to penetrate the crystalline areas [16].

For a better understanding of how ultrasound interacts with cell walls and enhance mass transfer of the cell contents, microscope observations were compared with the results obtained by differential thermal analysis (DTA).

DTA curves of the pyrolysis process appeared to be divided into three weight loss stages (Figure 4). For the three samples, the first weight loss below $130°C$ was mainly due to the removal of moisture when the samples were heated up. At the second weight lose stage, between 200 and $270°C$, may attribute to the decomposition of the polysaccharides. The last stage of weight loss ranging from 300 to $400°C$ was suggested to proceed through the combustion of lignin [17, 18]. A significant variation in peak intensity in the solid residues was observed; indicating that besides physically the extraction process altered chemically the roots. Comparing the DTA curves, both peaks which represent polysaccharides and lignin are shorter and less acute in the sample previously extracted using ultrasound irradiation than in unextracted sample and extracted sample without the use of ultrasound waves. This variation occurred probably because ultrasound irradiation is able to more effectively recover low and/or high molecular weight substances from plant materials [19]. Figure 4 also shows that only by the aid of ultrasound irradiation a fraction of lignin could be extracted using water as extracting solvent. Recently, Yuan et al. proposed a process named ultrasound assisted organosolv treatment for partial delignification of lignocellulosic materials also at ambient temperature (25°C). The results showed that the ultrasonic treatment and sequential extractions with aqueous solution with basic pH led to a release of 96.2% of the lignin and a subsequent recovery of 75.5% of the original hemicellulosic polysaccharides [20].

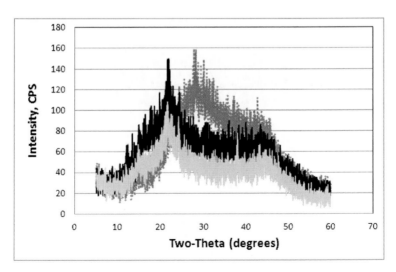

Figure 3. X-ray patterns of each sample. *Pffafia glomerata* roots before extraction process (Solid black line); *Pffafia glomerata* roots after extraction process with ultrasound irradiation (Dashed dark-gray line); *Pffafia glomerata* roots after extraction process without ultrasound irradiation (Solid light-gray line).

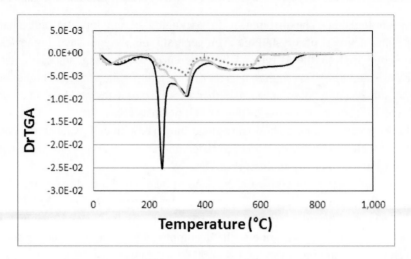

Figure 4. DTA curves of each sample. *Pffafia glomerata* roots before extraction process (Solid black line); *Pffafia glomerata* roots after extraction process with ultrasound irradiation (Dashed dark-gray line); *Pffafia glomerata* roots after extraction process without ultrasound irradiation (Solid light-gray line).

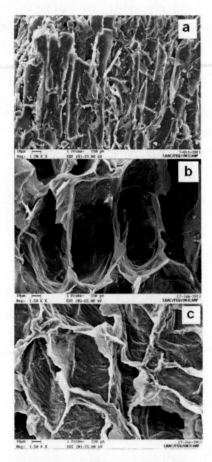

Figure 5. Scanning electron micrographs of: a) *Pffafia glomerata* roots before extraction process; b) *Pffafia glomerata* roots after extraction process with ultrasound irradiation ;c) *Pffafia glomerata* roots after extraction process without ultrasound irradiation.

Scanning electron microscopy analysis confirmed that both extraction processes altered significantly the Brazilian ginseng roots structure, being this change more pronounced when ultrasound irradiation was used (Figure 5).

Regular sponge-like structure with the remaining empty spaces after dynamic UAE process is clearly visible. The sponge-like structure formed may result from hydration of the amorphous phase and/or melting of the crystalline structures [21]. It was also possible to detect starch granules within the plant tissues (Figure 5a).

It is known that if starchy plant materials are mixed with water disruption of the cell wall structures accompanied by swelling and amylose solubilisation can occur. Native starch contains two main types of polysaccharides, namely amylose and amylopectin. Both polymers are composed of a-D-glucose units.

Comparing Figure 5b and c with literature we confirm that both solid residues consist predominantly of amylopectin, due to amylose leaching [21, 22]. Beyond amylose extraction dynamic UAE process using water an environmentally friendly solvent seemed to recover some of the others identified polysaccharides (cellulose and hemicellulose), lignin and protein. Similar studies that have demonstrated the potentiality of UAE process using water as extracting solvent for bioactive compounds recovery can be found elsewhere [3, 6, 19, 23].

## CONCLUSION

Dynamic ultrasound assisted extraction supplied sufficient energy to enhance mass transfer of the cell contents from Brazilian Ginseng (*Pffafia glomerata*) roots to the extracting solvent by disruption of the cell wall structures accompanied by swelling and amylose solubilisation. Besides amylose UAE process using water as an environmentally friendly solvent seemed to recover some amounts of the others identified polysaccharides (cellulose and hemicellulose), lignin and protein.

This study is part of a broader project that aims the integral use of this biomass using clean technologies. The use of ultrasound irradiation improved the release of different types of constituents with a consequent loss in selectivity, which can be undesired in some fractionation steps. Since, starch, non-starch polysaccharides (cellulose and hemicellulose) and lignin degraded by heat at different temperatures it seems obvious that it is preferred the use of heat instead of ultrasound energy in the first steps.

## ACKNOWLEDGMENT

Diego T. Santos is thankful to FAPESP (2010/16485-5) for a postdoctoral fellowship. Rodrigo B. Rabelo is thankful to FAPESP (2010/02819-9) for an undergraduate research fellowship. Renata Vardanega is thankful to CNPq for a master's fellowship.The authors acknowledge the financial support from CNPq and FAPESP (processes 09/17234-9; 12/10685-8).

# REFERENCES

[1] Kima, S., Murthy, H. N., Hahna, E. (2007). Parameters affecting the extraction of ginsenosides from the adventitious roots of ginseng (*Panax ginseng* C.A. Meyer). *Separation and Purification Technology*, 56, 401-406.

[2] Liu, Z., Li Y., Li, X., Ruana, C., Wanga, L., Suna, G. (2012). The effects of dynamic changes of malonyl ginsenosides on evaluation and quality control of *Panax ginseng* C.A. Meyer. *Journal of Pharmaceutical and Biomedical Analysis*, 64- 65, 56- 63.

[3] Roldán-Gutiérrez, J. M., Ruiz-Jiménez, J., Castro M. D. L. (2008). Ultrasound-assisted dynamic extraction of valuable compounds from aromatic plants and flowers as compared with steam distillation and superheated liquid extraction. *Talanta*, 75, 1369-1375.

[4] Zhang, S., Chen, R., Wu, H., Wang, C. (2006). Ginsenoside extraction from *Panax quinquefolium* L. (American ginseng) root by using ultrahigh pressure. *Journal of Pharmaceutical and Biomedical Analysis*, 41, 57-63.

[5] Leal, P. F., Kfouri, M. B., Alexandre, F. C., Fagundes, F. H. R., Prado, J. M., Toyama, M. H., Meireles, M. A. A. (2010). Brazilian Ginseng extraction via LPSE and SFE: Global yields, extraction kinetics, chemical composition and antioxidant activity. *Journal of Supercritical Fluids*, 54, 38-45.

[6] Sereshti, H., Rohanifar, A., Bakhtiari, S., Samadi, S. (2012). Bifunctional ultrasound assisted extraction and determination of *Elettaria cardamomum* Maton essential oil. *Journal of Chromatography A*, 1238, 46-53.

[7] Luque-García, J. L., Castro M. D. L. (2003). Ultrasound: a powerful tool for leaching. *Trends in Analytical Chemistry*, 22, 41-47.

[8] Engelberth, A. S., Clausen, E. C., Carrier, D. J. (2010). Comparing extraction methods to recover ginseng saponins from American ginseng (*Panax quinquefolium*), followed by purification using fast centrifugal partition chromatography with HPLC verification. *Separation and Purification Technology*, 72, 1-6.

[9] Lu, G., Zhou Q., Sun, S., Leung, K.S., Zhang, H., Zhao, Z. (2008). Differentiation of Asian ginseng, American ginseng and Notoginseng by Fourier transform infrared spectroscopy combined with two-dimensional correlation infrared spectroscopy. *Journal of Molecular Structure*, 883-884, 91-98.

[10] Albarelli, J. Q., Rabelo, R. B., Santos D. T., Beppu, M. M., Meireles, M. A. A. (2011). Effects of supercritical carbon dioxide on waste banana peels for heavy metal removal. *Journal of Supercritical Fluids*, 58, 343-351.

[11] Wu, Y., Zheng, Y., Li, Q., Iqbal, J., Zhang, L., Zhang, W., Du, Y. (2011). Study on difference between epidermis, phloem and xylem of Radix Ginseng with near-infrared and infrared spectroscopy coupled with principal component analysis. *Vibrational Spectroscopy*, 55, 201-206.

[12] Bledzkia, A. K., Mamuna, A. A., Bonnia, N. N., Ahmad, S. (2012). Basic properties of grain by-products and their viability in polypropylene composites. *Industrial Crops and Products*, 37, 427-434.

[13] Liu, Z., Zhang, F. (2008). Effects of various solvents on the liquefaction of biomass to produce fuels and chemical feedstocks. *Energy Conversion and Management*, 49, 3498-3504.

[14]  Jin, W., Zhang, Y., Mei, S., Xiong, Y., Yang, Q., Yu, L. (2007) Identification of *Lepidium meyenii* (Walp.) based on spectra and chromatographic characteristics of its principal functional ingredients. *Journal of the Science of Food and Agriculture*, 87, 2251-2258.

[15]  Katopo, H., Song, Y., Jane, J. (2002). Effect and mechanim of ultrahigh hydrostatic pressure on the structure and properties of starches. *Carbohydrate Polymers*, 47, 233-244.

[16]  Koo, H., Park, S., Jo, J., Kim, B., Hur, N., Baik, M. (2005). Physicochemical characteristics of 6-year-old Korean ginseng starches. *LWT*, 38, 801-807.

[17]  Franceschi, E., Luciano, G., Carosi, F., Cornara, L., Montanari, C. (2004). Thermal and microscope analysis as a tool in the characterisation of ancient papyri. *Thermochimica Acta*, 418, 39-45.

[18]  Lacerda, L. G., Almeida, R. R., Demiate, I.M., Filho, M. A. S. C., Vasconcelos, E.C., Woiciechowski, A. L., Bannach, G., Schnitzler, E., Soccol, C.R. (2009). Thermoanalytical and Starch Content Evaluation of Cassava Bagasse as Agro-Industrial Residue. *Brazilian Archives of Biology and Technology*, 52, 143-150.

[19]  Yuan, T., Sun, S., Xu, F., Sun, R. (2011). Isolation and physic-chemical characterization of lignins from ultrasound irradiated fast-growing poplar wood. *BioResources*, 6(1), 414-433.

[20]  Yuan, T., Xu, F., He, J., Sun, R. (2010). Structural and physico-chemical characterization of hemicelluloses from ultrasound-assisted extractions of partially delignified fast-growing poplar wood through organic solvent and alkaline solutions. *Biotechnology Advances*, 28, 583-593.

[21]  Blaszczak, W., Valverde, S., Fornal, J. (2005). Effect of high pressure on the structure of potato starch. *Carbohydrate Polymers*, 59, 377-383.

[22]  Svagan, A.J., Samir, M. A. S. A., Berglund, L.A. (2008). Biomimetic Foams of High Mechanical Performance Based on Nanostructured Cell Walls Reinforced by Native Cellulose Nanofibrils. *Advanced Matererials*, 20, 1263-1269.

[23]  Fu, L., Chen, H., Dong, P., Zhang, X., Zhang, A. (2010). Effects of Ultrasonic Treatment on the Physicochemical Properties and DPPH Radical Scavenging Activity of Polysaccharides from Mushroom *Inonotus obliquus. Journal of Food Science*,. 75, 322-327.

# INDEX

## C

# D

# E

# F

# G

## U

## V

## W

## X

## Y